CW00656183

THE ANCIENT GREEK COMPUTER FROM RHODES

KNOWN AS THE ANTIKYTHERA MECHANISM

Efstathiadis Group S.A.
Agiou Athanasiou Street,
GR - 145 65 Anixi, Attikis

ISBN 960 226 227 3

© Efstathiadis Group S.A. 1995

All rights reserved; no part of this
publication may be reproduced, stored in a
retrieval system or transmitted, in any form
or by any means, electronic, mechanical,
photocopying, recording, or otherwise, without the
prior permission of Efstathiadis Group S.A.

Printed and bound in Greece by Efstathiadis Group S.A.

To Anna Argyrou

"Not to know what happened before we were born is to remain perpetually a child. For what is the worth of a human life unless it is woven into the life of our ancestors by the records of history."
Cicero 106-43 B.C.

The Author fully acknowledges the many Archaeologists, Engineers and Academics who have contributed over the past 80 years to the sum of knowledge of this unique scientific instrument.
In particular, I must draw my reader's attention to the published work of Derek de Solla Price and all those individuals who assisted him in his detailed and comprehensive investigations.
Victor J. Kean

Contents

Appendices

Photographs

Illustrations

Foreword

The island of Rhodes lies in the eastern Mediterranean Sea enjoying some 300 days of sunshine each year. It is also blessed with clear night skies where the stars shine with a hard brilliance.

For the past 5000 years the island, situated along the ancient trade routes between Greece, Asia Minor and Egypt has witnessed the ever changing tides of history. During those tumultuous years the island has been attacked, dominated and exploited by conquerors and empire builders from many other lands envious of its natural blessings.

The story of the Antikythera Mechanism begins over two thousand years ago in the first century B.C. when the island of Rhodes was a centre of both cultural and intellectual activity within the Roman Empire.

At the ancient stadium which overlooks Rhodes Town, athletes trained prior to competing in the Olympic Games on the Peloponnese. Close by on the acropolis adjacent to the stadium, the famed school of Rhetoric was visited by such distinguished persons as Julius Caesar, Pompey, Brutus, Cato the Younger, Mark Antony, Cassius and Cicero.

It is the last named of these, Cicero who plays an important part in the story.

Our story begins in the year 74 B.C.

Victor J. Kean

Plate A: Main fragment of the Antikythera Mechanism on display in the National Archaeological Museum, Athens.

Part One

1. Preparations in the City of Rhodes

Each morning as the warmth of the rising sun lifts the cold sea mist, so the island of Rhodes emerges like Aphrodite from the waves. The ancient city which overlooks the harbours, is itself dominated by the Temple sanctuary of Apollo Pythios standing in splending isolation in the south-west corner of the town. Pale pink columns gleam in the early morning sunlight. The almost perfect silence that pervades the whole area is broken only by the occasional shouts of athletes which rise from the stadium. Small birds pecking for grain flutter up into the clear morning sky in alarm as a thrown javelin arches through the air.

The long rows of stone benches which flank the narrow running track are empty save for one solitary figure. Ignoring the efforts of the sweating athletes, Nikias a young Rhodian, is more intent on studying the shadow cast by the turning post set at the far end of the stadium. As it shortens with the climbing sun, so the shadow moves with the passage of time. Nikias, who is already known as a budding astronomer smiles inwardly as he sees the small group of men coming across the stadium entrance. They make their way to the small amphitheatre with its semi-circle of cool stone seats. Gathering his white robe around him, Nikias descends to join them, for this almost square enclosure has become the daily meeting place of the intellectuals of the island.

Taking his place a little apart from the others, Nikias listens with wrapt attention as Geminos, the calendar maker and astronomer explains the Metonic cycle of nineteen years*.

To have studied the monthly appearances of the Moon over such a long period was most impressive. Even more so was the calcuation that the New Moon occurred on exactly the same day of the year as it has done nineteen years previous. It was the sort of achievement that young Nikias would dearly love to emulate. Geminos, who had once been a pupil of the great Posidonius was always listened to

---

* See Appendix III.

with respect by his contemporaries. For it was Geminos who had encouraged all men to conduct their years in accordance with the Sun; their days and months in accordance with the Moon.

As the discourse continued, Nikias was filled with admiration at so much knowledge. The myriad of stars that could be seen from the island each night were discussed, as well as the stars known as the wanderers. Hermes and Apollo, the evening and morning stars. Could they be but one? Ares and Jupiter and pale Selene, the Moon herself. Sirius and Vega, two of the brightest stars in the night sky. Nikias began to wonder if there could be other worlds moving in stately procession through the heavens. It seemed like such an ordered sequence. A mathematical progression. As he gained more and more knowledge from these learned men, Nikias began to try to visualise a simple mechanical device that could simulate the orderly movements of the heavens, and thus be able to predict forthcoming events.

Although this concept was entirely his own, Nikias had obtained some of his ideas from a rare and much valued copy of "Mechanics" written by the renowned Archimedes. Sitting in the quietness of the old library that stood near the commercial harbour, Nikias had stared wide-eyed as he turned the leaves of parchment and saw the drawings and calculations of wheels with intermeshing teeth.

Not that it had taken very long before Nikias could understand how motion could be transmitted through a series of meshed wheels. He quickly saw that, by the careful choice of the number of teeth each wheel possessed, a specific ratio could be obtained at the end of the gear train.

Only the insistence of the keeper of books forced Nikias to abandon his studies as siesta approached and the library closed until the cool of the evening.

Nikias would walk to the harbour wall and find a shady place to sit. Watching the heavy merchant ships that lay at rest, Nikias would try to calculate involved gear ratios in his mind. Many were the times when he would fall off to sleep in the afternoon heat. The shouts of the workmen as they began their toil again into the

16

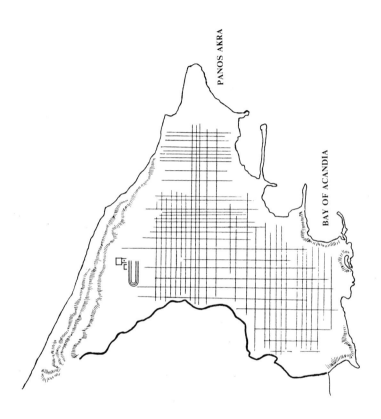

Fig. 1: Plan view of Ancient Rhodes showing the city's gridded
layout of streets on a N. - S. E. - W. axis.

evening usually woke him with a start.

He was certain that he could combine the mechanics of Archimedes with the calendars of Geminos, in such a way as to produce a mechanism to predict the future! Nikias found himself almost trembling with excitement at these ideas. Crown wheels and drive wheels, slip rings and pointers. If only he could afford to commit these ideas to parchment. Though he knew that was far too expensive for him to seriously consider.

As that summer began to approach and the days lengthened, so Nikias grew more certain that he now had the basic ideas for such an instrument. However, if it was to incorporate the Metonic cycle it would need a far more complex system of gears than the simple drive trains he had read about.

Leaving behind the bustling market place which stood beside the thriving harbour, Nikias would walk to the sandy northern point of the island alone with his thoughts. From here he could watch the merchant ships from Rome and Athens as they ploughed their way towards the harbours of Rhodes. Smaller vessels traded between the islands, bringing a constant supply of both people and produce. Beyond the island of Kos where Hippocrates, known as the father of medicine was born, lay Samos. This island was of special interest to Nikias, for it was here that Aristarchus had calculated that, in spite of appearances Helios — the Sun was stationary and that it was the Earth that moved. In one full year the Earth moves round the Sun exactly once, though the Sun appears to move along an ecliptic path through the 'zodiakos kyklos' — the circle of animals. Each of the twelve astrological signs were considered to occupy 30° of the great circle.*

Nikias had already decided that his mechanical device would have a fixed scale for these twelve segments of the Zodiac. He tried to visualise a movable scale which would carry the twelve months of the year. It had to be movable since the first day of the year had to coincide with the day of the first New Moon after the Summer Solstice and this varied every year. A pointer to represent the Sun,

---

* See Appendix VIII.

Plate B: Remains of the Temple of Apollo Pythios, Rhodes.

19

Plate C: View of the Ancient Stadium and probable site of School.

fixed to the main drive wheel and moved each day by turning a small handle at the side of the device. Then, by looking at the front face of the instrument one could read instantly which day of the year it was. For moving the pointer would be like moving the Sun! Nikias decided that it was time for him to talk to Geminos again. Each morning, after the day's lecture was over and in spite of the steadily rising temperature, the Elders remained deep in conversation reluctant to leave. Geminos, as was usual was discussing some of the finer points of his subject. Nikias was forced to wait impatiently to one side.

When Nikias finally began to explain his ideas for duplicating the movement of the Sun and the Moon he could see the look of disbelief on many of the faces of those in front of him. Only Geminos nodded with kind encouragement. "Be careful, my young friend. The Gods might not be pleased at a mere mortal copying their handiwork!" Somewhat chastened by this remark, Nikias continued a little more cautiously. He explained that he would need to make many wheels and other parts.

"Go to Kamiros" urged Geminos. "There in that once noble town lives a man who works with metals. Copper from the island of Cyprus and tin from far off Britain".

Almost reluctantly, the gathering slowly moved towards the cool of their individual homes. Nikias, his head full of practical ways of achieving his goal, hardly heard Geminos offering him the loan of the works of Eudoxos which included the Risings and Settings of the Fixed stars. Such information would have saved Nikias many cold nights of observation.

For the next two weeks Nikias prepared himself for his journey down the island. He expected that it would take three or four days following the western coast track, before he would reach Kamiros. Leaving the city, Nikias passed once more close to the stadium. Soon it would be time for the local games. Then the athletes would vie with each other in what had become preliminary heats which counted much towards selection for the games to be held at Olympia. The interest throughout the island of Rhodes in those more famous Games was intense. Ever since Diagoras of Rhodes had brought back to the island the laurels of victory from Olympia, so the young men had strove to achieve the same fame. Such was this interest that many of the people on the island of Rhodes and throughout Greece, referred to the current year as being the Third Year of the 176th Olympiad, with next year as the Fourth Year and so on until the next holding of the Games. Nikias was determined to incorporate a four-year dial on his mechanism that would indicated the current position in the Olympic cycle.

Nikias reached Trianda passing the ruins of the Minoan colony. Little remained now of the houses built by those early people from Crete at the foot of Mount Ialysos. Nikias continued his long journey, welcoming the stiff breeze which came off the sea. He spent the cooler nights under the stars. On the third day Nikias reached Kamiros-Ancient City. Once capital of the whole region, now laid to waste by successive earthquakes. He climbed the long hill up from the sea, threading his way through the pine and jasmine until he stood amongst the fallen columns of the once magnificent stoa. Nikias stared down at the remains of the city. Many of the houses on either side of the main street were without roofs. Those houses which were still intact seemed spacious and elegant. The once wide street narrowed where some of the walls had collapsed. Nikias, standing on the wide acropolis, filled his nostrils with the heady mixture of jasmine and honeysuckle. From where he stood he could look across the ruins to the sea. To his left, giant water cisterns had been dug into the ground where they had collected rain water from the roof of the stoa. The walls of the cisterns were covered in a white coating to lessen seepage. Underground conduits distributed the rain water to the houses below. Nikias wondered which man of Science had built such marvels.

2. Manufacture in Ancient Kamiros

With most of the once fine houses now abandoned, Nikias had no difficulty in finding a suitable empty house in which to stay. His new found friend, the blacksmith introduced Nikias to the handful of people still living in Kamiros, including a carpenter whose knowledge of wood was unequalled on the island. It was decided

Plate D: Ancient Kamiros looking towards the fallen stoa.

23

that when the mechanism was complete, it would be housed in a strong cabinet which would protect it in all weathers. The carpenter added that he would oil and polish it to perfection!

It was agreed between the three of them that they would keep silent about their work for fear that the Romans would covet such an object. "I hear that the Romans even dared to plunder Athens not so long ago" said the blacksmith. "They will do the same here on Rhodes one day. You mark my words", he added.

The work was slow and not without difficulty. Whilst Nikias spent the long afternoons trying to work out the various details of the mechanism, so the blacksmith cut and filed the teeth of each wheel. Small square holes in the centre of each wheel to take tiny square-sectioned axles taxed the abilities of the blacksmith to the limit. The work of assembling the mechanism with the few tools at their disposal and under such conditions was not easy. From the cogged centre of the main drive wheel, a set of toothed wheels took the movement up to the top of the mechanism. Another set took the movement downwards. Each toothed wheel was aligned with extreme care.

Nikias was fascinated by the remains of ruined Kamiros. The days when it had enjoyed the status of a city state were gone. Capital of the whole region which bore the same name, Kamiros at the height of its influence had minted its own coinage. Now the many statues around the damaged temple lay forlornly beside their bases. The fountain house and numerous altars were split asunder. Beneath the ruins, pebbled mosaic floors could still be seen in places. A concave shaped stone, smoothed worked, inscribed and marked in divisions to serve as a sun-dial lay broken and discarded. Other stones naming the philosopher, Panaitos could still be seen. Dedications to Helios, God of the Sun lay smashed underfoot. The handful of families that still lived amongst the ruins ignored these symbols of past glory.

It was a momentous day when Nikias finally worked out how to incorporate a simple form of differential gearing into the mechanism. Fed by two separate drive systems, it duplicated the difference between the apparent movement of the Sun and the revolutions of the Moon.

Plate E: View of sea from Ancient Kamiros, Rhodes.

25

All too soon the long summer passed. The mechanism neared its completion. Aided by a little grease from the pig, the meshed wheels turned smoothly. For the blacksmith it was the end of work which had been a diversion from his normal everyday tasks. For Nikias, it was only the beginning of a lasting involvement with the complexities of the stars.

On the morning that Nikias bade farewell to Kamiros and the many friends that he had made, the Sun rose against Virgo.

With the finished mechanism carefully wrapped in cloths, Nikias set out to reach the other side of the island.

The fertile plain of Keskinto with its ancient association with astronomy was shrouded in mystery. Most of the islanders had never heard that such a place existed. Even fewer knew its precise location.

For the first few kilometers Nikias followed the coast south. In the heat of the day the breezes off the sea were a welcomed blessing. Following the simple directions which he had been given, Nikias turned away from the coast. A young goatherd sitting beneath the shade of a spreading plane tree waved as he passed. Nikias refreshed himself at a natural fountain of fresh water that cascaded down from the hillside. Gradually he began to climb towards the foothills of Mt. Ataviros. Treading time-worn paths beaten hard by goats and men, Nikias made his way along the narrow paths that linked the tiny hamlets that lay amongst the hills. The three black summits of the mountain, sharp-etched against the sky, thrust upwards. Large herds of sure footed goats roamed high amongst the rocky outcrops searching for edible grasses. A white walled Temple of Zeus, built below the summit served as a landmark to the now weary climber. A little further on, Nikias was delighted to be able to see the island of Karpathos. In the clear air, the white peaks of Crete could also be seen in the far distance.

Following the course of one of the many rivers that flowed down the mountainside, Nikias made his way down into the lush valley. Herds of deer cropped their way across flat expanses of green grass. Olive, pine and citrus grew in profusion amongst oak and cypress trees. In the shaded depths of these thick forests, Nikias found shelter from the heat of the Sun.

Plate F: Remains of ancient Sun-Dial found at Kamiros, Rhodes.

Plate G: Smoke-blackened blacksmith's forge at Kamiros, Rhodes.

As Nikias made his way down into the last valley, he could see the glint of light upon the water in the Bay of Lardos. On the far horizon, the Temple of the Lindian Athene standing atop of its natural acropolis dominated the landscape. Nikias had reached Keskinto. High on the crest of the hill which overlooks the plain of Keskinto, Nikias could see the ancient observatory. Masses of pink and white oleander clustered over the crumbling walls. Green crested lizards scuttled between the stones. The flat roofed building was encircled by silver-grey olive trees, heavy with fruit.

A stone stele stood in one corner of the courtyard. Nikias ran his fingers over the columns of letters and numbers which had been chiselled into the face of the stone. The names of the planets could be read at the head of the neat columns. The numbers appeared to Nikias to indicated various positional data, phases and rotations far beyond his understanding. At the bottom of the stone stele, partially obscured by the long grasses which had begun to climb its smooth face, were larger size letters. Nikias cleared aside the grass in order to be able to read these last words... 'A thanksgiving to the Gods.'

Nikias was reminded that he also would have to pay homage to the old Gods. From the roof of this solitary building the view of the eastern horizon was magnificent. Here he would observe the risings of the fixed stars as they climbed into view.

3. Observations from Keskinto, Rhodes

During the year that followed, Nikias became a familiar sight to the few people who lived close by. Climbing up to the observatory each late afternoon, Nikias would study the heavens as the evening twilight turned to darkness and the first stars appeared in the night sky. With only a simple diopter to aid him*, Nikias struggled to remember the names of the principal stars as he searched for them in the sky.

In the tradition of all previous calender makers, the risings and settings of both the Pleiades and the Hyades were almost

---

* See Appendix VI.

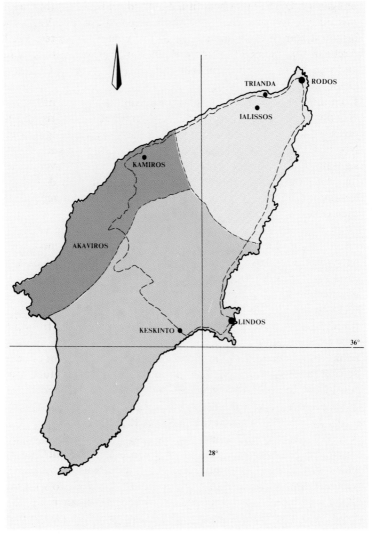

Fig. 2: Map of Ancient Rhodes.

obligatory. Of the other beautiful diamonds of the night that lay in this infinite treasure chest, the choice seemed endless. Vega, the brightest star in the summer sky. Sirius, winter's brightest jewel. Arcturus that seemed to shine with an orange glow... Altair, white and sparkling in the constellation of the Eagle... Capella... Orionis... Rigel... Antares...

Each morning Nikias was awake before sunrise, recording the last visibility of the stars before the brighter light of the rising sun obscured them. In spite of the island's normally clear night skies, Nikias found much difficulty in deciding the moment of first sighting of a particular star after sunset. He soon discovered that the eastern and western areas of the sky varied in their degrees of darkness. Nor did all the stars in one area appear at the same time as each other.

Gradually his list of recorded observations which he carefully inscribed onto the bronze plate of the mechanism, lengthened. Each entry was inscribed alongside a letter of the alphabet which was carefully copied in the correct place on the front calender dials of the mechanism.

As he worked, Nikias was conscious that the legendary Attulus of Rhodes was reputed to have carried out his observations from this very same building.

From time immemorial the island had been a focal point of both Science and Astronomy. The parallel of 36° of latitude was considered by the Greek geographers to be of great importance, linking the Pillars of Hercules — the Straits of Gibraltar, at one end of the Mediterranean with the island of Rhodes at the other.*

A year after he had begun his task, so Nikias completed his observations. The mechanism, now fully inscribed with all the data which he had so laboriously collected, was finished. All that remained was for Nikias to pay homage to the Gods to whom a giving of thanks was customary. Gathering together his few possessions, he took his leave of the few people who lived in that remote place and set out towards Lindos. As he neared that ancient

---

* See Appendix X.

acropolis, so he recalled the words spoken in jest by his friend Geminos, "The Gods might not be pleased at a mere mortal copying their handiwork!" Torn between a real respect for the old Gods and fear for his own safety, Nikias was in no hurry to reach his destination.

4. Lindos — Sanctuary of the Lindian Athene

For over a thousand years, the temple sanctuary that stood on the rock known as Lindos, had been the centre of reverence throughout the Mediterranean. Most of the prominent personalities of the past had visited the sanctuary and laid offerings at the foot of the statue which stood inside the Temple building. King Ptolemy I of Egypt; King Pyrrhos; Alexander the Great and Philip V had all climbed the ancient steps to the summit. It was a daunting task for Nikias to follow in such famous footsteps.

As he approached, his attention was caught by the detailed relief carving of a ship which had been hewn into the solid rock. Clearly detailed, the proud stern and the ornamental seat of the ship's Captain could be seen. A bronze statue of Agesandros stood amidships.

Climbing the remaining steps with some effort, Nikias entered the complex. Almost every space not occupied by buildings was filled with olive trees and statues. The magnificent buildings with their many columns and shaded arches, seemed to extend higher and higher towards the sky. A flight of steps led Nikias onto a flat patio. Either side of him, the arms of the stoa seemed to be open in invitation. Nikias walked through its centre columns. He found himself at the bottom of an even greater flight of wide stone steps. Nikias hesitated, aware that only his footsteps echoed through the deserted buildings.

At the top of this next flight of steps stood the Propylaeum. Red roofed; its columns and arches seemed like a miniature of the stoa through which Nikias had just passed. Clutching the mechanism tighter, Nikias passed into this majestic annexe. Standing within its cool interior, Nikias stood staring out into the harsh sunlight. The deep blue of the sea, white-flecked by the wind on its surface seemed

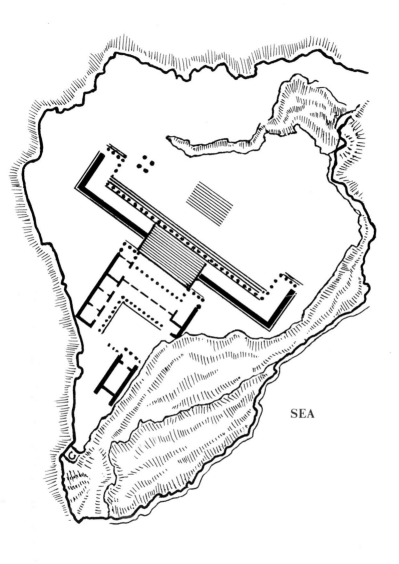

SEA

Fig. 3: Plan view of the Temple buildings at Lindos, Rhodes.

Plate H: Reconstruction of the sanctuary of the Lindian Athene.

Plate 1: Remains of the sanctuary buildings at Lindos, Rhodes.

35

remote and silent from this great height. A tiny boat, its white sail billowing out in the stiff breeze, ploughed its way through the troughs.

The Temple sanctuary was only some fifteen metres away. Summoning up his resolve, Nikias walked between the columns of the building and out into the sunlight. He entered the temple which had been built almost on the very apex of the acropolis. In the centre of the cella, standing on a raised dias stood the statue of the Lindian Athene. Made mainly of gold-covered wood, though her limbs and head were carved in marble, she stood crowned and garland surrounded by the many offerings which had been piled around her feet. In her right hand she held a phial of nectar. The fingers of her left hand rested upon a shield. She gazed into the far distance, unarmed and vulnerable. There was no altar in the temple, only this single statue. A shiver passed through Nikias, though whether it was caused by the coolness inside the temple or apprehension he could not answer. Placing the mechanism against the statue, Nikias quietly explained its workings adding his gratitude for the clear skies which only the Gods could have given him.

5. The Mysteries of Lindos

They had come from the surrounding villages walking along the narrow, dusty tracks towards Lindos. Whole families moving in groups towards that silent acropolis.

High on this natural dias, the Temple of the Lindian Athene stands poised above the sea. Patroness of Lindos, the Goddess Athene was worshipped as the protector of fertility and vegetation. Her temple had been rebuilt by the Lindians after the fire of 342 B.C. An almost exact copy of the Temple of the Wingless Victory on the acropolis of Athens; at Lindos a separate staircase served the temple. Hundreds of people were now climbing up the acropolis, joining those who had sat patiently in the open amphitheatre waiting. The days had almost been forgotten when the Rhodians had come in their hundreds to worship the Goddess. But here they were again,

Plate J: Remains of the East wing of Propylaeum at Lindos, Rhodes.

Plate K: Grand stairway to the Propylaeum of the Lindian Athene.

Plate L: *View from the Temple of Athene looking eastwards.*

Plate M: Remains of the Temple of Athene at Lindos, Rhodes.

streaming down from the mountains and up from the coast in a sudden revival of this almost forgotten cult.

They quietened as they reached the summit of the acropolis. High in the late afternoon sky, the Full Moon was already visible. Now an unknown priestess, contrary to the tradition that only priests served at Lindos, predicted the darkening of the Moon. Those who had heard her previous pronouncements had no doubt as to her accuracy.

They seated themselves on the hard rock facing the many columned stoa. Most eyes were upon the wide flight of steps which led down to the roof of this covered walkway. Others glanced with some nervousness up at the Moon. The crowds fell silent. As dusk approached all eyes turned towards the Moon. As the dark shadow of the earth moved slowly over the face of the Moon, a low troubled moan rose from the crowd.

A lone child whimpered in the uncanny light. Up in the foothills wild dogs began to howl as the face of the Moon took on a strange brown appearance. Minutes passed as the hushed crowd stared silently up at the darkened Moon. The priestess clapped her hands together. The face of the Moon began to slowly brighten to normality.

From behind the statue of the Lindian Athene the priestess stepped into view. The slight breeze moulded her thin white robe to the fullness of her bosom. To many of the onlookers it seemed as if Athene herself had come to life before their eyes. Suddenly, her voice ringing clear and echoing from the walls of the many buildings, she announced the forthcoming darkening of Helios-the Sun. The crowd stirred in fear. Some jumped to their feet ready for a swift departure. Others glanced anxiously towards the smaller temple of Psithyros, remembering how they had once paid homage to an evil spirit there.

With one arm raised aloft the priestess stilled their fears. For those who paid her homage all would be well. With those few words the Goddess Athene gained a thousand new adherents. Then, as the huge crowd began to make its way down from the acropolis, so the priestess returned into the temple. She stood smiling at the small wooden cabinet with its strange mechanism from which came her seemingly magical prophesies. Carefully she opened its doors running her fingers over their polished surfaces. The bronze plates and dials gleamed in the now strong moonlight. With the utmost care she turned the small handle at the side of the cabinet watching the long pointer move one day onwards.

6. The Pillage of Lindos

The afternoon was particularly hot. Beneath the shade of a large olive tree the goatherd slept. The goats moved silently from place to place searching for food. First one, then a few more until finally the whole herd began to move. Their bleating cries woke the boy who called out to them in reassurance. He glanced around looking to see what had disturbed his charges. On the horizon, a small cloud of dust kicked up by marching soldiers revealed their progress. The goats edged away from the track to be slowly followed by the boy. For the next five minutes the small group of soldiers came marching up the incline towards the herd, their helmets glinting in the sunlight. The goatherd urged his goats across the gully and climbed away from the track. For these men were Romans.

Having disembarked some two hours earlier in the harbour of Rhodes, they were now marching at a smart pace south towards Lindos. A brief rest beside the waters at Kallithea had done little to ease their aching muscles. "Why do we have to make such a pace?" muttered one of the soldiers to his companion. "We're going to collect Cicero's birthday present!" cried a voice. The others laughed. Their officer growled at them to be quiet. The track threaded its way between the forest and the river. Arriving at a grove of olives they halted. Thankfully, the soldiers sank to the ground amidst the trees. Five springs of fresh drinking water emerged from the ground, feeding the foliage which grew in wild abundance. The soldiers dashed water into their faces and refilled their water bottles. The officer, sitting apart from his men was deep in thought. He recalled his meeting with Cicero in Rome. "Go to the island of Rhodes. Find the device that fortells the future of the stars. Bring it back to Rome."

Plate N: General view of Temple complex at Lindos, Rhodes.

Plate O: Section of the Hellenistic colonnade on the acropolis.

44

Cicero the orator had studied here in 78 B.C. At that time he had met with his old teacher, Molon. It was at the school of Rhetoric that he had improved his ability to command and to persuade with the use of words. With this ability to silence a noisy rabble with his eloquence, Cicero had also learnt how to achieve personal ambitions without the use of force. Yet, deep down he had never forgotten how direct action could result in swift achievement.

Whilst he had lived on Rhodes, he had been much impressed with an astronomical device made by Posidonius. It was somewhat ironic that a man who was known to consider the work of the mechanic degrading, should have come to covet this new device. Writing that there was "nothing noble about a Workshop", he nevertheless would be happy to possess its fruits.

The Roman officer shouted to his men to reform ranks. As they cursed and shuffled into some sort of order, an owl startled by their noise screeched over their heads. The Roman soldiers, many of them superstitious labourers from the farms, cowered in fear. The owl had always been considered by the Romans to be an omen of impending disaster.

The sight of the Temple buildings of Lindos standing high on its acropolis overlooking the sea was most impressive. As the soldiers neared the village, so the people stood in their doorways to watch their progress in silence. The reputation of the Romans did nothing to make them welcome on the island. None doubted that they had arrived in Lindos for their own ends.

7. The ill-fated voyage to Rome

In the still waters of Rhodes harbour the Roman merchant ship lay heavy with cargo. Laden with amphorae and marbles from the islands of Paros, Delos and Kos the ship was the centre of much activity. Earlier that very morning, one of the crew had slipped on the gangplank and plunged between the ship and the harbour wall. Now the gangplank was covered with dry matting to avoid any repetition. It was not without some satisfaction that the Captain had noted that the unfortunate man had not been carrying any prized booty when he slipped.

A line of men passed amphorae filled with fruits and spices from one man to the next. Each shaped container bore the distinctive marks of the island of Rhodes, the rayed head of Helios and the Rose emblem proclaiming its origins.

It took six men to carry the heavy bronze statue swathed in protective cloths onto the deck of the ship. Set upright, it stood over two metres tall. The athletic figure of the youth was naked, the right arm oustretched. The hand open as if grasping an unseen globe. A modest expression enhanced the handsome face. The statue was a sheer marvel of rythmn and pose. For almost 300 years this fine work of art had stood outside the gymnasium adjacent to the stadium. Now, on the orders of their Roman masters, the islanders were forced to part with this priceless work of art. The Roman ship settled a little lower in the water. Its Captain paced back and forth on the small bridge of his heavily built vessel. High on the yard arms, the sails of the ship flapped in the light breeze. When loading was complete, the oarsmen would row the ship out of the harbour. An uncanny hush descended upon the noisy quayside. Men looked at each other for an explanation of this sudden silence. In the narrow alleys which ran down to the harbour, crowds began to gather. A small detachment of Roman soldiers trooped along to the ship. Within their ranks, one man carried a polished wooden cabinet onto the ship. The watching crew muttered uneasily amongst themselves. Was this the object that had set all of Rhodes against them? The mechanism that could foretell the future.

Ropes were loosened. The bow of the ship turned slowly towards the mouth of the harbour. Long oars dipped into the water in unison and the Roman ship moved away from the crowded quay. The crowds of islanders stood silent at their departure. The ship edged through the swarm of small boats that surrounded it. The furled sails were released to catch the winds.

The clear blue sky bright with the afternoon sun seemed to augur well for the voyage. Rome lay some twenty five days ahead of them. The astronomical device stood on the bridge of the vessel in full sight of the crew. Each sunrise the Captain turned the small handle at the side of the cabinet moving the Sun pointer on to another day.

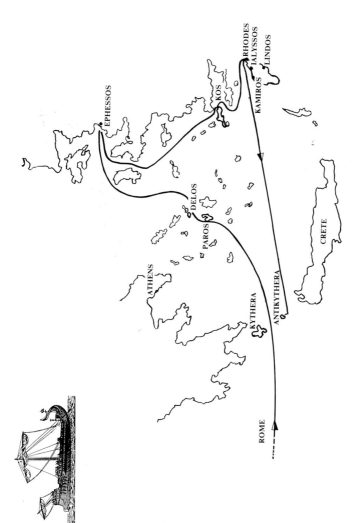

Fig. 4: Probable route of the Roman merchant ship through the Aegean Seas.

The progress of the ship was slower than usual. Nevertheless, the fine days of sunshine and light winds made for a smooth passage. The crew, anticipating in their minds their eventual arrival in Rome had forgotten those earlier feelings of unease about their cargo. Ahead of the ship, the Ionian Sea beckoned them on.

The storm which came towards them from the horizon ahead, came swiftly with a rapidly darkening sky. A curtain of torrential rain swept over them. Splashes of lightning followed by long rumbles of thunder filled the air. Spumes of white froth engulfed the plunging bows of the ship. Sharp gusts of wind tore at the sails with ferocious energy. The sound of ripping sail cloth sent fear through the crew. Eager hands lowered the sails to the deck. Others bent to their oars. Almost midway between the island of Kythera and the western most tip of the island of Crete, the small island of Antikythera stood alone amongst the white-capped waves offering sanctuary from the violence of the storm. Seeking the lee of the island to escape the north-westerly gale, the Roman Captain brought his ship as close as he dared to this apparent haven. Swimmers were ordered into the boiling storm waters to take lines to the rocky shore some 25 metres away. The lightning, now flashing almost directly overhead, reflected in the polished surface of the wooden cabinet which housed the mechanism. Its bronzed plates gleamed dully in the ozone filled air.

The sound of splitting timber filled the crew with terror. Built mainly of elm planking, the timbers of the hull fastened with long bronze nails, tore itself apart. The sound ran from bow to stern as swiftly as the panic of the crew. For a few moments the deck seemed to rise up beneath their feet. Weighing some 300 tons, the Roman ship overburdened with its illicit cargo, split asunder.

The weight of the filled amphorae, bronze and marble statues and other priceless works of art took it to a submerged shelf some 60 metres below in less than twenty seconds. The mud and sand which covered the underwater shelf cushioned the inital impact, but the timbers of the aged merchant ship opened like an overripe piece of fruit disgorging its contents. Pottery and eating utensils, drinking cups, almonds, oil-jars, grinding stones and glass bowls lay amongst the shattered statuary. A thick cloud of disturbed sand and mud rose from the shelf obscuring the tumultuous scene. Of the Roman crew none survived. The mechanism, partially protected by its solid cabinet rested in the murky depths.

The date indicator was locked in its final position where it would remain for all time.

By the Greek calender of the day, it was the 22nd day of Mounichon in the 1st Year of the 180th Olympiad.

Part Two

8. Sponge divers from the Island of Symi

The two small caiques plunged deep through the waters of the Mediterranean. The men on board were recovering from the weeks of underwater diving work which they had recently completed off the Tunisian coast. Their trip had been highly successful and now that they were heading back to their beloved island, their spirits were high. Under the command of Captain Demetrios Kondos, the twenty two oarsmen and six divers were all brave men. It required strong nerves to still their fears as they dived beneath the waves into the depths of the ocean.

The gathering of the natural sponge from the ocean bed was the island's main source of income. The work however was extremely dangerous, with no equipment save a belt of heavy weights to keep them below.

Captain Kondos was an experienced master diver. Knowing the hazards of diving and in particular the dangers of the 'bends', he took great care of his crew. On each day's work he carefully noted how many dives each man made, how many minutes he stayed below.

Ahead of the two small boats, the crew looked forward to the warm homecoming from their wives and girl-friends. Soon it would be Easter. It was the year 1900 A.D.

A cry came from the stern of the leading boat and the weatherman could be seen pointing to the sky off the port bow. Dark, thunder-filled clouds began to cover the sky. Captain Kondos ordered his steersman to turn to the North and, urging his oarsmen to maximum effort, headed for the island that lay a few hundred metres off their port bow. It was the island of Antikythera.

The two small boats tucked themselves as close as they dared into the lee of the island, letting go the anchors. The island at this point was inaccessible, and so for the next six hours Captain Kondos and his crew had no choice but to ride out the fury of the storm in their small but sturdy boats.

Plate P: The underwater salvage operation at Antikythera in 1901

From N. Svoronos (Das Athener Nationalmuseum)

Plate Q: (detail) Main fragment of the Antikythera Mechanism on display in the National Archaeological Museum, Athens.

Eventually the wind dropped, the sea calmed and the crew began to laugh and joke with relief. As the sky brightened some of the crew began to dive overboard in the vague hope of finding sponges in such a remote place. Suddenly a cry was heard. Emerging from the depths, one of the divers, Elias Statiadis was quickly hauled on board. Recovering his breath, he told the members of the crew how he had seen the figure of a man beneath the waves. Arm outstretched, the figure seemed to be beckoning him to come closer! Without hesitation the other divers disappeared overboard to investigate this unbelievable claim. The figure stood in a mound of amphorae, many of them still intact. They had found the Roman shipwreck. It lay at a depth of some 60 metres (180 feet) on a submerged rock shelf. The length of the hull could clearly be seen lying in the mud. Captain Kondos also dived down to confirm the find. Having taken careful bearings, the two boats immediately set sail for their native Symi, with an arm from one of the statues lying in the bottom of the boat as proof of their find. They were all aware that this new find was even more valuable than their recent haul of sponges.

Whilst the members of his crew joyfully greeted their relatives and friends who had been standing on the quayside watching their approach, Captain Kondos made his way to the house of the Elders with the sculptured arm from the wreck. After much deliberation and with some caution, the Greek archaeological authorities in Athens were informed of the discovery.

9. Recovery operations off Antikythera

On the 6th of November 1900, a small Greek warship, the 'Mykale' accompanied by the divers of Symi and their two boats arrived off Antikythera. It was the start of the world's first underwater dig. Such was the position of the wreck that even on that first day the efforts of the divers were rewarded. A bronze head, thought to be a portrait of a third century philosopher and two 5th century statuettes were brought to the surface. Nevertheless, without the use of proper diving equipment and with constant interruptions due to the deteriorating weather, the recovery operations began to prove hazardous.

Diving down to such depths with so little knowledge of the dangers of narcotic poisoning, the divers were limited to just five minutes beneath the surface. The mixture of sand and mud in which the wreck lay was so easily disturbed by any great movement. Thus the scene would suddenly become obscured by clouds of sand adding to the diver's problems. Each time a diver lifted an object, these would be tied onto the ropes which had been let down from the ship on the surface. Occasionally these ropes broke under the weight of the statues sending them plunging back into the depths.

Unless they were fortunate enough to settle again onto the narrow submerged shelf upon which the wreck lay, these precious art treasures sank into deeper water where they were lost forever.

Amongst the fine bronze and marble statues recovered from the wreck was the famous bronze known as the "Youth from Antikythera". Now on permanent display in the National Archaeological Museum in Athens (Room 28) it is the only existing large-scale bronze from the first quarter of the fourth century B.C. (Plate Q). Smaller finds included many amphorae from the island of Rhodes, easily identified by the emblem of the Rose and the rayed head of Helios imprinted on the inside of the handles. Alabaster flasks used to carry perfumed oils were recovered, as were many glass vessels in almost faultless condition. One particular blue-green moulded and carved bowl which possibly originated in the city of Alexandria, had an Eight-petalled Rosette decorating its underside. Roman pottery, wine amphorae, small jugs and a single Ephesos-shaped oil lamp were lifted from their watery store where they had lain for almost two thousand years.

These art treasures were not recovered without human cost. One diver died and two others were permanently paralysed during the underwater operations which were finally abandoned on September 30th 1901.

Captain Kondos and his crew were rewarded by the Greek Government with the sum of 150,000 Drachmas, plus a bonus of 500 Drms. for each diver.

Plate R: Youth from Antikythera (340 B.C.).

10. Archaeological Museum, Athens

The painstaking task of cleaning and examining all the salvaged objects began immediately. Teams of archaeological experts from all over Greece worked long hours at the Museum in Athens, patiently removing the thick calcified crust which covered many of the recovered objects.

Such was the condition of one unidentifiable lump of formless material that had been raised from the sea along with the bronze and encrusted marbles, that it was surprising that the divers had bothered to send it up to the salvage vessel. Placed at the back of a shelf along with many other pieces waiting to be cleaned, this shapeless lump slowly began to dry. For the next eight months this natural slow drying process continued. Free of the protective properties of the sea mud which had encased it for almost two thousand years, what little remained of the wooden cabinet deteriorated rapidly. This single lump of as yet unidentified debris broke into four separate pieces.

On 17th May 1902, Valerios Stais — a former minister, then working as an archaeologist at the Museum in Athens, began to examine these four lumps of calcified material. To his utter astonishment he realised that he was looking at parts of a mechanical device. Furthermore, he could just recognise inscribed letters in Ancient Greek script upon parts of it. Surrounded by the few colleagues who were also working in the Museum on that particular Saturday morning, Stais stared at the strange pieces. One or two of the expert onlookers offered tentative ideas as to what they were examining. So began the scientific controversy which was to continue unabated for the next fifty years. For trying to assess this new discovery divided the scientific community for many years.

11. The Scientific controversy

Apart from the questions concerning the origin of the mechanism, the pieces of the mechanical device posed two fundamental questions:

      1) What was the purpose of the mechanism?

and 2) What was its age?

The first account describing the mechanism was published in May 1902. This was a joint account by two numismatists, Svoronos and Wilhelm who, by virtue of their expertise in the study of ancient coinage, had studied the forms of the ancient Greek inscriptions on the mechanism. Of the 220 inscribed letters that could be read at that early stage of cleaning, Svoronos and Wilhelm came to the conclusion that these could be attributed to the period from 200 B.C. to 200 A.D. They described the mechanism as having spherical projections on a set of rings, and thus decided that it was an astrolabe — a simple navigation device.

Immediately there was strong opposition to this first report from many of the other experts who also had the opportunity of examining the device. According to one Constantine Rados, the device was far too complex to be an astrolabe and appeared to him to contain a spring. In order to dampen down the heated debates that were raging through Athens, a committee of learned men were convened to carefully re-examine the mechanism. After much deliberation they also decided that it was an astrolabe. This new finding also raised a storm of criticism. Conflicting opinions as to the purpose of the find continued to be offered from all quarters of the scientific world. Constantine Rados staunchly maintained his conviction that the device was not an astrolabe.

Meanwhile, Valerios Stais the expert who had originally recognised the mechanism at the Museum, had concentrated his efforts on the continued study of the forms of the inscribed letters. He was able to narrow the possible time span to the First century B.C.

Two years later in 1907, the device was examined by Professor Albert Rehm of Munich University. He agreed with Rados that the device was far too complex to be a simple navigation instrument. He also began what was to become for him, a life-long study of the Antikythera Mechanism.

12. Dating the Mechanism

In 1913, Professor A. Rehm stated that he was able to read the month name ΠΑΧΩΝ (Pachon) on the front dial of the mechanism. From the appearance of this name which was one of the months of

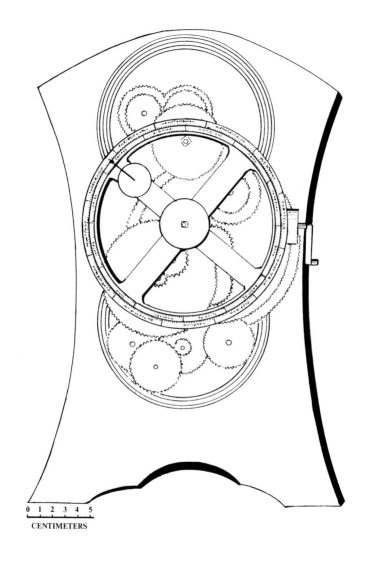

0 1 2 3 4 5
CENTIMETERS

Fig. 5: Artist's impression of the original mechanism

an Egyptian styled calender, Rehm concluded that the device must be dated after the Julian calendar reform of 46 B.C. He therefore proposed a date of around 30 B.C. for the date of the disaster which had sunk the Roman ship.

This date of "around 30 B.C." was repeated by George Karo who was Director of the German Archaeological Institute in Athens between 1911 and 1920. He also stated that the inscriptions on the 'astrolabe' prove it to be made "shortly after 30 B.C." He offered no evidence to substantiate this statement.

The mystery deepened further when the report by Prof. Derek de Solla Price, dated June 1959 appeared in "Scientific American"; for although he subjected the device to microscopic examination, he made no mention of the reading of the month name ΠΑΧΩΝ upon which this proposed date had been based. Nevertheless by 1965 this proposed date had become part of accepted folk-lore in the world of archaeology. For it was now being stated that "an exact date of 30 B.C. had been hit upon for the unique mechanism", with George Karo being credited as the originator.

Prof. Price in later reference to Rehm's claim stated that "Rehm's argument loses all validity since the Egyptian style calendar occurs already in Plato" i.e. *prior* to 46 B.C.

Having carefully measured the 'out of phase' condition of the two scales of the Front Dial as being 13 1/2°, Prof. Price concluded that the setting of the device as preserved, could only have occurred in the year 80 B.C. and "because we do not know the Month", at all years 120 years before or after that date.

From this statement we can only wonder what had become of the Month name ΠΑΧΩΝ (Pachon) which Prof. Rehm was able to read in 1913. In fact the only letters on the Month scale which could be identified by Prof. Price with the aid of a powerful microscope, were the letters ΠΑ.

From the position of a fiducial mark outside the Month scale, it was suggested in this 1959 report that 82 B.C. was the date of manufacture of the mechanism.

These two dates were later confirmed by Gladys Weinberg in her 1965 report entitled, "The Antikythera Shipwreck Reconsidered".

In this comprehensive report, the evidence of the timbers of the Roman ship, as well as the pottery and glass which had been recovered from the wreck were futher studied. This report concluded that the shipwreck took place within the period 80-50 B.C. As to the crucial dating of the mechanism, this was re-assessed by Prof. Price. In his comprehensive report dated 1974, he wrote that the Month name ΠΑΧΩΝ could now be seen. Though stating that this month name is difficult to evaluate since it appears 120° out of position, Prof. Price was nevertheless convinced that the markings indicated two consecutive months of a Greco-Egyptian calendar. He now came to the conclusion that the 'out of phase' condition indicated 85 B.C. as the year of the preserved setting and 87 B.C. as the likely year of manufacture.

For archaeologists a fixed date on a particular artifact is an invaluable aid in dating other objects found in the same locality. The discovery of the Antikythera Mechanism can therefore be compared with the finding of a ship's chronometer — still set at the moment of disaster — even though smashed beyond repair.

If the ship obviously came from an age outside the limits of our present knowledge, both the technology of its design and method of manufacture would be of immense value in answering the vital question of exactly when the disaster occurred. But the reading of the last setting of the chronometer would be even more revealing. It was towards these questions that many of the experts who studied the mechanism turned their attention.

An examination of some of the timbers of the Roman merchant ship which were recovered from the wreck were subjected to dating by the Carbon 14 method. This showed that the wood could be dated between 273-177 B.C. Thus the timbers of the ship were over one hundred years old when it floundered.

The identification of the inscribed letter forms on the mechanism could be dated to a period spanning just one hundred years (100-0 B.C.). The identification of the style and shapes of the amphorae found in the wreck were dated close to the decade 80-70 B.C. Whilst G. Roger Edwards found that the Hellenistic pottery belonged to circa 80-65 B.C.

61

In keeping with the high degree of technical knowledge that has been incorporated into the design of the Antikythera Mechanism, the provision of an accident-proof locking system would have surely been an essential feature.

Fortunately, the fragment which contains a vital part of the two front dials is sufficiently preserved to provide us with evidence pointing to the exact date of the wrecking of the Roman ship.

13. The Front Dial Fragment

Front Dial Fragment

This particular fragment is all that remains of the front dial plate (See Fig. 6). It is however in a good state of preservation. It contains part of the two annular scales which can be seen to be divided into 30° divisions and further inscribed at 1° intervals.

The inner scale is fixed and contains the names of the segments of the Zodiac. The name ΧΥΛΑΙ (Libra) can be clearly identified.

In the adjacent division, in an anti-clockwise direction, close examination reveals the letters NO. These are identified as the 6th and 7th letters of the name ΠΑΡΘΕΝΟΥ (Virgo). Thus it is accepted that this fragment contains part of the Zodiac cycle which proceeds clockwise and probably began with the division for the segment of Cancer.

The Outer scale was movable in relation to the fixed scale. This movable scale was also inscribed with letters which refer to the names of the months. In the major division of this movable scale of Months the letters ΠΑ can be clearly seen. It is possible that these are the first two letters of ΠΑΝΟΠΣΙΟΝ, a corrupt form of the month name Pyanopsion. This was the fourth month of a Greek calendar in use during the first century B.C.

This movable month scale is some half a major division out-of-phase with the fixed Zodiac scale.

The significance of this out-of-phase condition is vital in establishing the date at which the mechanism was set. An alternative calendar system used by both the Athenians and the Ionians in the First Century B.C. proclaimed that the day upon which the first New Moon occurred after the Summer Solstice, was the first day of the New Year.

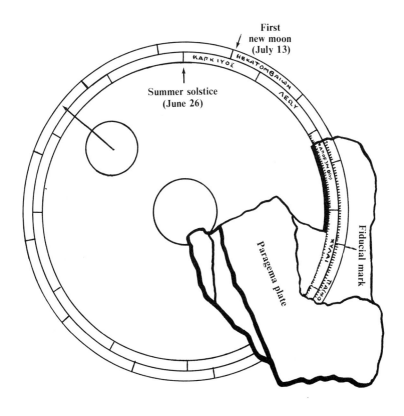

First
new moon
(July 13)

KAPKIYOΣ

HEKATOMBAIΩN

ΛEΩN

Summer solstice
(June 26)

ΠAPΘENO (Σ)

KYΛΛI

ZYГ(OΣ)

Fiducial mark

paragema plate

Fig. 6: Recovered paragema plate with Front scales.

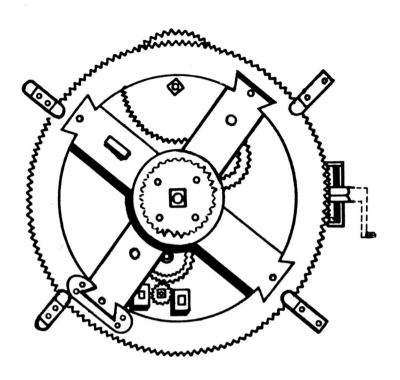

Fig. 7: Front View - Simplified.

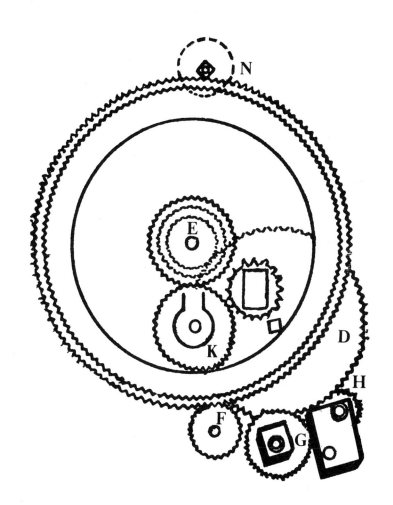

Fig. 8: Rear View - Simplified.

Thus to set the mechanism each year, the first day of the first Greek month (Hekatombaion) would have been aligned with the precise degree of the Zodiac indicating when this phenomenon occurred. On the front dials of the Antikythera Mechanism, the inscribed 18° line of the fixed Zodiac scale aligns with the first (day) division of the movable Month scale. This setting indicates that the first New Moon after the Summer Solstice occurred when the Sun rose against the 18° of ΚΑΠΚΙΥΟ (Cancer). During the First Century B.C. the Summer Solstice took place on June 26th. Thus the setting of the mechanism as preserved, indicates a Julian date of July 13th. From Standard Tables accurate to within ten minutes, it can be established that, within the limits indicated by all the other evidence available, the year 60 B.C. is the year in which the last setting of the mechanism was carried out*

At the beginning of each New Year, when the movable Month scale had been locked in its correct position relative to the fixed Zodiac scale, a single pointer mounted in line with one of the wide spokes of the Main Drive wheel would sweep both the Month and Zodiac scales. This single pointer would be moved 1° each day. Thus it would follow the apparent movement of the Sun against the Zodiac. By reference to the front dials, the particular day of the current year could be instantly read. As preserved, it would appear that this pointer was indicating the 9° of Taurus i.e. May 5th (Julian Calendar).

Since this must have occurred in the year which followed the year of the preserved setting of the scales, it would appear that the Roman merchant ship on its last ill-fated voyage sank on May 5th 59 B.C. as attested by the Antikythera Mechanism.

Confirmation of the hazardous sailing conditions in the waters off the island of Antikythera at that time of the year, was provided by the sponge divers from the island of Symi almost two thousand years later.

---

* New and Full Moons 1001 B.C. to A.D. 1651 GOLDSTINE 1973

14. The Fiducial Mark

This short, but clearly incised line which has been carefully inscribed at right-angles to the Month scale of the mechanism, is accepted as having been inscribed at the time of the completion of manufacture.

In reference to the fixed Zodiac scale, the fiducial mark has been carefully measured to be displaced by a half degree. This indicates that the mechanism was finally completed in a year when the first New Moon after the Summer Solstice appeared on Cancer 19 (July 14th).

This phenomenon took place in the year 71 B.C. according to the Standard Tables previously referred to in the text.

15. The Inscriptions

There are four main areas of inscriptions which are attached to the mechanism. The positive identification of the form of the individual letters as being those used in the first century B.C. puts beyond doubt the period during which the Antikythera Mechanism was manufactured.

This was first attested by Wilhelm in 1902 —At that time 220 individual letters were recognizable.

Since those early days, careful cleaning and the removal of encrusted debris has revealed a further 573 letters.

Paragema Plate Inscription

Originally contained at least 24 lines of text. Each line began with a Key letter of the Greek alphabet. These Key letters are duplicated at specific intervals around the Zodiac scale. Thus by reference to the paragema plate the information of the risings and settings of certain notable stars and constellations could be read.

In Fig. 9 the remaining piece of paragema plate is illustrated. The area marked thus *********** is no longer in existence, but was recorded by Prof. Albert Rehm.

Whilst only a small fragment of the paragema plate from the mechanism has been recovered, it nevertheless contains a remarkable amount of information.

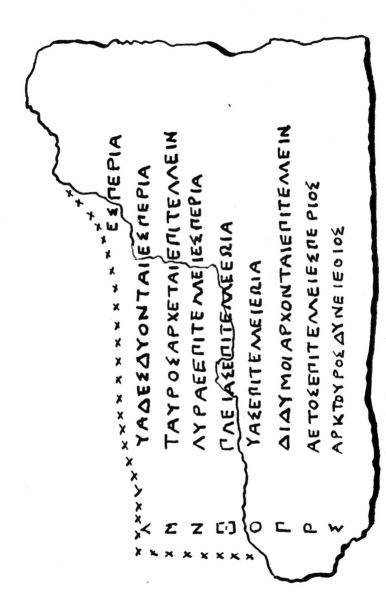

Fig. 9: Recovered inscription on the Paragema plate.

K

∧   Hyades in the Evening sets.

M   Taurus begins to rise.

N   Lyrae in the Evening rises.

Ξ   Pleiades in the Morning rises.

O   Hyades in the Morning rises.

Γ   Gemini begins to rise.

P   Eagle in the Evening rises.

ϛ   Arcturus in the Morning sets.

Fig. 10: Translation of the inscription.   *(Dale Mallory)*

Five known stars or groups of stars are referred to, in addition to two segments of the Zodiac. These are: —

The Hyades, for which both a Morning rise and a Evening set are given. (Aldebaran)

The Pleiades, for which a Morning rise is recorded. (Alycone)

Arcturus, for which a Morning setting is noted.

Lyrae, the constellation containing the bright star-Vega.

Eagle, the constellation containing the star-Altair.

Taurus and Gemini, two of the segments of the Zodiac are also named.

These eight entries cover a period of about two months which would seem to suggest that there were originally two plates in order to cover the whole year. However there is no evidence to support this suggestion, which is discussed in more detail later.

The omission of any reference to the star Sirius on the paragema plate, caused some of the experts to doubt the authenticity of Prof. A. Rehm's translation. Certainly Sirius being the brightest star in the sky (See Appendix VII) had been used by many ancient cultures as a calendar event of great significance. In the year 2768 B.C. the Morning Rise of Sirius (Sothis) coincided with the onset of the annual flooding of the Nile. This particular day; July 19th was selected as the beginning of the Egyptian calendar.

Over the years the fragile nature of the paragema plate has resulted in some loss of the material. Thus the first three extant lines, L, M, N cannot now be completely read.

If the inscriber of the paragema plate had wished to insert the Evening Set of Sirius it would have had to appear on Line N if the works of Geminos were being followed.

It is more likely that, faced with the need to make certain selections due to the limited space available, the omission of Sirius was a deliberate choice.

It has often been overlooked that the incorrect placing of events on the paragema plate did not necessarily throw the calender into confusion. The insertion of the Key letters in their correct places on the Front Dial (Zodiac Scale) would have rectified such apparent errors.

16. The Zodiac Scale

The recovered portion of this particular scale is in a good state of preservation and thus provides us with a lot of evidence as to its purpose. Divided into twelve major divisions, one for each of the segments of the Zodiac; the scale was further inscribed with graduations for each single degree.

On the recovered segment there is a 30° division which is clearly inscribed XYΛAI (Libra). Within this major division the first four letters of the Greek alphabet can be seen adjacent to specific degree marks.

A	Libra	1		Γ	Libra	14
B	Libra	11		Δ	Libra	16

These are followed by the fifth letter of the Greek alphabet E shown at the beginning of the next major division in a clockwise direction:

E   Scorpio   1

A tentative reading of the last letter of the alphabet next to the eighteenth degree of Virgo was made:

Ω   Virgo   18

With only 24 letters in the Greek alphabet, we must assume that the number of entries on both the Zodiac scale and the paragema plate was limited to twenty four.

The distribution of phenomena which matches all the available evidence is as follows:—

Libra	Four entries
Scorpio	One entry
Sagittarius	One entry
Capricorn	One entry
Aquarius	One entry
Pisces	One entry
Aries	Two entries
Taurus	Four entries
Gemini	Three entries
Cancer	Two entries
Leo	Two entries
Virgo	Two entries

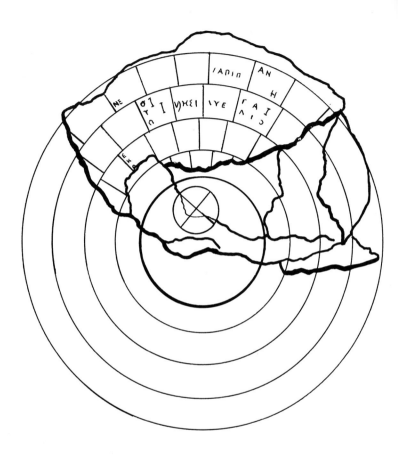

Fig. 11: Upper Back Dial.

Though the Antikythera Mechanism has been subjected to many hours of consideration by many of the leading experts in the field of archaeology, the importance of the inscribed letters found on the recovered portion of the Zodiac Scale has been completely overlooked.

Each of these six entries was recording an event of some importance which was occurring in the sky in the year that the mechanism was being completed.

Knowing the present position of the fixed stars and the rate of change of both their Right Ascension (R.A.) and Declination, it is possible to calculate with accuracy the position of any fixed star in the First Century B.C.

We can also put a Day to the Zodiac reference. With Cancer 1 being the day upon which the Summer Solstice occurred, then the entry for Libra 1 refers to the 91st day after the Summer Solstice. Thus: —

Libra 1	Day +91
Libra 11	Day +101
Libra 14	Day +104
Libra 16	Day +106
Scorpio 1	Day +121
Virgo 18	Day +78

During the First century B.C. the Morning Rise of the Arcturus coincided with Day +78 (Virgo 18).

Day 101 (Libra 11) would have seen the Evening Rise of Pleiades, with the Evening Set of Spica being observed three days later on Day +104 (Libra 14).

The Evening Rise of the Hyades would have been observed on Day +106 (Libra 16).

In order to complete the proposed paragema plate which follows, the Morning Rise of Sirius is entered upon Line 20, since it coincided with Cancer 9 during the First century B.C. The entry of Line 22 records Altair Morning Setting.

Thus the complete paragema plate with the matching entries on the Zodiac scale could have been as follows: —

		Zodiac Scale		**Paragema Plate**	
1	A	Libra 1	Libra rises	(18)
2	B	Libra 11	Pleiades Evening Rise	(17)
3	Γ	Libra 14	Spica Evening Set	—
4	Δ	Libra 16	Hyades Evening Rise	(20)
5	E	Scorpio 1	Scorpio rises	(21)
6	Z	Sagittarius 1	Sagittarius rises	(25)
7	H	Capricorn 1	Capricorn rises	(29)
8	Θ	Aquarius 1	Aquarius rises	(31)
9	I	Pisces 1	Pisces rises	(32)
10	K	Aries 1	Aries rises	(1)

Recovered portion of
Paragema Plate

11	Λ	Aries	Evening Set of Hyades	(3)
12	M	Taurus 1	Taurus begins to rise	(5)
13	N	Taurus	Evening Rise of Lyrae	(4)
14	Ξ	Taurus	Morning Rise of Pleiades	(7)
15	O	Taurus	Morning Rise of Hyades	(9)
16	Π	Gemini 1	Gemini begins to rise	(8)
17	P	Gemini	Evening Rise of Altair	(10)
18	Σ	Gemini	Morning Set of Arcturus	(11)
19	T	Cancer 1	Cancer rises	(12)
20	Y	Cancer 9	Sirius Morning Rise	(13)
21	Φ	Leo 1	Leo rises	(14)
22	X	Leo 2	Altair Morning Set	(15)
23	Ψ	Virgo 1	Virgo rises	(16)
24	Ω	Virgo 18	Arcturus Morning Rise	(19)

Note: The last line of figures in parenthesis ( ) shows the sequence of Geminos.

The recording of the Evening Set of Spica, the second event to be noted (Libra 14) on the Zodiac scale, no doubt led to the eventual exclusion of the Evening Setting of Sirius from the paragema plate inscription. From the evidence of both the Zodiac scale and the paragema plate it would seem that the maker of the mechanism had

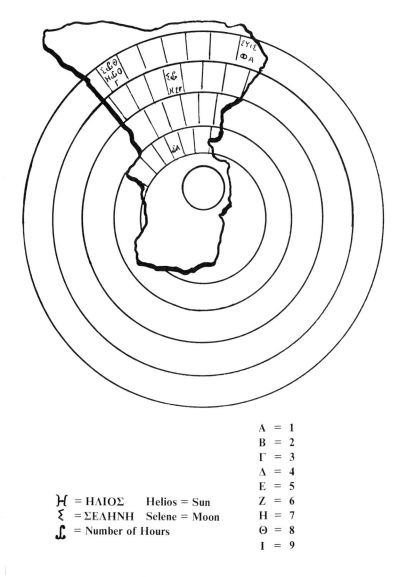

H = ΗΛΙΟΣ Helios = Sun
Ξ = ΣΕΛΗΝΗ Selene = Moon
ↄ = Number of Hours

A = 1
B = 2
Γ = 3
Δ = 4
E = 5
Z = 6
H = 7
Θ = 8
I = 9

Fig. 12: Lower Back Dial.

originally set out to record two events from each of just six Fixed stars: Sirius, Vega, Arcturus, Altair, Aldebaran (Hyades) and Alycone (Pleiades). These twelve observations, added to the twelve datelines of the Risings of the Zodiac filling the 24 available letters of the Greek alphabet.

However, having recorded the Morning Rise of Spica just three days after recording the Morning Rise of Arcturus, he would have realised the necessity of omitting one of the previously chosen observations.

From the evidence obtained from both the fragment of the paragema plate and the recovered section of the Zodiac Dial, it is probable that the maker of the mechanism used the following sequence:

Firstly, in line with his direct observations, he inserted the Key letters of the alphabet adjacent to the correct dates on the Zodiac scale. (Lines 2, 3, 4, 11, 14, 18, 20, 22 and 24).

Secondly, he inscribed the paragema plate with the names of the twelve segments of the Zodiac. (Lines 1, 5, 6, 7, 8, 9, 10, 12, 16, 19, 21 and 23).

On certain days of the year, faced with adverse observing conditions, he resorted to copying the recorded data which Geminos ascribes to Eudoxos, thus inadvertently duplicating errors. (Lines 13, 15 and 17). As has been mentioned earlier, though these appear to be misplaced on the paragema plate they may well have been correctly dated on the Zodiac scale, thus accurately recording these events for any future user of the device.

The apparent uneven distribution of the twenty-four entries would seem to suggest that having commenced the observations in late Autumn, adverse conditions for naked eye viewing forced them to be discontinued over the Winter months. Even on the island of Rhodes with its normally clear skies, such difficulties as inclement weather, atmospheric refraction and other problems would have to be contended with. These observations were resumed the following Spring when conditions improved.

The task of establishing the moment of first visibility of a particular star in the evening sky; or the last visibility of a star in the morning

76

sky is extremely difficult. Nor did these early astronomers have a wealth of tabulated data or precise star maps to which they could refer. It is therefore not surprising that the published information of many of the ancient astronomers is far from accurate.

The data which Geminos attributes to Eudoxos was mostly calculated mathematically and not by direct observation. This can lead to certain events (Risings or Settings), being dated in advance of their actual occurrence.

It is to Professor Price that we owe most of the detailed knowledge of both the construction and purpose of the Antikythera Mechanism. Appreciating the deep significance of such advanced technology emerging from Ancient Greece, and aided by detailed photographs of the mechanism, Prof. Price attempted to build a reconstruction of the device.

In June 1961, having again examined the mechanism in Athens he began to make significant progress in its reconstruction. Though he continued to work at the puzzle for many years, it was not until 1972 when, with the aid of Gamma-radiographs and X-ray pictures provided by the Greek Atomic Energy Commission, he was able to complete the reconstruction.

In 1974 he was able to publish a complete elucidation of the mechanism and the workings of its complex and sophisticated gear trains. (See Bibliography)

Professor Price concluded that the device was a mechanised calendar which gave the places of the Sun and Moon, as well as the Risings and Settings of other fixed stars through the cycle of years and months.

17. The Rear Dials

Each of the two Rear dials (Figs. 11 and 12) consists of a small subsidiary dial, Radius 44 mm in the centre of a number of movable scales, each of approx. 6 mm in width. These scales have been divided into separate divisions containing various inscriptions.

The inscriptions are a meaningful combination of astronomical symbols, numerical symbols and hour signs. A pointer swept both Rear dials.

Upper Rear Dial

Slip Ring	48 Divisions	7.5° each
Slip Ring	»	»
Slip Ring	»	»
Slip Ring	»	»
Sub. Dial	4 Divisions	90° each (Olympiad)

Mainly inscribed with planetary information. Mercury, Mars, Venus, Jupiter and Saturn.

Lower Rear Dial

Fixed Scale	60 Divisions	6° each
Slip Ring	»	»
Slip Ring	»	»
Slip Ring	»	»
Sub. Dial	12 Divisions	30° each (Synodic Month)

Inscribed with Lunar information.

Visitors to the National Archaeological Museum in Athens can see for themselves in the Second Room of Bronzes, the condition of the recovered parts of the Antikythera Mechanism. Looking at these ancient mechanical fragments with their delicate inscriptions one can only admire the work of Prof. A. Rehm and Prof. Derek de Solla Price in providing so much detailed knowledge from such little evidence.

In recognition of the latter, I quote his final conclusions regarding the significance of this unique find: —

"It is a bit frightening to know that just before the fall of their great civilization the Ancient Greeks had come so close to our age, not only in their thought, but also in their scientific technology."

In order to assist those readers who may wish to make a further study of the mechanism, I have followed the nomenclature used by Solla Price.

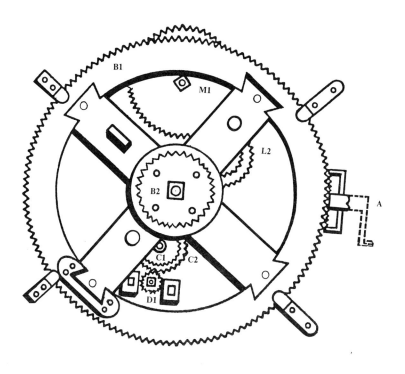

Fig. 13: Front view showing Main Drive wheel (B1) and other wheels.

Appendix I

Material Analysis and Usage

Extracts from the comprehensive reports of
>   Prof. Earle R. Caley
>   Prof. Cyril S. Smith
>   Institute for the Study of Metals. Univ. of Chicago. March 1959

Material Analysis - Bronze
>   Copper 89-98%   Tin 10-1%

>   Trace Elements 0.7% (Lead, Arsenic, Sodium, Nickel, Iron, Antimony, Bismuth).

(Analysed by Damberge in 1910, and said to contain about 4.1% of Tin alloyed to basic Copper.)

Cold hammered and annealed at about 500-600° C.

Material Usage
>   Rolled Bronze   Thickness 2.0-2.3mm.

>   85 sq.mm. (Including double-thickness Base Plate and four 19mm wide spokes.)

Appendix II

Basic design concept

As seen from the Earth, the Sun appears to move through the constellations of the Zodiac in just over 365 days, whilst the Moon revolves once every 27 1/3 days. The difference between these two rates of motion produces the cycle of Moon phases — once every 29 1/2 days.

The Antikythera Mechanism was designed to reproduce this phenomena by incorporating a differential gear fed by two separate drives.

The first was a straight drive from the Main Drive wheel, but in a reverse direction. The second drive was through a series of gear wheels in the forward direction. The differential gear took these two different rates and produced a calculated difference. Thus, turning the Main Drive wheel through nineteen complete revolutions resulted in the turntable receiving nineteen reverse turns, whilst simultaneously being fed with 254 revolutions through the series of gears. The resultant motion producing 235 revs. of the differential turntable.

Appendix III

Modern measurements of the Metonic cycle

	Days	Hours	Mins	Secs
Length of Mean Lunar Synodic Month (New Moon to New Moon)	29	12	44	3
235 Mean Lunar Months are: —	6939	16	31	45
Length of Mean Solar (Tropical) Year	365	5	48	47
19 Mean Solar Years are: —	6939	14	26	53
Difference between 235 Mean Lunar Months and 19 Solar Years: —		2	4	52

Appendix IV

Table A

Showing the *nominal* number of Teeth based on multiples of 3

Gear Wheels

Letter	1	2	3	4	5	
A	45	—	—	—	—	Handwheel
B	225	63	33	33	—	Main Drive Wheel
C	39	48	—	—	—	
D	24	126	—	—	—	
E	33 33	33	192	222	48	
F	48	30	—	—	—	
G	21	60	—	—	—	
H	60	15	—	—	—	
I	60	—	—	—	—	

J	63	—	—	—	—
K	33	48	—	—	—
L	36	54	—	—	—
M	96	15	—	—	—
N	63	—	—	—	—
O	33	48	—	—	—

Table B

Showing the quantity of Wheels having similar nominal numbers of Teeth.

Nominal No. of Teeth	Gear Wheel	
15	2	H2 M2
21	1	G1
24	1	D1
30	1	F2
33	7	B3 B4 E1 E2 E2 K1 O1
36	1	L1
39	1	C1
45	1	A1
48	5	C2 E5 F1 K2 O2
54	1	L2
60	3	G2 H1 I1
63	3	B2 J1 N1
96	1	M1
126	1	D2
192	1	E3
222	1	E4
225	1	B1
	32	

Appendix V

Gear train incorporated in the Antikythera Mechanism to duplicate the relationship between Solar Years and Synodic Months.

A1   45t   (Handwheel)
       ⟨⟨
B1   225t ═══════ B2   64t
                    ⟨⟨
                    C1   38t ═══════ C2   48t
                                      ⟨⟨
                                      D1   24t ═══ D2   127t
                                                    ⟨⟨
                                                    B4   32t

$$\frac{64}{38} \times \frac{48}{24} \times \frac{127}{32} = 13.368421 = \frac{254}{19}$$

One complete revolution of the Main Drive Wheel-B results in Gear Wheel B4 completing just over thirteen revolutions. Thus 19 complete revs. (i.e. 19 Solar Years) results in 254 revs. of B4 (i.e. 254 Synodic Months)

Note: – The number of Teeth(t) shown above is that accepted by Prof. Price as being consistent with the count obtained by Dr. Ch. Karakalos from X-radiography. (Greek Atomic Energy Commission Radiography Laboratory).

Gear train incorporated in the Antikythera Mechanism possibly to enable each Olympiad of Four Years to be displayed in the centre of the Upper Back Dial.

A1   45t (Handwheel)

B1   225 t ═══ B2   64t

L1   36t ═══ L2   54t

M1   96t ═══ M2   16t

N1   64t

$$\frac{64}{36} \times \frac{54}{96} \times \frac{16}{64} = \frac{55296}{221184} = 0.25$$

One complete revolution of the Main Drive Wheel-B results in Gear Wheel N1 completing one quarter of a revolution. Thus 4 complete revs, (i.e. 4 Solar Years) results in 1 rev. of N1 (i.e. One Olympiad).

Note: – The number of Teeth(t) shown above is that accepted by Prof. Price as being consistent with the count obtained by Dr. Ch. Karakalos from X-radiography. (Greek Atomic Energy Commission Radiography Laboratory).

Appendix VI

Diopter

A simple instrument made of bronze consisting of a horizontal support upon which are mounted two vertical plates.
1) A fixed plate in which is a small viewing hole.
2) A sliding plate with two holes in vertical alignment.

Method of use:
The eye was placed against the viewing hole in the fixed plate and focused upon a particular star. The sliding plate was then moved until its two holes coincided with both the upper and lower edges of the star.
From this setting the angular diameter of the star could be determined.
An instrument of the description is known to have been used by Hipparchus 167-127 B.C. in the course of his observations made at Alexandria and on the island of Rhodes.

The Commentary to Aratus by Hipparchus deals specifically with Risings and Settings for the horizon of Rhodes.

Appendix VII

Some 4000 fixed stars are visible to the naked eye from the island of Rhodes. The ancient Greeks grouped some 1000 of these into 48 separate constellations. This method of grouping the stars in this way was called astronomy, from the word 'astronomos' — one who arranges the stars.

These early astronomers also realised that certain of the stars did not remain on fixed courses, but appeared to move erratically through the skies. These stars they named the 'wanderers'. Today we call them the planets.

The brightest objects in the sky are listed below: —

Sun	−26.8
Moon	−13.6
Venus	−4.6
Mars	−1,6
Mercury	−1.6
Jupiter	−1.5
Saturn	−1.4

The brightest fixed stars which can be seen from Keskinto, Rhodes

	Sirius	−1.47		Betelguese	0.8
*	Vega	0.04	∘*	Aldebaran	0.86
∘*	Arcturus	0.06	∘	Spica	0.96
	Rigel	0.08		Pollux	1.15
	Capella	0.09		Deneb	1.26
	Procyon	0.34		Regulus	1.36
*	Altair	0.77	∘*	Alycone	2.80

∘ On recovered portion of Paragema plate
* On Zodiac Scale

Appendix VIII

Zodiakos Kyklos		**Greek Month**
Cancer	ΚΑΡΚΙΝΟ	Hekatombaion
Leo	ΛΕΩΥ	Metageitnion
Virgo	ΠΑΡΘΕΝΟΥ	Boedromion
Libra	ΧΥΛΑΙ	Pyanopsion
Scorpio	ΣΚΟΡΠΙΟΣ	Maimakter
Saggitarius	ΤΟΣΕΥΙΟΣ	Poseidon
Capricorn	ΑΙΥΟΚΕΡΩΣ	Gamelion
Aquarius	ΑΥΔΡΟΧΟΥ	Anthester
Pisces	ΙΧΘΥΕΣ	Elaphebolion
Aries	ΚΡΙΟΣ	Mounichion
Taurus	ΤΑΥΡΟΣ	Thargelion
Gemini	ΔΙΔΥΜΟΙ	Skirophorion

Appendix IX

Inscription from Keskinto

Modern maps of the island of Rhodes do not show the location of Keskinto. It lies some 5 km. to the south-west of Lindos, just beyond the modern village of Lardos. Nothing now remains of the ancient site.

It is situtated almost exactly along the 36° latitude which Hipparchus had noted as the nominal latitude for Rhodes.

In 1893, a worker in the fields from nearby Lindos accidentally stumbled upon the lower part of a stone stele bearing various inscriptions. These have been interpreted as a list of planetary parameters. These are based on the assumption that 29140 sidereal years contain a whole number of revolutions and phases for the outer planets. Mercury, Mars, Jupiter and Saturn are referred to in that order.

Known as the Inscription from Keskinto – the stone fragment measures 78×31×12 cm. and is now in the Antikensammlung of the Staatliche Museum in East Berlin. Due to weathering the inscriptions are extremely indistinct. The inscription has been dated around 100 B.C. though this date is not secure. It was thought by some that Keskinto was the site where Attulus of Rhodes carried out his observations and that the stele was possibly erected by him. For a comprehensive assessment of the Inscription see, 'A History of Ancient Mathematical Astronomy' by O. Neugebauer.

(Springer, Berlin, 1975)

Appendix X

First and Last visibility
Observations calculated for the year 71 B.C. as seen from Keskinto, Rhodes. (36° N. 28°E).

Event	Julian Calender
Aries rises	March 27th
Pleiades Morning Rise	March 31st
Hyades Morning Rise	April 15th
Taurus rises	April 27th
Arcturus Morning Set	May 3rd
Vega Evening Rise	May 5th
Pleiades Evening Set	May 13th
Altair Evening Rise	May 22nd
Hyades Evening Set	May 26th
Gemini Rises	May 27th

The references to the signs of the Zodiac (Aries, Taurus and Gemini) shown above, relate to the artificial segments in the sky each of 30°, and not the constellations of the same names.

The above astronomical information was computed with the aid of the "STARTRACK" program compiled by Discovery Software

291 Cricklewood Lane
London. England. U.K.

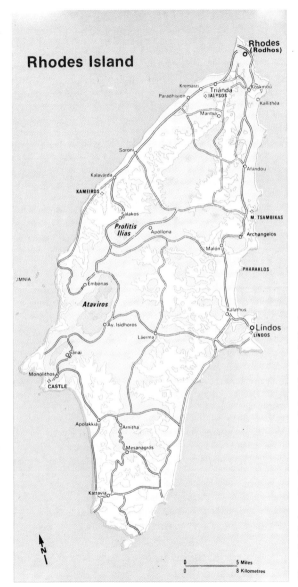

Rhodes Island

Rhodes
(Rodhos)

Kremasti
Paradhision
Triánda
IALYSOS
Koskinoú
Kallithéa
Maritsá
Soroni
Kalavárda
Afándou
KAMEIROS
Salakos
Profítis Ilias
Apóllona
M. TSAMBIKAS
Archángelos
Malón
PHARAKLOS
IMNIA
Embonas
Ataviros
Kalathus
Áy. Isidhoros
Lindos
LINDOS
Láerma
Fanai
Monólithos
CASTLE
Apolakkiá
Arnitha
Mesanagrós
Kattavía

N

| 0 | | 5 Miles |
| 0 | | 8 Kilometres |

Fig. 14: Modern Road network of the island of Rhodes.

Postscript

The salvage operations which took place off the island of Antikythera in 1900-1 were finally abandoned due to the difficult weather conditions encountered, and not because the site was exhausted.

In August 1950 one of the divers who had taken part in this extremely hazardous work some fifty years previous declared that, "For the twenty-seven amphorae which we were able to bring to the surface some fifty others remained".

This statement was later confirmed by Frederic Dumas, chief diver of the exploration vessel the "Calypso". According to Dumas, the sponge divers of Symi had really only cleared the surface of the wreck and a great deal of the Roman ship remained for future investigation under some 50 cm. of sand.

In 1977, the "Calypsò" returned to the site under the command of Jacques Cousteau. Using modern equipment and up to date diving techniques, his divers brought to the surface more treasures. Two statuettes in athletic poses were amongst the amphorae brought to the surface, and a tiny arm broken from a statuette which had been recovered seventy-seven years earlier was found. Amongst these later finds was a small pile of silver coins encrusted together in one solid lump. Separated and cleaned by the experts at the National Archaeological Museum in Athens, they were eventually identified as originating from Pergamum and dated to 86 B.C. thus adding to the other indicators as to the date of the shipwreck.

Amongst the priceless works of Art which may well still remain awaiting recovery, some missing pieces of the Antikythera Mechanism may also be lying beneath the waves.

One can only look forward to the day when the Greek Archaeological Service sets out to finally complete the work which began many years ago.

There can be no doubt that such an event will provoke as much interest and excitement as did the original discovery.

Victor J. Kean published the first complete elucidation of "The Disk from Phaistos" in 1985. Now be brings to his readers the story of the manufacture and use of the Ancient Greek mechanical computer on display in the National Archaological Museum in Athens.

Made on the island of Rhodes ca. 71 B.C. the computer was lost beneath the waves for almost two thousand years until its recovery in 1910. The "Antikythera Mechanism" as it became known, caused much controversy in the scientific circles of the day for the technology incorporated in the device was far ahead of its time.

BIBLIOGRAPHY

1 Art salvaged from the Sea	George Karo	Archaeology I	1948
2 An Ancient Greek Computer	Solla Price	Scientific Am.	1959
3 Antikythera Shipwreck Reconsidered	G. Weinberg	Amer. Phil. Soc.	1965
4 Archaeology under Water	G.F. Bass	Thames and Hudson	1966
5 Gears from the Greeks	Solla Price	Amer. Phil. Soc.	1974
6 Ancient Engineers	Sprg. de Camp	Balantine	1974
7 Science since Babylon	Solla Price	Yale Univ. Press	1976

93

BATTLE OVER MALTA

AIRCRAFT LOSSES & CRASH SITES 1940–42

ANTHONY ROGERS

SUTTON PUBLISHING

THE AUTHOR

Anthony Rogers grew up in Malta and, in the mid-1970s, served there in the Royal Marines Commandos. He continued to use the Island as a base while working in the oil industry until recession, and an interest in the media, led to a new career as a photojournalist. He maintains links with Malta through visits and his membership of various associations.

First published in 2000 by
Sutton Publishing Limited · Phoenix Mill
Thrupp · Stroud · Gloucestershire · GL5 2BU

Copyright © Anthony Rogers, 2000

All rights reserved. No part of this publication may be reproduced, stored in a retrieval system, or transmitted, in any form, or by any means, electronic, mechanical, photocopying, recording or otherwise, without the prior permission of the publisher and copyright holder.

Anthony Rogers has asserted the moral right to be identified as the author of this work.

British Library Cataloguing in Publication Data
A catalogue record for this book is available from the British Library

ISBN 0 7509 2392 X

Typeset in 10/11 pt Bembo
Typesetting and origination by
Sutton Publishing Limited
Printed in Great Britain by
The Guernsey Press Company Limited,
Guernsey, Channel Islands.

CONTENTS

To the memory of my mother, who actually witnessed some of the events that follow. And to my son, Chris, who hopefully will never have to endure such times.

FOREWORD

BY WING COMMANDER
P.B. 'LADDIE' LUCAS CBE DSO DFC

Only those who knew Malta at the peak of the Mediterranean battle in the spring and early summer of 1942 can truly comprehend its intensity – or measure the courage of the gallant Maltese people in standing up to the weight of the Axis powers' devastating onslaught.

What is not generally appreciated is the extent of the concentration of the aerial bombardment against an island measuring little more that 17 miles long and 8 wide – just a shade smaller than our Isle of Wight. So mark well this fact: in March and April 1942 – two calendar months – twice the tonnage of bombs fell on Malta as were dropped on London during the worst 12 months of the Blitz. And there were only four principal targets to absorb this attack: Grand Harbour and its environs and the three operational airfields – Takali in roughly the centre with Luqa and Hal Far a few miles to the south.

Well might Winston Churchill write of this period, 'In March and April, all the heat was turned on Malta and remorseless air attacks by day and night wore the island down and pressed it to the last gasp.'

And why did Churchill and the War Cabinet in London decide that this beleaguered island must be held, no matter what the cost, what the odds and what the sacrifice? Because, as a base for our strike aircraft and Submarine Flotilla – the glorious Fighting 10th – it enabled the Allies to straddle the enemy's supply lines from southern Europe to General Erwin Rommel and his Afrika Korps, slogging it out with the British 8th Army in the Libyan Desert.

A few years ago, when I was researching the details of my personalized story of the island conflict, *Malta – The Thorn in*

Rommel's Side, a good German friend, one of the ablest and most popular of all the Luftwaffe wartime commanders, came to dinner with me at the Royal Air Force Club in London. Oberst Eduard Neumann, a highly accomplished officer, had commanded Jagdgeschwader 27, the Air Force Group supporting the Afrika Korps in the Western Desert. Neumann had been as well placed as anyone on 'the other side' to assess the strategic importance of Malta in terms of Germany's prosecution of the North African campaign. I posed my question with care. 'Edu', I said, 'you were on the receiving end and saw at first hand the effect of Malta's strike capability on the supplies for your forces. How did you actually regard the Island's impact at the time?'

Neumann put down his knife and fork and held up a cautionary finger. 'Laddie,' he said decisively, 'Malta was the key.' Hitler's failure to invade the Island had been a grave misjudgment.

To retain control of this outpost as an effective operational base for offence and defence we had to win the air battle. With no more than four or five squadrons of fighter aircraft facing Feldmarschall Albert Kesselring's Luftflotte 2 with its front-line strength of some 600 or 700 aircraft – fighters and bombers, based across the Straits in Sicily and southern Italy, Malta's defending air force and gunners, sustained heroically by the Royal Navy, the Merchant Navy and the United States Navy, had to hold the line. Impotence in operations and, still less, surrender could never be countenanced.

It followed that in the great air battles which ensued, casualties on both sides were heavy. For weeks, those in Malta, enduring one air raid after another, had a grandstand view of heavily damaged and stricken aircraft plunging earthwards from thousands of feet above.

While a few of the pilots from the Island's fighter squadrons, in a gesture of chivalry, would make a practice of exchanging experiences with wounded Luftwaffe and Regia Aeronautica aircrew in hospital, sometimes taking them cigarettes and chocolate, there was rarely any disposition on our part to visit the scene of crashed aircraft. Generally, once an aeroplane had been dispatched in the air that was the end of it. Morale would not have been aided by seeking out the location of shattered remains.

What a surprise it is, therefore, more than half a century on, to find in the pages that follow the most complete and comprehensive examination yet made of the sites and remains of aircraft crashes which so often formed a feature of the island battle all those years ago. By diligent and extraordinary application and research, the author has compiled a unique picture of the spread of these incidents.

By listing 184 aircraft crashes -- Allied and enemy -- from those awful days and identifying 125 of these sites, Anthony Rogers has performed a signal factual service. Individual accounts are supported with detailed background information about a particular aircraft, its pilot or crew, the unit designation and the date and hour of its final moment. I take leave to doubt whether such an intimate picture has ever been attempted, let alone compiled, before.

One thing is sure. By undertaking this work, the author has enhanced immeasurably the detailed record of this decisive island battle of the Second World War but, more than that, he has provided us with a sad yet meaningful picture of the appalling sacrifice which it all entailed.

Read on and I'll be surprised if you disagree.

P.B. 'Laddie' Lucas
2 September 1915–20 March 1998

ABBREVIATIONS

AA, A/A	Anti-Aircraft		MG	Machine Gun
A/C, a/c	Aircraft		MI	Medical Inspection
AC (1, 2)	Aircraftman (1st, 2nd Class)		M.llo	Maresciallo
AFM	Armed Forces of Malta		MNFU	Malta Night Fighter Unit
AI	Air Interception		MT	Motor Transport
AOC	Air Officer Commanding		MTM	Motoscafo Turismo Modificato
1° Av	Primo Aviere			(Modified Tourist Motorboat,
Av Sc	Aviere Scelto			or explosive motor boat)
BEM	British Empire Medal		OADU	Overseas Air Delivery Unit
BSM	Battery Sergeant Major		Obgfr	Obergerfreiter
Cap	Capitano		Obltn	Oberleutnant
Cpl	Corporal		Ofw	Oberfeldwebel
CO	Commanding Officer		OP	Observation Post
DA	Delayed Action		ORB	Operations Record Book
DFC	Distinguished Flying Cross		OTU	Operational Training Unit
DFM	Distinguished Flying Medal		Plt Off, P/O	Pilot Officer
DLI	Durham Light Infantry		PRU	Photographic Reconnaissance
DSO	Distinguished Service Order			Unit
EK II	Eiserne Kreuz II (Iron Cross		P/W	Prisoner of War
	2nd Class)		RA	Royal Artillery
FAA	Fleet Air Arm		RAC	Royal Armoured Corps
Fg Off	Flying Officer		RDF	Radio Direction Finding
F/L, F/LT,	Flight Lieutenant		RNAS	Royal Naval Air Service
F/Lt, Flt Lt			R/T	Radio Telephone
FS, F/SGT,	Flight Sergeant		RTR	Royal Tank Regiment
F/Sgt			SA	Small Arms
Fw	Feldwebel		Serg	Sergente
Gefr	Gefreiter		Serg Magg	Sergente Maggiore
HAA	Heavy Anti-Aircraft		Sgt	Sergeant
HE	High Explosive		S/L	Searchlight
Hptm	Hauptmann		SLC	Siluro a Lenta Corsa (Slow-
HSL	High Speed Launch			running Torpedo, or 'human
IAF	Italian Air Force			torpedo')
Jabo	Jagdbomber (Fighter-bomber)		SNCO	Senior Non-Commissioned
KOMR	King's Own Malta Regiment			Officer
LAA	Light Anti-Aircraft		S.Ten	Sottotenente
LAC	Leading Aircraftman		Sub Lt	Sub Lieutenant
LMG	Light Machine Gun		TD	Territorial Decoration, or
Ltn	Leutnant			Efficiency Decoration
Maj	Major		Ten	Tenente
MAS	Motoscafo Anti Sommergibili		Uffz	Unteroffizier
	(Anti-Submarines Motorboat,		W/Comm,	Wing Commander
	or Motor Torpedo Boat)		Wg Cdr	
MC	Military Cross		WO	Warrant Officer
ME, Me	Messerschmitt		W/T	Wireless Telegraphy

INTRODUCTION AND ACKNOWLEDGEMENTS

When I was younger, my mother, who was Maltese, some-times related to me her experiences as a little girl during the war. She did not talk often about such events, however, and would sometimes become agitated by my insatiable curiosity. Later, I understood why.

One day, she told me how she had been instructed to take some soup, prepared from the meagre rations available, to one of the menfolk employed at a local gun site. During the journey there was an air raid, the intensity of which terrified my mother. As nearby anti-aircraft guns opened fire, she crouched against a rubble wall and looked up at the bursting shells and attacking aircraft, one of which received a direct hit and began to descend, out of control, directly overhead. As the panic stricken child fled, the doomed aircraft slammed into the ground where she had been sheltering moments earlier. In the confusion, the soup bowl and its precious contents were lost. This so concerned my mother that she was reluctant to return home, fearing a scolding for being careless. When she eventually explained what had happened, she was teased by an elder brother, who considered the subject a source of amusement for some years. Whenever the incident was mentioned, my mother would become terribly upset. Of course, it wasn't the loss of the soup that caused the reaction. Somewhat insensitively, I asked to be shown where the aircraft had crashed. My mother refused. She died in 1986, without ever taking me to the scene of that eventful day.

I shall never know for sure, but the aircraft that very nearly ended my mother's life may have been Unteroffizier Werner Mirschinka's Messerschmitt Bf 109, which is thought to have crashed near Bubaqra after being hit by AA on 3 January 1942. The event is described on page 98.

Some might think that after sustaining two and a half years of aerial warfare Malta must be a veritable aircraft graveyard. However, many aircraft lost during the battle lie beneath the Mediterranean, while Malta's rocky terrain ensured that those which crashed on land frequently broke up on impact. This was no doubt welcomed by salvage crews, whose thoroughness was partly attributable to the Island's geological structure. All that remains at many locations are easily overlooked scraps of aluminium and fragments of shattered perspex; even less survives in areas where there has been development. Sometimes, though, one may come across a significant find – such as the pair of Hispano cannon, still firmly lodged in bedrock in a field near Siggiewi, thought to be the crash site of a Spitfire of 126 Squadron from which American Pilot Officer Richard McHan baled out on 3 July 1942, apparently as a result of engine failure.

Some crashed or wrecked machines were disposed of in pits which were then covered over. Occasionally, these sites are re-located. In the early 1980s, construction work at the western edge of Ta'Qali uncovered, and soon obliterated, a dump containing, among other things, sections of airframe, aircraft instruments and fittings. Another dump, believed to exist nearby, has so far escaped a similar fate.

Numerous battles took place over south and south-east Malta, as shown by the concentration of crashes in this area. The south coast has remained relatively unspoilt for centuries, and any wreckage still remaining is likely to be found along the region's cliffs and among its ravines, as well as beneath the shallow top-soil of the little fields that predominate here. Often, farmers have used pieces of wreckage in the construction of the rubble walls that divide Malta's fields.

It is, of course, impossible to compile a list of every crash site. Some simply could not be located, and most aircraft lost offshore are likely to remain so. Nevertheless, *Battle Over Malta* does provide the only detailed reference for those sites that have been found. Gathering this information necessitated spending more than 450 hours at the Public Record Office in Kew, where in excess of 200 documents were consulted; and many more hours at the Imperial War Museum, the RAF Museum and elsewhere. Along the way

I was assisted by many who selflessly gave of their time to corroborate events and/or to provide their own recollections. To this end, *Battle Over Malta* is as accurate as can be expected, but if there are any errors, the responsibility is mine.

My sincere thanks and appreciation to everyone who helped to make this work possible. They include former Service personnel: John Alton, Ron Backhouse, H.J.S. (John) Beazley, the late Howard Bell and Jimmy Booth, Pat Bing, Fred Callus, Carmelo Cassar, the late Phil Chandler, Emanuel Ciantar, the late F.F. Clark, George Dale, D.J. (John) Eaborn, Gordon Farquharson, Dave Ferraby, Ted Filby, Phil Francis, Stan Fraser, John Galea, Bob Garraghan, Steve Haffenden, P.L. Hammond, N.P.W. (Pat) Hancock (Honorary Secretary/Treasurer of the Battle of Britain Fighter Association), J.S. Houghton, Professor Quentin Hughes, Bill Jackson, Lars Larsen, R.L. Ledbrook, P.G. (Graham) Leggett, the late George Lord and P.B. 'Laddie' Lucas, The Honourable Judge Ian McKay, Bill Metcalf, the late Reg Morse, Thomas Neil, Leo Nomis, Malcolm Oxley, the late Denis Parker, Jim Pickering, Jack Rae, Frank Rixon, Peter Rothwell, Conyers Rutter, T.C. (Charlie) Savage, Alan Sheppard, Bill Sheppard, F.E. (Ted) Shute, Peter Simpson, Rod Smith, Jim Somerville, Tony Spooner, Don Stones, Peter Thompson, Peter Watson, Bill Welford, Pat Wells, the late Phil Wigley, and Roger Woodhouse. Thanks, too, to Brian Cook, Honorary Secretary of the 89 Squadron Reunion Club; D.P.F. 'Mac' McCaig, Honorary Secretary/ Treasurer of the 249 Squadron Association, and Joachim Louis and Hermann Neuhoff (both ex-Luftwaffe); Gino Battaggion, Generale Francesco Cavalera and Silvio De Giorgi (all former Regia Aeronautica).

Many crash sites would not have been located without the invaluable assistance and expertise of Robert Farrugia in Malta. Thanks, too, to Brian Cull and Roland Symons for their generosity in providing material intended for their own publications. I am also grateful to Horst Amberg, Joe Azzopardi, Oliver and Mrs Diana Barnham, the family of the late Ernie Broad, Squadron Leader Rodney Burges, Tony Busuttil, Don Caldwell, Gavin Cooper, George Curmi, Lord James Douglas-Hamilton MP, Mrs Carmen Fenech, Francis

Galea, Alfred Gatt, John Hamlin, Chris John, Mrs Lydia Lord, Carlo Lucchini, Lex McAuley, Phil Nobbs, Mrs Ena O'Connell, John Ormrod, Dr Jochen Prien, Lieutenant Mark Said AFM, Andy Saunders, Mrs Elizabeth Scratton, Chris Shores, Edgar Smith, John Weal and John Wigley. Frederick Galea and the late Philip Vella, present and past Honorary Secretaries of Malta's National War Museum Association, were equally helpful, as was the staff of the RAF Museum and the Imperial War Museum (London), the Royal Marines Museum (Eastney), the Air Historical Branch (London), the Public Record Office (Kew), the Lufwaffen-museum der Bundeswehr (Germany), the Volksbund Deutsche Kriegsgräberfürsorge e.V. (Germany), the Ministero Della Difesa (Italy) and the German and Italian embassies in London.

I also wish to thank the publishers and authors who kindly gave permission to quote from their works, all of which are acknowledged in the Notes section towards the end of this book and express my gratitude to Sonja Stammwitz who helped with the typing and, along with the late Phil Wigley, took on the laborious task of translating German material. Last, but no means least, thank you to Sarah Moore, my editor at Sutton Publishing for helping make this book what it is.

MALTA 1940–42

Measuring just seventeen and a half miles by eight and a quarter, Malta is the largest of three main islands situated in the middle of the Mediterranean south of Sicily and is almost equidistant from Gibraltar in the western approaches and Suez in the east. The Island boasts one of the best natural harbours in the region and has provided a succession of rulers with an enviably dominant position. In 1814, Malta freely became part of the British Empire, serving as an ideal base for the Royal Navy, the Army and, more than a century later, for the Royal Air Force.

In the summer of 1939, the Committee of Imperial Defence approved a long-term air defence programme in recognition of Malta's strategic importance. The plan was designed to improve existing anti-aircraft capabilities and also took into account the requirement for fighter planes. Malta had already been provided with its first Radio Direction Finding Station (radar); there was an airfield at Hal Far, an airport at Ta'Qali, and construction on a third aerodrome near Luqa was also well under way. (In addition, there was a seaplane station at Kalafrana and seaplane facilities at Marsaxlokk and St Paul's Bay.)

On 10 June 1940, Italy entered the war against Britain and France. Luqa aerodrome was soon to become operational, but there were still only 34 heavy anti-aircraft guns, 8 Bofors and 24 searchlights available, together with several Royal Navy Gloster Sea Gladiators recently taken over by the RAF[1]. At dawn on 11 June, the Regia Aeronautica's 2ᵃ Squadra Aerea commenced operations against Malta; 18 Macchi C.200s escorting some 55 Savoia Marchetti S.79s across the 60 miles of sea that separates the Island from Sicily.[2] Hal Far, Kalafrana and the Dockyard area were each targeted. The raiders were intercepted by three of Malta's Gladiators in this engagement, the first of many during the next two and a half years.

The Fighter Flight's outdated biplanes were Malta's sole aerial defence for nearly two weeks following Italy's declaration of war. Eventually, they would be immortalised as 'Faith', 'Hope' and 'Charity' (notwithstanding the fact that there were at least four aircraft on strength with others stored in crates). Reinforcements did not arrive until 21 June when two Hurricanes, followed on the 22nd by three more, were retained after landing in Malta en route to the Middle East.[3]

It was also on 22 June that the RAF achieved its first victory when Flight Lieutenant George Burges, flying a Gladiator, was credited with destroying an S.79: there were two survivors, both of whom became prisoners of war. Air battles continued throughout July, with losses on both sides. On the morning of 3 July, Flying Officer John Waters chased and shot down an S.79 before his own aircraft was attacked by FIAT CR 42s. Waters crash-landed as a result, but survived unhurt. His Hurricane was written off. The first RAF fatality occurred on 16 July, when CR 42s shot down a Hurricane piloted by Flight Lieutenant Peter Keeble. On 31 July, the first of Malta's Gladiators was lost, Flying Officer Peter Hartley baling out into the sea from where he was rescued and rushed to Mtarfa Military Hospital suffering from severe burns.

The Maltese were only too aware that their island urgently needed more fighters, and on 30 July 'The Fighter Plane Fund, Malta', was launched to enable the public to purchase their own aircraft for the Island's defence. In three months enough was raised to pay for two Spitfires. These were duly assembled and christened 'Malta' and 'Ghawdex', the latter after the Maltese name for the neighbouring island of Gozo. Ironically, neither machine ever reached Malta. Both were released to 74 Squadron in May 1941; W3210 'Malta' was reported missing during a sortie over northern France on 27 June 1941, while W3212 'Ghawdex' was eventually transferred to the Royal Navy.[4]

Malta had been at war for nearly two months before an operation was launched to reinforce the Island's fighter force. On 2 August, twelve Hurricane Mk Is of 418 Flight left the aircraft carrier HMS *Argus* to be flown 380 miles to Luqa where they joined the surviving fighters there to form 261 Squadron.

Malta was to experience a new mode of aerial attack when 96° Gruppo Bombardamento a Tuffo became the first Italian unit to be equipped with Junkers Ju 87Bs; operations against the Island commenced on 4 September with the dive-bombing of Delimara by five Picchiatelli.

At the end of October 1940, Headquarters and Maintenance staff from RAF Luqa were dispatched to Ta'Qali preparatory to its transition to a fighter base. On 17 November, HMS *Argus* again flew off twelve aircraft, this time accompanied by two Fleet Air Arm Blackburn Skuas. Tragically, eight of the RAF fighters ran out of fuel before reaching their destination, while one of the Skuas was shot down by AA fire after becoming hopelessly lost and flying over Sicily.

Malta's fighter pilots were extremely courageous men whose achievements cannot be overemphasised but in addition to fighters, Malta also provided a base for various other machines, including flying boats, bombers, torpedo and reconnaissance aircraft, all of which were kept operational through the skill and dedication of the often-overworked maintenance crews. Neither should one forget the magnificent efforts of the Royal Navy and Merchant Marine, or the heroism of Malta's land forces, particularly the anti-aircraft gunners. All would continue to play a vital role throughout the siege.

Mussolini's offensive against Malta, the North African campaign and Italy's invasion of Greece finally led Hitler to send reinforcements to his ally in the Mediterranean. Towards the end of 1940, elements of the Luftwaffe's X Fliegerkorps, commanded by Generalleutnant Hans-Ferdinand Geisler, began to arrive in Sicily from Norway. By mid-January 1941, the Luftwaffe had gathered in Sicily a formidable array of front-line aircraft that included Junkers Ju 87s and 88s, Heinkel He 111s and Messerschmitt Bf 110s. For Malta, the war was about to begin in earnest.

In January 1941, Operation 'Excess' delivered to the Island troops, supplies and a number of crated Hurricanes, though not without cost. The destroyer HMS *Gallant* was severely damaged by a mine, while the carrier *Illustrious* was singled out for attack by the Germans during the debut of the Luftwaffe over the central Mediterranean. At 1238 hours on

10 January, following an attack by S.79s, German Ju 87 Stukas arrived overhead and moments later achieved the first of six direct hits. The assault lasted just six and a half minutes and was later described by the carrier's Captain Denis Boyd as, 'severe, brilliantly executed, and pressed home with the utmost skill and determination'.[5]

Despite further attacks by both the Regia Aeronautica and the Luftwaffe, during which she was struck yet again, the badly damaged *Illustrious* was able to limp into Grand Harbour during the evening of the 10th. Incredibly, the carrier was virtually ignored by the enemy until 16 January, when she was targeted by a combined force of some forty-four Ju 87s and seventeen Ju 88s escorted by Bf 110s, CR 42s and Macchi C.200s. But the defenders, having learned much from previous raids by Italian dive-bombers, had prepared a formidable 'box barrage'. The attackers also had to contend with the Island's fighters, supplemented by Fulmars off the *Illustrious*. It is recorded that during one of the raids, a Fulmar followed a bomber through the barrage to level out at only 15 feet before shooting down the German machine just beyond the harbour entrance.[6]

Two days later, the German bombers returned, this time concentrating on the airfields at Hal Far and Luqa. On Sunday 19 January, *Illustrious* was again subjected to a day of intensive bombing, with the attackers having to face a terrifying repetition of Thursday's barrage. On the 23rd, the carrier slipped her moorings and quietly left Grand Harbour on the first stage of her journey to the shipyards of the United States. Her remaining Fulmars stayed as welcome reinforcements for the Island's air force.

Events in Libya between January and March led to the departure of a number of Axis aircraft from Sicily (though some Ju 88s would return in early April). Early in February, Messerschmitt Bf 109 Es of 7/JG 26 were also transferred from Germany to Gela in Sicily, under the command of Oberleutnant Joachim Müncheberg, whose outstanding performance had already gained him twenty-three victories and earned him the coveted *Ritterkreuz* (Knight's Cross).

At the end of January six more Hurricanes arrived in Malta from North Africa. However, the Hurricane was no match for the faster, cannon-equipped Messerschmitt Bf 109.

During the next four months 7/JG 26 would claim at least forty-two air victories, twenty of which were credited to Müncheberg (including one during his unit's brief involvement in the invasion of Yugoslavia) and all without a single operational loss.[7]

Notwithstanding German efforts to neutralise Malta, the Island was still able to provide the Royal Navy with a base from which to strike at Axis supply routes, thus creating a constant drain on enemy shipping in the Mediterranean.

The Island's fighter strength was sustained by occasional reinforcements from North Africa coupled with the constant attention of RAF ground personnel. On 3 April, Malta received its first batch of Hurricane IIAs. During the next two months there were three major naval operations in which the carriers *Ark Royal* and *Furious* flew off a total of eighty-one Hurricanes, although many were to continue to the desert after refuelling. During this time – mid-1941 – the air forces on both sides in the central Mediterranean underwent some reorganisation. In Malta, a newly reformed 185 Squadron was created using pilots from 261 Squadron shortly before the latter unit was replaced by 249 Squadron, flown in off *Ark Royal* on 21 May. April and May also saw the arrival of the first Blenheim and Beaufighter units. On 1 June, Air Vice-Marshal Forster Maynard, Malta's Air Officer Commanding since the start of hostilities, was finally relieved by Air Commodore Hugh Pughe Lloyd. That month more Hurricanes, including the latest four-cannon IICs, were ferried in by the Royal Navy and on the 28th, 126 Squadron was also re-formed from the recently arrived 46 Squadron to operate from Ta'Qali with 249. In July, twelve Hurricane MK IIs were allocated for a new night fighter unit. Malta's defences were further improved following the arrival of extra troops and the delivery of more AA guns and ammunition.

The Allied build-up in Malta coincided with the run-down of the Luftwaffe in Sicily. Most of its aircraft were withdrawn in May for Operation 'Barbarossa', the German invasion of Russia. The following month, 7/JG 26 also left, flying south to Libya.

Tasked once again with subjugating Malta, the Italians proceeded with an audacious plan whereby they would simultaneously strike at the submarine base at Marsamxett Harbour and the recently arrived 'Substance' convoy in neighbouring Grand Harbour. Following the withdrawal of the Luftwaffe, there had been a noticeable decrease in the number of raids. The Islanders were, therefore, amazed when, during the night of 25/26 July, the Italian Navy's élite La Decima Flottiglia MAS deployed two SLC 'human torpedoes' and nine MTM explosive motor boats to a point north of Grand Harbour. Unfortunately for the Italians they were detected while still 20 miles short of their target. Furthermore, when the attack began, the SLCs failed to reach their objectives, which included the destruction of the anti-torpedo net across the harbour mouth. This task was taken over by one of the MTMs. At 0445 hours, it hit and blew up the mole bridge of the breakwater, causing the west span to collapse and this effectively blocked the entrance. The attack now turned into a rout for the Italians. As searchlights illuminated the scene the shore defences opened up, sending tracer rounds ricocheting off the sea into the night sky. The Italians were in a hopeless situation made all the worse when Hurricanes took off at dawn to attack the survivors as they tried to withdraw back to Sicily. Fifteen Italians were killed in the raid and eighteen captured.

There was a sharp decline in Italian aerial activity during August and September 1941. For the first time, Malta's forces were able to meet the enemy on an equal footing after the Navy delivered, between July and September, seven Swordfish and twenty-two Hurricanes in addition to thousands of tons of supplies. The Italians did what they could to disrupt operations, but of some sixty-seven vessels comprising the convoys 'Substance' and 'Halberd', just two ships were sunk and four damaged.

In September, several Hurricanes were fitted with Light Series bomb racks capable of holding 40lb General Purpose and 25lb incendiary bombs; the 'Hurri-bombers' subsequently carrying out a series of raids against Sicily. While attacking Còmiso on 30 September, 185 Squadron encountered the new Macchi C.202s for the first time. Powered by the same model Daimler Benz DB601 engine as the latest Messerschmitt Bf 109 F, the Folgore was considerably more powerful than the Hurricane as 185 Squadron quickly discovered when one of its aircraft was shot down with the loss of Pilot Officer Donald Lintern.[8]

On 12 November, thirty-four Hurricanes flown by pilots of 242 and 605 Squadrons arrived from the carriers *Argus* and *Ark Royal*. The following day, *Ark Royal* was sunk by U-81. The previous month she had also delivered one Swordfish and eleven Albacore torpedo bombers for the Island's strike force. Information on potential targets was frequently obtained through the interception of enemy messages confirmed by reconnaissance missions flown by such men as Flying Officer Adrian Warburton, who was active from the very early days of the battle. Warburton and others like him were vital to the offensive operations of the Royal Air Force, the Fleet Air Arm and the Royal Navy, whose efforts were having a telling effect on Italo-German supply lines to North Africa. Axis land bases were also prone to attack if they came within range of Malta's aircraft.

In November, Generalfeldmarschall Albert Kesselring, commanding Luftflotte 2 in Russia, was designated Commander-in-Chief South, and with the onset of winter, the Germans began to transfer aircraft from the Eastern Front and elsewhere to Sicily. It was the beginning of the end for the Hurricane's short-lived reign over Malta. In December, Generalleutnant Bruno Loerzer's II Fliegerkorps replaced the Regia Aeronautica in day operations over the Island. German raids began on a relatively small scale, increasing in intensity towards the end of the month. Daylight bomber attacks were heavily escorted by Bf 109 Fs against which the Hurricanes could do little.

Besides being scrambled too late, Malta's fighters tended to use the outdated vic or line astern formations, leaving themselves vulnerable to attack by the Luftwaffe, whose fighter pilots had adopted the procedure of flying in pairs and fours in line abreast, with the pilots able to look inwards so as to cover as much sky as possible.

In February 1942, Squadron Leader Stan Turner arrived to take command of 249 Squadron. He quickly decided on some radical changes. It was due largely to his intervention that the RAF in Malta began to follow the example of the Luftwaffe, flying in pairs and in loose 'fingers four' sections.

Another decisive tactic implemented by Turner and Malta's outstanding Operations Controller, Group Captain A.B. 'Woody' Woodhall, saw fighters scrambled as the raids were approaching, thus giving the Hurricanes time to gain altitude south of the Island, well away from the enemy's course of attack. Then, on the word from ground control, they would dive on the intruders, gaining precious speed in the process.[9]

In order to survive as an Allied base, the Island had continued to be resupplied by sea, but there still remained an urgent requirement for more fighters. On 7 March, fifteen Spitfire Mk VB(Trop)s were flown in off HMS *Eagle*. At last, here was a machine with the speed to match the Bf 109 and the firepower required to destroy the Ju 88. At about this time, 1435 Flight (formerly the Malta Night Fighter Unit) also received a welcome addition to its own Hurricanes – four Beaufighters on detachment from 89 Squadron in Egypt.

Soon after the arrival of the Spitfires, the Luftwaffe devised another strategy and dispatched large formations of bombers against the Island's air bases, initially in an attempt to destroy the fighters on the ground. First to be targeted was Ta'Qali, where aerial reconnaissance had revealed to the Germans the construction of what appeared to be an underground hangar. To deal with this latest development, a number of Ju 88s were provided with rocket-assisted bombs with an alleged capability of penetrating up to 45 feet of solid rock.[10] On 20 March, a powerful force including some sixty Ju 88s opened the new phase by attacking Ta'Qali. These efforts were wasted on what was actually a dummy target. Although the RAF had indeed attempted to excavate a hangar in the cliff face bordering the airfield's south-west perimeter, the stone had proved unsuitable for such a scheme and the project was abandoned. Instead, the site was painted with mock hangar doors, and damaged fighters were left at the 'entrance' in order to lure the enemy into attacking the site.[11]

On 21 and 29 March, Malta was reinforced with sixteen more Spitfires. In the interim, the survivors of convoy 'MW10' had reached the Island. Consequently, the Luftwaffe redirected its efforts against the harbours, thereby easing the pressure on Ta'Qali which had been rendered temporarily unserviceable after attacks on 20 March. One merchantman,

Clan Campbell, and an escorting destroyer, HMS *Southwold*, were lost. All the remaining cargo ships, *Talabot* and *Pampas* and the Commissioned Auxiliary Supply Ship *Breconshire* (the latter a veteran of the Malta run) were among those vessels sunk as a result of heavy raids on 26 March.

During March, the fighter units underwent some reorganisation with 242 and 605 Squadrons taken over by 126 and 185. On the 27th, Hurricane IICs of 229 Squadron were transferred to Malta from North Africa, with further reinforcements arriving in April and early the following month, when aircraft were flown in to replace those lost in the previous five weeks of combat. Due to the high attrition rate of the Hurricanes and Spitfires, the RAF was finding it increasingly difficult to meet the enemy fighters on an equal basis. The Bf 109s frequently outnumbered their opponents and sometimes encountered no aerial opposition whatsoever. On such occasions, the RAF adopted a rather unorthodox 'defensive' procedure, as explained by Flight Lieutenant Hugh 'Tim' Johnston of 126 Squadron:

> When we can put up no aircraft at all, Fighter Control lays on a dummy R/T conversation. The other day, after a corporal in a cubicle had announced that he'd spotted four 109s and was going to attack them, the German listening device picked it up and broadcast a warning which confused the Huns so much that there was a good deal of nattering in high-pitched German and finally a burst of cannon fire![12]

The Island's strike aircraft also suffered fearful losses. Surviving machines were kept operational by all available means, with ground crews, often using spares scavenged from the wrecks that littered the airfields, and frequently working through the night to service a grounded aircraft. To protect the precious aeroplanes and service vehicles, dispersal pens were constructed from sandbags, rubble, stone, earth-filled petrol cans and whatever else could be utilised. By the end of April, around 300 pens had been built along with 27 miles of dispersal runway. This mammoth task was achieved by civilian labour, the Navy and Air Force and as many as 3,000 soldiers at a time who toiled under the most oppressive conditions in the cold, mud and rain, while in constant danger of air attacks.[13]

II Fliegerkorps was relentless in its efforts to pound Malta into submission. The Spitfire deliveries and Hurricane reinforcements were barely sufficient to sustain Malta's fighter defence. Yet the Maltese displayed an unshaken belief in the RAF, the artillery, the Navy and God – and not necessarily in that order. The Governor and Commander-in-Chief, General Sir William Dobbie, himself a religious man, was not averse to expressing his own trust in Divine Providence, and in April 1942 it seemed as though nothing short of a miracle could save Malta.

The arrival of several supply ships in early 1942, however welcome, hardly improved the worsening food shortage. The poor diet combined with the permanent stress and tension so affected the health of some that it was not unusual to see people being carried into air-raid shelters. A vivid and evocative depiction of Malta's ordeal is provided in the diaries of Stan Fraser, who served in 4th Heavy Anti-Aircraft Regiment Royal Artillery. The entry for 8 April 1942 reads:

As the raids have been so intense during the past week, especially during yesterday, I decided to pay my regular visit to Valletta today, being on 24 hour leave, to see the extent of the damage for myself.

Our first lift was to Luqa 'drome in a small van. It took us right across the landing field and we alighted in the centre of the camp. What a desolate scene! Hardly a building remained intact, and most of the portable-type buildings had weird shapes reminding me of these sideshows we see in England – the world's ugliest house, or the crooked house at the fair – buildings with bulging sides, no doors or windows and a few sheets of corrugated iron missing or, usually, all except a few sheets blown out until they hung by a single bolt, etc. Inside, a clerk or picket may be seated at a table using the telephone, the lines of which are kept constantly in repair. The main occupation seemed to be salvage work by RAF ground staff and also Maltese labourers, bomb holes were filled as fast as possible, mainly by PBI [Poor Bloody Infantry], especially on the runway; fittings, etc, were piled onto trucks – fire extinguishers, light switches, telephones. Many planes were strewn about the field, most of them crippled from bomb splinters or flying debris, others through crash landings, etc. Altogether a disheartening scene.

From the aerodrome we managed to get a lift in a small car being used by a Flight Lieutenant – incidentally, there were no windows in the car and there was an unintentional sunshine roof! Before leaving the camp the siren had sounded and the guard informed us that 30 bombers were coming in and we had just reached Marsa Creek when the guns opened up in greeting for them. The car stopped and we witnessed a dive bombing attack by Stukas on Marsa itself. The raid only lasted 10 minutes and so we continued on our way, having squeezed another Flight Lieutenant in the tiny car. A bomb crater right across the road, about 80 feet wide, which had burst the sewer main, made it imperative for us to make a detour to arrive eventually in the city of Valletta.

Throughout the journey we had been passing through stones and debris scattered across our path but here, in the city, it was impossible to drive around owing to the many fallen buildings. We alighted at the Castille, which is the War HQ of the island, and decided to make a methodical tour in order to ascertain the extent of the damage.

Looking into the harbour first we could see many gaps in the dock which had earlier been occupied by destroyers, tugs, floating cranes, merchantmen of the recently arrived convoy, now the tips of the funnels or mastheads were just visible above the water, or, if they had been berthed in shallow water, then they now rested at a rakish angle on the bottom. Most of the convoy cargo had already been salvaged thank goodness.

We next viewed the larger buildings around the Castille, which had received a direct hit itself and, although the front wall still stood, the interior was reduced to a heap of rubble. The Opera House, the Museum and the Governor's Palace had all been directly hit and the two former were now useless, as also was the Education Office. Walking down the main street – Kingsway – I noticed that *every* street running from it, to the right or left, was blocked with fallen masonry.

Three raids took place within the first hour of our tour, all on the harbour area and the sky filled with JU 88s and ME fighters. Never have I seen bombs bursting at such close range and with such a feeling of comparative safety. Three of us were sheltering in a small electric switch room, about 5 feet square, cut into a wall overlooking the harbour; the doors had been blown off and thus we had a good view of the bombs bursting as they struck the rocks and water less than ¼ mile away, the blast was terrific. Floriana houses also received several direct hits which caused clouds of dust to envelop the district all around.

We managed to get a lift out of Valletta having seen the main damage, and found that we were unable to get anything to eat or drink; our next visit was via the districts of Hamrun and Birkirkara in search of food. Eggs, chips and coffee we found, and also the lucky find of a shop selling soap – Palmolive.

More raids followed whilst in Hamrun but we were out of the target area, although we noticed carcasses of horses and a donkey lying in the road – casualties from a previous raid. Our fighters have taken to the air again and, in spite of terrific odds against them, are putting up a very good show. Later we were caught in Marsa area when it was raided and saw many aerial combats, our fighters diving in to attack the Junkers in spite of the barrage which AA were putting up. One of our planes was blown in two and the pilot [Flight Lieutenant Philip Heppell 249 Squadron] baled out as it spun to earth in flames.

The general scenes in the town and fields are just like those of the battered villages of Belgium and France during the last war, debris, bomb craters, twisted girders, etc. The Maltese are bearing it very well and making the best of a hopeless situation equally as well as the people of Britain did during the 1941 winter.[14]

The bravery and fortitude of the islanders was formally recognised on 15 April 1942 by the award of the George Cross by King George VI. It was the highest honour that an appreciative British sovereign could bestow on a community.

On 20 April, forty-six Spitfires comprising 601 (County of London) and 603 (City of Edinburgh) Squadrons were flown off the American carrier USS *Wasp*. The Germans waited until the aircraft landed before launching the first in a series of raids against the aerodromes.

Late in April, the 10th Submarine Flotilla quietly left Malta for the safety of Alexandria. The submarines were not to return until the end of July. It was also at this time that reconnaissance aircraft photographed what appeared to be three airfields being levelled in Sicily. Reports indicated that these were intended for gliders for a proposed Axis invasion of Malta. Codenamed 'Herkules' by the Germans and 'C3' by the Italians, the operation was planned for that summer. The attack force was to be five times the strength of that deployed during the 1941 invasion of Crete. Yet 'Herkules' was destined never to materialise, with Hitler instead giving priority to his offensives in North Africa and Russia. The decision ultimately sealed the fate of Rommel's Afrikakorps, thereby affecting the course of the entire war. But in April 1942, the threat of invasion was still very real, and would remain so for months to come.

Luftwaffe records show that between 20 March and 28 April 1942, Malta was subjected to 5,807 sorties flown by bombers, 5,667 by fighters and 345 by reconnaissance aircraft – a total of 11,819 sorties. In this five and a half week period, the weight of bombs dropped is reported to have exceeded 6,557 tonnes.[15]

By May, the Regia Aeronautica had begun to reappear over Malta during daylight hours. On the 9th, Operation 'Bowery' culminated in the delivery of sixty Spitfires flown from USS *Wasp* and HMS *Eagle*. The new arrivals were quickly introduced to the desperate fighting conditions of Malta since the Germans and Italians timed their attacks to catch the Spitfires as they came in to land. The enemy's efforts were countered by ground crews who immediately re-armed and refuelled the aircraft; and by experienced Malta pilots who replaced the original crews and sat strapped in the cockpits, ready to scramble. Meanwhile, enemy fighters were held at bay by the Island's available Hurricanes and Spitfires. One of the reinforcements, Flying Officer Richard Mitchell, recounted:

The tempo of life here is just indescribable. The morale of all is magnificent – pilots, ground crews and army, but it is certainly tough. The bombing is continuous on and off all day. One lives here only to destroy the Hun and hold him at bay; everything else, living conditions, sleep, food, and all the ordinary standards of life have gone by the board. It all makes the Battle of Britain and fighter sweeps seem like child's play in comparison, but it is certainly history in the making , and nowhere is there aerial warfare to compare with this.[16]

On 10 May, the minelayer-cruiser HMS *Welshman* completed a lone run from Gibraltar with supplies and RAF ground personnel. The enemy responded with a series of concentrated attacks countered by the magnificent efforts of the RAF and ground defences, which enabled the *Welshman* to depart later that evening. Although the odds were still stacked against Malta, the situation had changed: the defenders could again feel that they were achieving significant results as opposed to simply disrupting the enemy's efforts.

As the battle continued, the fighting became increasingly ruthless. In February 1942, Messerschmitt Bf 109s strafed Air-Sea Rescue Launch 129, killing four of the crew. Neither were Axis ASR floatplanes exempt from RAF attack. Baled-out aircrew were also liable to be targeted. On 12 May, Flight Lieutenant Denis Barnham of 601 Squadron observed three Italians parachuting into the sea off Malta's rocky south coast. After ensuring that they had climbed onto a cliff ledge, he landed at Luqa and reported the incident. A few days later, he learned that all had been killed (see pages 155–8).

Some considered such an event amusing, as men often do in time of war, and later joked about it in the mess. When Barnham protested at the callous indifference of his fellow pilots, he was told: 'Denis, you need re-educating, this is total war.'[17]

'Total war' meant that anxious Allied pilots, only too aware of the danger of being mistaken for an Italian or German if forced to bale out, prudently took to carrying identification marks on their Mae Wests – words like, 'Spitfire – British', in bold lettering. In 'total war' it was not unknown for pilots to collapse the parachute of an adversary, or to attack those awaiting rescue after they had been shot down into the sea.

Flight Lieutenant P.B. 'Laddie' Lucas of 249 Squadron
recalled such an episode, apparently carried out in reprisal for
the death of Rhodesian, Pilot Officer Douglas Leggo (see
pages 118-21):

> A Junkers 88 had been shot down south-east of the Island.
> The aircraft had ditched in the sea and now the crew of
> three were in a dinghy ten miles or so from Delimara
> Point. Their chances of being picked up must have been
> good. The sea was calm and sparkling. A Dornier 24
> would have had no trouble making a landing. As we
> headed home for Takali, my eye caught sight of a single
> Spitfire away to my left, at the bottom of a shallow, fast
> dive, heading straight for the dinghy. A sustained burst of
> fire sent geysers of sea water creeping up on the tiny,
> inflated boat. Not content with one run, the pilot pulled
> up into a tight climbing turn to the left and dived again.[18]

By the end of May 1942, developments in the Western
Desert and on the Eastern Front again led to the departure of
most Sicily-based Luftwaffe units. As in 1941, operations
against Malta were left primarily to the Italians and, as before,
the reduction of German aircraft in Sicily provided a
temporary respite that enabled Malta to strengthen and
reorganise its defences. On 7 May, General Sir William Dobbie
was relieved by Field Marshal Lord Gort VC. On the 18th,
HMS *Eagle* ferried seventeen Spitfires to the Island. Aircraft
also arrived for the RAF's strike units. With sufficient
Spitfires to hand, 229 Squadron departed for the Middle East
late in May. On 3 June, thirty-one Spitfires took off from
HMS *Eagle*. All but four reached Malta. Six days later, the
carrier delivered another thirty-two aircraft. One of the
pilots was Sergeant George Beurling, a Canadian who was
subsequently assigned to 249 Squadron. 'Laddie' Lucas
described him as: 'untidy, with a shock of fair, tousled hair
above penetrating blue eyes. He smiled a lot and the smile
came straight out of those striking eyes . . . He was highly
strung, brash and outspoken . . . something of a rebel . . .'[19]
He was also 'a positive master of air combat and possessed
phenomenal skills in deflection gunnery', according to Pilot
Officer Leo Nomis, an American in 229 (Spitfire) Squadron,

who recalled that of all the fighter pilots in Malta: 'The only person I ever met who liked it there was Beurling.'[20]

'Screwball' Beurling, as he became known, opened his Malta account during his first engagement there on 12 June when he claimed to have shot the tail off a Bf 109. Though credited with only a 'damaged', he then went on to run up a string of victories, including twenty-six and one-third aircraft destroyed (in addition to two Focke Wulf 190s claimed over Europe the month before), before being shot down and wounded in October 1942.

In June, convoys 'Vigorous' and 'Harpoon' made a simultaneous attempt to reach Malta, the former from the Middle East and the latter via Gibraltar. After suffering heavy losses, 'Vigorous' was aborted. With Malta-based aircraft providing air cover, the survivors of Operation 'Harpoon' continued to battle through. Two merchantmen reached the Island, as did the *Welshman* on another, unescorted run.

On 21 June, Tobruk changed hands yet again, this time falling to the Deutsch Afrikakorps. Soon after, 601 Squadron departed Malta to join the hard-pressed RAF in North Africa. Meanwhile, II Fliegerkorps was bolstered by Ju 88s and Bf 109s transferred from other sectors, and the Regia Aeronautica commenced a build-up of its forces in Sicily.

July began with a renewed Axis offensive that continued unabated for two weeks, with substantial losses on both sides. On the 14th, Air Vice Marshal Keith Park took over as Air Officer Commanding from Air Vice Marshal Lloyd. Soon after, the new AOC issued an order for raids to be intercepted en route to Malta in an attempt to force the bombers to jettison their loads before they could cross the coast. The tactic duly became standard procedure.

RAF losses during the first two weeks of July were alleviated when the *Eagle* delivered thirty-one Spitfires on the 15th followed on the 21st by twenty-eight more. Subsequently, 1435 Flight, previously rendered ineffective as a Hurricane unit, was reformed as a Spitfire squadron. 229 Squadron was also reconstituted with pilots and Spitfires of 603 Squadron, which now ceased to operate as a Malta-based unit.

Although the Spitfire was vital to the continued survival of Malta, the overall situation was still critical. On 3 August, Operation 'Pedestal' left Scotland on the first stage of its journey to the Mediterranean. 'Pedestal' consisted of fourteen merchantmen under Royal Navy escort. By the time the convoy reached the beleaguered Island, nine cargo vessels and four warships had been sunk. Of the five surviving merchantmen, the most famous was undoubtedly the Texaco oil tanker, *Ohio*. After being disabled during torpedo and bombing attacks, in which one bomber actually crashed onto her deck, the battered ship finally reached Grand Harbour lashed between two destroyers and with another secured to the stern as an emergency rudder. The date was 15 August, the Feast of the Assumption, known locally as the Feast of St Mary. Ever since, the Maltese have referred to Operation 'Pedestal' as *Il-Convoy ta'Santa Marija*.

On 17 August, thirty-two Spitfires were launched from HMS *Furious*. Twenty-eight reached Malta. During the second half of the month, Allied attacks against Sicily increased with fighter sweeps by Spitfires, and raids by Hurri-bombers flown by RNAS pilots and these continued until they were curtailed in September due to fuel shortages. During this period there was a noticeable decline in enemy air activity, but the Axis Command was still very much concerned about the ongoing disruption of Rommel's Mediterranean supply routes, and by October the Luftwaffe had gathered a formidable force in Sicily.

The final Italo-German offensive against Malta began early on 11 October. Raids were almost invariably carried out by small formations of bombers heavily escorted by fighters. After seven days, during which both sides suffered substantial losses, the enemy changed tactics, resorting instead to attacks by fighters and fighter-bombers. But it was becoming increasingly clear that Hitler had lost the opportunity of defeating Malta.

On 29 October, the *Furious* transported another batch of Spitfires to a departure point west of the Island. All twenty-nine aircraft reached their destination. Meanwhile, in Egypt, a successful Allied offensive against Axis forces at El-Alamein was followed, on 8 November, by the Anglo-American landings in French North Africa, prompting the diversion of Axis resources from Sicily to these battle fronts. For a while, attacks on Malta continued, but never with the same tenacity as before. The main problem now was the shortage of provisions, although the situation was alleviated somewhat by supply runs undertaken by individual ships and submarines. It was not until 20 November 1942, that the siege was finally lifted with the arrival of all four merchantmen of Operation 'Stoneage'.

In May 1943, the Afrikakorps surrendered in Tunisia. Two months later, Malta played a prominent role as Allied headquarters and as a forward air base during Operation 'Husky' – the Allied invasion of Sicily. Italy capitulated on 8 September 1943, and two days later the Italian Naval Fleet began to arrive under escort at Malta, the triumphant occasion prompting a delighted Admiral Sir Andrew Cunningham to signal the Admiralty: 'Be pleased to inform their Lordships that the Italian Battle Fleet now lies at anchor under the guns of the Fortress of Malta.' For the heroic Maltese and all who had defended their Islands, it was a fitting tribute.

AIRCRAFT CRASH SITES

In excess of 1,000 RAF, Italian and German aircraft were lost during the Battle of Malta.[21] Many disappeared beneath the Mediterranean; some crashed in Sicily; others came down in or close to the Maltese Islands. The crash sites of 184 of the latter are listed below. An asterisk indicates losses which are documented in the following pages. Insufficient information about crash locations precluded similar accounts to be written about the remainder. Fatalities are shown by a cross alongside the name of the deceased.

While every care has been taken to ensure accuracy, some details, indicated by a question mark, could not be cross-checked due to discrepancies or omissions in available records. It should also be noted that in some cases personnel may have held a more senior rank but were still awaiting notification of recent promotion.

Note: in the table l/o = limits of

AIRCRAFT	PILOT/CREW	UNIT	PLACE	DATE/TIME
S.79*	S.Ten Felice Filippi † (Crew believed to have also included) Serg Magg Enzo Muratori † Av Sc Cesare Ottavini † 1° Av Antonio Serafini †	195ª Sqd	It-Torri Ta' Triq il-Wiesgħa, Żonqor	10-7-40/0800
Hurricane*	Flt Lt Peter Keeble †	Fighter Flt	Wied il-Għajn, l/o Marsaskala	16-7-40/0916
CR 42* (MM4368)	Ten Mario Benedetti †	74ª Sqd	Wied il-Għajn, l/o Marsaskala	16-7-40/0916
Gladiator* (N5519)	Fg Off Peter Hartley	Fighter Flt	(Probably) in sea, off Ras il-Fenek, l/o Marsaxlokk	31-7-40/0930–0943
Hurricane* (N2700)	Sgt Frederick Robertson	418 Flt	Between Ta' Daniel and Ta'Bir Miftuħ, l/o Luqa	2-8-40/0830
CR 42*	S.Ten Francesco Cavalli	70ª Sqd	L'Iskorvit, l/o Mgarr	17-9-40/1040–1115
MC 200*	M.llo Lino Lagi †	79ª Sqd	It-Tumbrell (Delimara)	25-9-40/1208
MC 200*	Ten Mario Nasoni †	6° Gruppo Aut CT	Sea, (probably off) Fomm ir-Riħ Bay	4-10-40/1015
MC 200*	Serg (or Serg Magg) Abramo Lanzarini †	72ª Sqd	Buleben il-Kbir, l/o Żejtun	2-11-40/1220

Aircraft	Crew	Unit	Location	Date/Time
Wellington* (T2743)	Sgt Raymond Lewin Plt Off David Allen † Sgt Archibald Hunter Sgt Thomas Reay LAC John Hollingworth	Wellington Flt	Near Tal-Handaq	3-11-40/Approx 2325
Wellington* (R1094)	Sgt Philip Forrester † Sgt David Rawlings † Sgt Thomas Wood (or Woor) † Sgt Douglas Palmer Sgt Arthur Smith †	Wellington Flt	Dun Mario Street, Qormi	4-11-40/Approx 0005
Hurricane* (N2622)	Sgt William Timms †	261 Sqn	West end of Wied Qirda, I/o Zebbug	11-1-41/0745-0848
Ju 87* (5530/A5+JK?)	Fw (or Uffz) Richard Zehetmair† Gefr Heinrich Müller †	I/StG 1	Wied il-Qoton, I/o Birzebbuga	18-1-41/1415-1537
(Probably) Ju 87* (5431/A5+BK)	(Probably) Ofw Kurt Zube † (and) Uffz (or Fw) Franz Bussek (or Buczek) †	(of) I/StG1	South of Corradino and west of Ghajn Dwieli, I/o Paola	19-1-41/1247-1325
CR 42*	(Probably) Serg (or Serg Magg) Andrea Baudoni †	(of) 156° Gruppo Aut CT	Ta'Gokondu (south-west perimeter of St Andrew's Barracks)	1-2-41/Approx 1145
Hurricane*	Flt Lt James MacLachlan	261 Sqn	Paola	16-2-41/0915-0949

AIRCRAFT	PILOT/CREW	UNIT	PLACE	DATE/TIME
Bf 110* (3723/KB+NC?)	Obltn Günther Rudolf † Uffz Hans Dittmayer †	(Probably) Stab III/ZG 26	Tas-Sriedak, l/o Mosta	5-3-41/1710–1805
Maryland* (AR706)	Flg Off John Boys-Stones † Sgt J.M. Alexander Sgt Jack Levy †	69 Sqn	Wied il-Busbies, l/o Rabat	7-3-41/1230
Bf 110* (2057/L1+BH?)	(Possibly) Obltn Horst von Wegmann († ?) (and) Uffz Wilhelm Banser († ?)	(Possibly) 1/NJG 3	West of Nadur (Gozo)	9-3-41/0725
Sunderland* (L2164)	(None aboard at time?)	228 Sqn	Sea, St Paul's/Mistra Bays	10-3-41/1221
Hurricane* (V7495)	Sgt Frederick Robertson	261 Sqn	Approximately 150m south-west of Rabat reservoir (south of Rabat)	23-3-41/1530
Hurricane* (V7430)	Sgt R.J. Goode	274 Sqn attached to 261	Pwales Valley	28-3-41/1726
Hurricane* 	Sgt Peter Waghorn †	261 Sqn	Erba'Mwiezeb, l/o St Paul's Bay	11-4-41/1154
Ju 87* (5724/J9+BL?)	Ltn Werner Zühlke † Obgfr Hans Feldeisen †	9/StG 1	Near Chapel of St Mary, Maghtab, l/o Gharghur	11-4-41/2234

Aircraft	Crew	Unit	Location	Date/Time
Sunderland* (L5807)	Plt Off L.G.M. Rees Fg Off F.M. Goyen Plt Off N.M. Maynard LAC D.A.J. Taylor	228 Sqn	Sea, off Kalafrana	27-4-41/1007
Ju 88* (2279/L1+BT?)	Fw Rudolf Lenzner Fw Wilhelm Heller Fw Helmut Hartlich Uffz Paul Kletzmann	9/LG 1	Between Naval Rifle Range and Ix-Xhaghra L-Hamra, l/o Manikata	29-4-41/Early evening
Hurricane* (Z3061?)	Sgt B.C. Walmsley	'C' Flt, 261 Sqn	Ghaxaq	1-5-41/Early evening
Ju 88* (3199/4D+FS?)	Uffz Werner Gerhardt † Uffz Heinz Demmer † Obgfr Heinz Franke † Obgfr Alfred Starke († ?)	8/KG 30	Ospizio (between Gwardamanga and Floriana)	6-5-41/2020
Hurricane*	Sgt Henry Jennings †	261 Sqn	Wied id-Dis, l/o Gharghur	7-5-41/Approx 1600
Hurricane	(Unidentified)	(Unidentified)	Marsa Sports Club	14-5-41/1628–1700
Hurricane (Z3035)	Sgt E.V. Wynne †	185 Sqn	Between Safi and Kirkop	15-5-41/1212–1242

AIRCRAFT	PILOT/CREW	UNIT	PLACE	DATE/TIME
BR 20M*	Ten Sergio Reggiani Serg Magg (or M.Ilo) Guglielmo Mazzolenis 1° Av Francesco Minuto † 1° Av Michele Turco † 1° Av Giovanni (or Ugo) Bonanno †	243ª Sqd	Guarena, south of Qrendi	8-6-41/0330
Hurricane* (Z4317?)	Sgt Robert MacPherson †	260 Sqn	Near dam just west of Hal Farrug, l/o Luqa	14-6-41
MC 200	Serg Alfredo Sclavo †	90ª Sqd	Near XHB 7 HAA gun position, Ta'Karach, l/o Gudja/Ghaxaq	27-6-41/Approx 1145
Hurricane* (Z3055)	Sgt Thomas Hackston †	126 Sqn	Sea, at Hamrija Bank (south coast)	4-7-41/Morning
Blenheim (Z9575)	Sgt Walter Rand Sgt Alfred Murcutt † Sgt Jack Oaten † Cpl Wilfred Gape	82 Sqn	Gudja area	5-7-41
Wellington (Z8775)	Sgt Ralph Askin † Sgt Lionel Clay † Sgt William Ramsey †	15 OTU	Safi landing strip, St Nicola area	12-7-41/2230

Aircraft	Crew	Unit	Location	Date/Time
	Sgt Desmond Thomas † Sgt Eugene Townsend † Sgt Arthur Worsfield †			
MC 200*	S.Ten Francesco Liberti †	98ª Sqd	Near Church of St Francis, Valletta	25-7-41/1059
Ju 87* (MM7072 or MM7074?)	(Probably) STen Vittorino Bragadin † (and) Serg Magg (or M.llo) Angelo Gatti †	238ª Sqd	Il-Fiddien (between Birzebbuga and Marsaxlokk)	5-11-41/2132
MC 202* (MM7736 or MM7746?)	Cap Mario Pluda †	73ª Sqd	Wied Qasrun, l/o Dingli	8-11-41/1210-1220
Hurricane*	Sgt Alan Haley	126 Sqn	400m west of XHC 14 HAA gun position, Halq Dieri, l/o Zebbug	8-11-41/1210-1220
Hurricane* (Z3495?)	Flt Lt Donald Stones	MNFU	Between Hal Dragu and Zebbieh	9-11-41/Approx 2200
Ju 88* (0547/R4+HH)	Ltn Wilhelm Brauns Gefr Johannes Matuschka † Obgfr (or Uffz) Erwin Heese	1/NJG 2	Bin Gemma (Gozo)	19-12-41/1058-1148
Hurricane*	Plt Off Robert Matthews †	249 Sqn	West of Addolorata Cemetery, l/o Paola	22-12-41/1429-1522
Hurricane	Sgt W.E. Copp	126 Sqn	Near 'Cisk' chimney, Santa Venera	26-12-41/1600

AIRCRAFT	PILOT/CREW	UNIT	PLACE	DATE/TIME
Ju 88* (0636/R4+CL?)	Ltn Wilfried Babinek † Gefr (or Obgfr) Heinrich Schwarz † Gefr (or Obgfr) Wilhelm Gutt †	3/NJG 2	West perimeter of Hal Far aerodrome	28-12-41/2030
Ju 88* (1346?/M7+AK)	Obltn Viktor Schnez Fw (or Ofw) Ulrich Arnold Obgfr Gerhard Hoppe Fw Heinrich Freese	2/KGr 806	Ta'Srina, I/o Zebbug	3-1-42/0925
Hurricane*	Sgt J.A. Westcott	185 Sqn	Kalafrana	3-1-42/0850–0925
Maryland* (AR721)	Wg Cdr John Dowland GC † Plt Off Arnold Potter Plt Off Robert Gridley †	69 Sqn	Sea, off Tigné	13-1-42/1245
Hudson* (V9126)	Sgt Alan Story † Sgt Colville Sgt Noel Wouldes † Sgt Percy Hankins †	59 Sqn	Ghajn il-Kbira, I/o Rabat/Dingli/ Siggiewi	18-1-42/0620
Ju 88* (0149/R4+MM?)	Ltn Felix-Dieter Schleif † Gefr (or Obgfr) Rolf Wiegand † Gefr Karl-Heinz Bülow †	I/NJG 2	Ghar Mundu, I/o Rabat/Dingli/ Siggiewi	18-1-42/0645
Hurricane* (BE346?)	Sgt Donald Neale †	242 Sqn	Hemsija area, I/o Mdina	22-1-42/1130–1200

Aircraft	Crew	Unit	Location	Date/Time
Hurricane*	Plt Off Albert Anderson (or) Plt Off C.A. Blackburn (or) Plt Off C.F. Sluggett	(of) 126 Sqn (of) 126 Sqn (of) 242 Sqn	Il-Hotba, I/o Qrendi	25-1-42/1025–1115
Hurricane*	(As above)	(As above)	South-west perimeter of Qrendi airfield	(As above)
Hurricane*	(As above)	(As above)	Ta'Marianu, I/o Zejtun	(As above)
Hurricane* (Z3571?)	Plt Off Alexander Mackie †	1435 Flt	Southern outskirts of St Katerina	27-1-42/1735–1754
Bf 109* (7463/Yellow 4?)	Ofw Otto Göthe †	6/JG 53	North-east of Post HF5, Hal Far	7-2-42/1120
Ju 88* (8581/3Z+FP?)	Ltn Waldemar Stadermann † Ofw Walter Heese (†?) Ofw Albert Stahl (†?) Uffz Martin Knobloch †	6/KG 77	Tal-Qortin, I/o Bubaqra	15-2-42/0800–0910
Maryland* (AR714)	Sqn Ldr W.E.M. Lowrey Fg Off J.E. Bosley Sgt N.E. Rasmussen Sgt Durant	69 Sqn	Sea, off Benghisa	15-2-42/1700
Bf 109* (7541/+ 10?)	Uffz Walter Schwarz †	9/JG 53	Il-Hotob, I/o Qormi/Birkirkara	22-2-42/1325–1355

AIRCRAFT	PILOT/CREW	UNIT	PLACE	DATE/TIME
Hurricane (Z3562)	Fg Off Denis Winton	1435 Flt	Near Rabat	3-3-42/Night
Bf 109* (6649/Black 3?)	Uffz Benedikt Wegmann	5/JG 3	Pembroke Ranges	4-3-42/1250
Ju 88* (1392/7T+JK?)	Uffz Albert Degenhardt † Uffz Friedrich Engelmann (or Engelbert) † Uffz Hermann Gessele † Uffz Werner Rehschütz †	2/KüFlGr 606	Gebel Cantar, I/o Siggiewi	5-3-42/0237–0625
Bf 109 (7475/Yellow 4?)	Obltn Hermann Raab	10 (Jabo)/JG 53	Bir Ir-Riebu, I/o Rabat	6-3-42/1659–1745
Hurricane*	Plt Off Howard Coffin	126 Sqn	Between Safi airfield and Gudja	9-3-42/1520
Ju 88* (8660/3Z+JP or 3Z+LP)	Obltn (or Hptm) Gerhard Becker † Uffz Arnulf Thiemann † Uffz Walter Kunzi Uffz Anton Schwäger (or Schweiger) †	II/KG 77	Hal Far	9-3-42/Approx 1600
Hurricane* (Z5140?)	Sgt John Mayall †	126 Sqn	Mriehel, I/o Qormi/Birkirkara	10-3-42/1020
Spitfire* (AB343?)	Plt Off Kenric Murray †	249 Sqn	Ta'Zuta, I/o Rabat/Dingli/Siggiewi	10-3-42/1640–1842

Aircraft	Unit	Crew	Location	Date/Time
Spitfire* (AB3377)	249 Sqn	Plt Off Douglas Leggo †	Midway between Ta'San Niklaw reservoir and Guarena Tower, l/o Qrendi	20-3-42/0805-0840
Hurricane* (Z5302?)	185 Sqn	Sgt Archibald Steele †	Approx 200m west of Tas-Silg Battery, l/o Marsaxlokk	31-3-42/1000
Mosquito (W4063)	69 Sqn	Plt Off Philip Kelley / Sgt Pike	Hal Far	31-3-42/1025
Bf 109* (8668/Black 11?)	II/JG 3	Uffz Hans Pilz (?)	Off Luqa Road, l/o Paola	1-4-42/Approx 1820
Ju 87* (2147/T6+FN?)	8/StG 3	Uffz Winfried Günthert / Gefr Wilhelm Neubauer †	Il-Qali, l/o Marsaxlokk	1-4-42/1825
Ju 88 (8605/R4+CL?)	I/NJG 2	Ofw Alfred Vogel † / Uffz Ernst Schillung (†?) / Obgfr Kurt Böhme (†?) / Obgfr Helmut Aumann (†?)	Kirkop area	8-4-42/2030-2044
Hurricane*	185 Sqn	Sgt Charles Broad	Is-Simblija, l/o Naxxar	10-4-42/Approx 1800
Hurricane*	185 Sqn	Plt Off Philip Wigley	Hagra s-Sewda (Ghar Lapsi)	10-4-42/Approx 1800
Ju 88* (5520/3Z+HS?)	8/KG 77	Uffz Harry Müller † / Obgfr Peter Dressen (†?) / Uffz Fritz Haas (†?) / Uffz Karl Gellenkirchen (†?)	Tal-Munxar (east coast)	11-4-42/Afternoon

AIRCRAFT	PILOT/CREW	UNIT	PLACE	DATE/TIME
Bf 109* (8724?/Double Chevron)	Hptm Karl-Heinz Krahl †	Stab II/JG 3	North-east of Post HF5, Hal Far	14-4-42/1130
Spitfire	Flt Lt Hugh Johnston	126 Sqn	Wied Hanzir, I/o Siggiewi	20-4-42/Afternoon
Spitfire*	Plt Off Hiram Putnam †	126 Sqn	Ta'Kandja valley, I/o Siggiewi/Mqabba	20-4-42/1800
Hurricane*	Sgt John Fullalove †	229 Sqn	San Leonardo, I/o Zabbar/Marsaskala	21-4-42/0735–1020
Spitfire*	Plt Off Frank Jemmett †	126 Sqn	Tal-Virtu, I/o Rabat	22-4-42/1725–1838
Ju 87* (2180/S7+CM?)	Uffz Jürgen Schwengers † Gefr Franz Netelnbeker († ?)	III/StG 3	Sea, Marsaxlokk Bay	23-4-42/1054–1202
Spitfire* (BP973?)	Plt Off Kenneth Pawson †	601 Sqn	Il-Qadi, I/o Bur Marrad	25-4-42/1250–1354
Hurricane*	FS Lucien Brooks †	229 Sqn	Bajda Ridge (just west of Victory Chapel), I/o St Paul's Bay	25-4-42/1741–1907
Spitfire*	Plt Off Walter Cripps †	601 Sqn	High Street, Qormi	26-4-42/1425–1534
Ju 88* (5717/L1+GM?)	Ltn Hans-Georg Witt † Sonderführer Dr Eduard Perertil (or Petertil) †	4/LG 1	Santu Rokku, I/o Kalkara	27-4-42/1055–1150

Aircraft	Crew	Unit	Location	Date/Time
	Uffz Josef Mirlenbrink († ?) Ofw Hans Steus († ?)			
Hurricane	Plt Off Thomas Foley †	229 Sqn	Hal Far	28-4-42/Morning
Hurricane* (Z2698?)	Plt Off John Fletcher †	185 Sqn	Approx 250m east of Dingli reservoir	28-4-42/0745–0850
Ju 87*	Gefr Karl Haff † Gefr Fritz Weber	9/StG 3	Zonqor, I/o Marsaskala	3-5-42/1815
Spitfire*	Flt Lt Norman MacQueen †	249 Sqn	San Pawl Tat-Targa, I/o Naxxar	4-5-42/1745–1820
Spitfire (BR116)	Flt Lt Hugh Johnston	126 Sqn	Near Villa Azzopardi, Zebbug	6-5-42/Morning
Bf 109* (7513/Black 3?)	Uffz Heinrich Becker	8/JG 53	Marsa Sports Club	8-5-42/Approx 0900
Ju 87* (2151/S7+HN?)	Fw Walter Obermellländer † Uffz Albert Westphalen †	III/StG 3	Sea, east of Ahrax Point	8-5-42/0930
Spitfire*	Plt Off Harry Milburn †	249 Sqn	Wied Maghlaq (south coast)	9-5-42/1055–1150
Spitfire* (BR248)	Sgt Gordon Tweedale †	185 Sqn	Saviour Street, Lija	9-5-42/1609–1656

AIRCRAFT	PILOT/CREW	UNIT	PLACE	DATE/TIME
Ju 87* (2149/S7+GN?) (or) (2057/S7+FM?)	(Probably) Uffz Gerhard Nikolai † ?) (and) Uffz Walter Kern († ?) (or) Uffz Christian Appmann († ?) (and) Uffz Heinrich Schäfer († ?)	III/StG 3 III/StG 3	Sea, Dockyard Creek	10-5-42/1040–1135
Cant-Z.1007 Bis*	1° Av Antonio Braschi † S.Ten Salvatore De Maria † Av Sc Celestino Giovannini † 1° Av Vittorio Rey † Ten (or S.Ten) Domenico Robilotta † Av Sc Giovanni Zancan †	211ª Sqd	Kalkara area	10-5-42/1810–1949
Ju 87* (2051/S7+EM?)	Uffz Walter Rastinnes Uffz Walter Rauer †	III/StG 3	Senglea	10-5-42/1900
S.84*	Ten Vinicio Vego Scocco † Av Sc Francesco Carabellese † 1° Av Lino Conte † Av Sc Sergio Orsingher † 1° Av Gustavo Petrai † Serg Eugenio Rivolta †	14ª Sqd	Tal-Pitkal, I/o Dingli	12-5-42/1730–1918
Spitfire*	Sgt Colin Finlay †	185 Sqn	Sea, off Wied iz-Zurrieq	14-5-42/0950

Aircraft	Crew	Location	Unit	Date/Time
Spitfire*	Sgt John Boyd †	Near west end of east-west Luqa runway	185 Sqn	14-5-42/1305
Ju 88* (140166/M7+CH?)	Fw Günter Schwerdt († ?) Gefr Rudolf Hertzler († ?) Fw Paul Stahl († ?) Uffz Johannes Meinel (†?)	Ta'San Gakbu (Ta'Qali)	KGr 806	14-5-42/1235–1400
(or) (140181/M7+FH?)	Hptm Emil Braun († ?) Obgfr Karl-Heinz Stadtmann († ?) Uffz Otto Richter († ?) Obgfr Rolf Hüppop († ?)			
Ju 88* (140156?/M7+BL)	Uffz Johannes (or Hans) Prokesch † Obgfr Herbert Burger Obgfr Hermann Köster † Obgfr Ferdinand Lechner †	Ta'Karach ridge, l/o Gudja/Ghaxaq	KGr 806	14-5-42/1811
Bf 109* (7295/Yellow 12?)	Ltn Herbert Soukup	South of Marsa Creek	6/JG 53	15-5-42/1536–1644
Spitfire*	Plt Off Peter Nash †	Bieb ir-Ruwa, l/o Rabat	249 Sqn	17-5-42/1154–1234
Spitfire	Sgt Frank Howard †	Ta'Luretu, l/o Gudja	601 Sqn	17-5-42/1728–1837
Re 2001*	Ten Remo Cazzolli	North side of Fort San Leonardo, l/o Zabbar/Marsaskala	152ª Sqd	18-5-42/0545–0646

AIRCRAFT	PILOT/CREW	UNIT	PLACE	DATE/TIME
Re 2001*	Cap Annibale Sterzi †	358ª Sqd	Ta'Garda, I/o Ghaxaq	26-5-42/1519–1559
Wellington*	Sgt Raymond Hills Sgt Eric (or Erix) Martin † Sgt (or FS) George Davis † Sgt Andrew McColl † Sgt Elwyn Roberts † Sgt (or FS) Kenneth Ross †	104 Sqn	Il-Hotob, I/o Qormi/Birkirkara	29-5-42/2310
Spitfire* (BR285)	Plt Off John Halford	185 Sqn	Sea, off Marsaxlokk	2-6-42/0910–0945
BR 20M* (MM24133?)	(Crew believed to have been) S.Ten Aldo Ruggieri † Serg Olinto Lentini † Giovanni Ruggero † Av Sc Bruno Gandolfi † Alberto Constantini †	277ª Sqd	Just north of Zebbug Cemetery	17-6-42/0150
Albacore*	Sub Lt P.A. Jordan Sub Lt R.S. Todd †	(Probably) 828 Sqn	Tal Bakkari (between Bubaqra and Hal Far)	19-6-42/1045
Hudson (FH248?)	Plt Off Frederick McBrath FS Francis Grosvenor † Sgt John Purdham Sgt Jack Pitchford	(Probably) 1 OTU	Kirkop area	19/20-6-42/Night

Aircraft	Crew	Unit	Location	Date/Time
Ju 87*	S.Ten Fulvio Papalia 1° Av (or Av Sc) Pietro Natale Gianini †	239ª Sqd	Near Qasam San Gorg, I/o Kercem/Victoria (Gozo)	24/25-6-42/2339–0014
MC 202*	Serg Magg Alberto Porcarelli †	151ª Sqd	800m north-east of Ghajn-Snuber Tower, I/o Mellieha	2-7-42/1944-2017
Ju 88* (1570/M7+GK?)	Ltn Oskar Kasimir († ?) Uffz Johann Haugenthal († ?) Uffz Rüdiger Telle († ?) Fw Walter Behnisch († ?) (or) Uffz Luitpold Martin († ?) Gefr Ludwig Ebner († ?) Uffz Willi Böhmer († ?) Obgfr Anton Fischer († ?)	(of) KGr 806 (of) 4/KG 77	Qawra	4-7-42/0015–0024
(or) (1348/3Z+BM?)				
S.84 Bis* (MM24008?)	(Probably) Serg Magg Romolo Cristiani † (and) Serg Magg Manca Gesuino † Av Sc Arduino Pelleschi 1° Av Giovanni Genovese † 1° Av Gino Pascalizzi † Av Sc Giovanni Lunati †	14ª Sqd	Ta'Garda, I/o Ghaxaq	4-7-42/0807–0908
Ju 88*	(Crew unidentified) († ?)	(Unidentified)	Approx 150m south-west of Zammitello Palace, Mgarr	6-7-42/0336–0440

AIRCRAFT	PILOT/CREW	UNIT	PLACE	DATE/TIME
Spitfire* (AB500 or BR165)	FS David Ferraby (or) FS Thurne Parks	(of) 185 Sqn (or) 249 Sqn	Ta'San Gwakkin, l/o Qormi	7-7-42/0730–0810
Spitfire*	(As Above)	(As Above)	Near the Chapel of Our Lady of the Abandoned, Zebbug	(As Above)
Cant-Z.1007 Bis*	Ten Francesco Antonelli † S.Ten (or Ten) Giovanni Casadio † 1° Av Gaetano Pisarra † (Probably) Av Sc Giuseppe Burratti † (Probably) Serg Calogero Dragotta †	60ª Sqd	Ta'Brija Street, Siggiewi, and l/o Ta'l-Ghasfur	7-7-42/1716–1741
Spitfire* (BR108)	Flt Lt Lester Sanders	603 Sqn	Sea, Marsalforn Bay (Gozo)	8-7-42/0732–0800
Ju 88* (5513/3Z+ET?)	Uffz Herbert Schlitt † Uffz Josef Forster † Gefr (or Obgfr) Andreas Pollak † Uffz Franz Schmiedl †	9/KG 77	Callus Street, Mosta	9-7-42/0852–0923
Bf 109 (13148?)	Ltn Heinz Riedel	Stab/JG 53	Ta'Giorni, l/o Silema	11-7-42/0924–0951
Spitfire (BP861)	Sgt Joseph Otis †	126 Sqn	Between Luqa and Gudja	19-7-42/1510
Ju 88*	Fw Karl Bonk †	8/KG 77	Near junction of Salvu Sacco	20-7-42/2346

Aircraft	Aircrew	Unit	Location	Date/Time
(6579/3Z+FS?)	Uffz Johann Gerstel † Uffz Gerhard Priewisch † Uffz Josef Pohl †		and Nerik Xerri Streets, Kirkop	
Hurricane (Z2825)	Plt Off David Kent †	185 Sqn	West Hal Far	23-7-42/Morning
Ju 88* (140247/M7+KH?)	Ltn Sepp Hörmann † Obgfr Josef Popp † Ltn Heinz Heuser Uffz Wolfram Quass †	KGr 806	Mnajdra/Hagar Qim (south coast)	24-7-42/1039–1115
MC 202* (MM7842)	Serg Magg Faliero Gelli	378ª Sqd	Between Dabrani and Ta'Kuljat, l/o Zebbug (Gozo)	27-7-42/0915
Spitfire (EP189 or BR303)	Sgt Donald Hubbard †	1435 Flt	Kirkop area	28-7-42/0835–0920
Ju 88* (14075/3Z+HP?)	Uffz Albert Führer † Gefr Peter Bolten † Uffz Karl Max Bauer Uffz Gustav Frick	II/KG 77	Wolseley Camp (near Il-Biez), l/o Marsaxlokk	28-7-42/1745
Spitfire	Sgt David Ritchie	126 Sqn	Qormi area	30-7-42/1115–1155
Spitfire* (BR362)	Plt Off James Guthrie †	185 Sqn	Limits of Zebbieh	2-8-42/1414–1445

AIRCRAFT	PILOT/CREW	UNIT	PLACE	DATE/TIME
Spitfire (BR357?)	Sgt R.H. Richardson	126 Sqn	Limits of St Paul's Bay	4-8-42/ 1446–1528
Spitfire* (EN973?)	Plt Off George Beurling	249 Sqn	Ta'Salib, l/o Gudja	8-8-42/1050
Beaufighter (T5143)	Flt Lt I.U.M. Gallaway FS Keech	248 Sqn	Rabat area	12-8-42/1915
Wellington* (DV542)	Plt Off Douglas Shepherd Sgt John Maslin Sgt Harry Fox † Sgt Keith Thompson Sgt Jacob Langley	(Probably) 221 Sqn	Tal-Ibrag (between Zebbug and Luqa)	13-8-42/0500
Spitfire* (EP207)	FS George Hogarth	249 Sqn	800m north of XHB 10 HAA gun position, l/o Qrendi	14-8-42/ Approx1845
Spitfire (EP467)	Plt Off Gray Stenborg	185 Sqn	Siggiewi area	17-8-42/ 1207–1238
Beaufort* (DW805)	Plt Off Ernest Moody Sgt Griffith Sgt O. Pritchard Sgt S. Gill	OADU	Sea, 1,300m north of Ghar id-Duhhan, l/o Marsaskala	21-8-42/ Approx 0930

Aircraft	Crew	Unit	Location	Date/Time
Ju 88* (140137/3Z+CS?)	Fw Ernst Klaus Uffz Franz Rohringer † Uffz Kurt Klawitter Uffz Franz Diedl (or Riedl) †	8/KG 77	Ta'Tingi, I/o Xewkija (Gozo) 0104	27-8-42/0003–
Spitfire (BR488?)	Sgt E.H. Francis	229 Sqn	Naxxar area	28-8-42/1710
Spitfire (BR374)	Sgt Lawrence Swain †	185 Sqn	Boundary of Luqa airfield, Gudja area	13-9-42/0830
Beaufighter* (V8268)	Flt Lt John Waddingham † Plt Off Alfred Cumbers	89 Sqn	200m north-east of XHE 33 HAA gun position, I/o Naxxar	26-9-42/2005–2036
Spitfire (BR379)	FS George Hogarth†	249 Sqn	Qrendi area	4-10-42/0900
Spitfire* (BR368?)	Sgt T.R.D. Kebble (or Kebbell)	1435 Sqn	Sea, St Julian's/Balluta Bay	12-10-42/0940–1030
MC 202*	S.Ten (or M.llo) Maurizio Iannucci †	352ª Sqd	Sea, off Tignè	13-10-42/1310–1344
Spitfire*	Plt Off James Stevenson †	126 Sqn	Near Gharghur Cemetery	18-10-42/1543–1654

AIRCRAFT	PILOT/CREW	UNIT	PLACE	DATE/TIME
Bf 109* (10524/Black 12?)	Uffz Heribert Wagner †	5/JG 53	Zebbieh	23-10-42/Approx 0700
Spitfire* (EP685)	Fg Off Alec Lindsay †	185 Sqn	Ta'Netta ta'Falzon, l/o Dingli	23-10-42/0640–0738
Spitfire (EP467)	Sgt Raymond Saunders †	185 Sqn	Ta'Wied Rini, l/o Rabat	24-10-42/1304–1350
Bf 109 (8349/White 14?)	Obltn Richard Eckhardt †	I/SchG 2	Ta'Qali area	25-10-42/Approx 0827
Spitfire* (EP138)	Plt Off Russell Wright †	1435 Sqn	Near Tal-Hlas Chapel, l/o Zebbug	1-11-42/1210–1225
Bf 109 (10045/Yellow 3?)	Otw Heinrich Slany (or Joachim Schanina) †	(Probably) I/SchG 2	Kirkop area	2-11-42/1340–1411
Wellington* (Z8590)	Sgt (or FS) Lincoln Craig † Fg Off Samuel Morrison † Sgt (or FS) Herbert Earney † Sgt (or FS) Alastair Paterson † Sgt Keith Donald † Sgt Oliver Holmes †	104 Sqn	Gebel Cantar, l/o Siggiewi	7-11-42/Approx 2040
Spitfire (EP609)	(Possibly) Sgt D.J. Harwood	(of) 185 Sqn	Birzebbuga area	8-11-42/1700
Spitfire	FS Martin Lundy †	229 Sqn	Naxxar area	21-11-42/1215

Aircraft	Crew	Unit	Location	Date/Time
Beaufighter (X7809)	Wg Cdr J.K. Buchanan Flt Lt J. Diamant FS J.W. Harper	272 Sqn	Rabat area	1-12-42/1155–1635
Halifax* (DT542?)	Maj The Lord Allen Apsley DSO, MC, TD, MP (1st Royal Gloucestershire Hussars, RAC) † LAC Cyril Browne (138 Sqn) † LAC Richard Clegg (138 Sqn) Plt (or Fg) Off Krzysztof Dubromirski (or Dubromisski) (138 Sqn) † Flt Lt Peter Earle (138 Sqn) † Cpl Douglas Hounslow (138 Sqn) † Fg Off Zbigniew Idzikowski (138 Sqn) † AC 1 Stanley Kelly (138 Sqn) † Sergeant (or FS) Alfred Kleniewski (138 Sqn) † Maj Arthur Millar (or Curtis-Miller) (Indian Army) † Fg Off Stanislaw Pankiewicz (138 Sqn) † Sgt Dennis Spibey (138 Sqn) † Flt Lt Leonard Vaughan DSO, DFC (40 Sqn) † Sgt Alexander Watt (138 Sqn) † Sqn Ldr Jefferson Wedgwood DFC (92 Sqn) † Sgt Roman Wysock (or Wysocki) (138 Sqn) † FS Oskar Zielinski (138 Sqn) †	138 Sqn	Between Il-Bajjada and Ta'San Girgor, l/o Zejtun	18-12-42/0405
Beaufighter	(Probably) Flt Lt Schmidt (and) FS Campbell	272 Sqn	Ghaxaq area	25-12-42/1000

The crash dates and other details of the following have yet to be confirmed:

AIRCRAFT	PILOT/CREW	UNIT	PLACE	DATE/TIME
Ju 87 (5152/6G+ER?)	(Probably) Uffz Heinz Langreder † (and) Gefr Erwin Suckow †	(of) II/StG 1	North perimeter of Luqa aerodrome	(Probably) 26-2-41/ Approx 1300–1400
Ju 87 (5718/6G+PR?) (or) (5509/GG+GT)	(Probably) Fw Johann Braun † (and) Fw Justin Kästle † (or) Obltn Kurt Reumann † (and) Uffz August-Wilhelm Schulz †	(of) II/StG1	Ghar Hanzir, l/o Luqa	(Probably) 26-2-41/ Approx 1300–1400
Bf 109* (7091/White 12?)	(Probably) Uffz Werner Mirschinka †	(of) 4/JG 53	125m south-west of Chapel of St Agata, l/o Safi/Bubaqra	(Probably) 3-1-42/Approx 0920
Hurricane* (Probably Z5147)	(Probably) Flt Lt Peter Thompson	(of) 185 Sqn	Hal Tartarni, l/o Dingli	(Probably) 25-1-42/1025–1115
Ju 88 (3556/B3+CK?)	(Probably) Fw Klaus Ahrens (and) Obgfr Gernet Hartmann † Gefr Hans-Wilhelm Peter Gefr Karl Schäfer	(of) I/KG 54	Ghallis (east of Salina)	(Probably) 6-2-42/1200–1348
Bf 109* (7375/Yellow 1?)	(Probably) Ltn Hermann Neuhoff	(of) 6/JG 53	Ta'Bir Miftuh, l/o Luqa/Gudja	(Probably) 10-4-42/Approx 1737

Aircraft	Crew	Unit	Location	Date/Time
(Possibly) BR 20M	(Possibly) Cap Alberto Zampini † (and) Serg Gianfranco Viola † Serg Fausto De Sanctis † 1° Av (or Av Sc) Ettore Pizzi † Av Sc Andrea De Vito †	(of) 276ª Sqd	North-west Nadur (Gozo)	(Possibly) 12-4-42/Approx 0335
Bf 109 (7373/Black 8?)	(Probably) Fw Alexander Kehlbuth	(of) 5/JG 53	Tal-Millha Farm, l/o Mqabba	(Probably) 25-4-42/Approx 0606
Hurricane*	(Probably) WO Douglas Corfe †	(of) 229 Sqn	Ras il-Qammieh (north-west coast)	(Probably) 25-4-42/1250–1354
(Possibly) Spitfire	(Possibly) Flt Lt William Douglas (or) Plt Off R. Bairnsfather	(both of) 603 Sqn	South of Bidnija	(Possibly) 11-5-42/1720–1820
(Probably) Spitfire	(Probably) Plt Off Richard McHan	(of) 126 Sqn	Between Siggiewi and Gebel Cantar	(Probably) 3-7-42/0805–0935
(Possibly) Bf 109 (13060/Yellow 2?)	(Possibly) Uffz Karl-Heinze Witschke †	(of) I/JG 77	Sea, 800m north-east of Dragut Point, Sliema	(Possibly) 29-7-42/0942–1030
(Possibly) Spitfire	(Possibly) Flt Lt Roderick Smith	(of) 126 Sqn	Sea, 800m north-east of Dragut Point, Sliema	(Possibly) 15-10-42/1031
(Probably) Blenheim			Sea, approx 700m south-east of Xrobb il-Ghagin (east coast)	

AIRCRAFT	PILOT/CREW	UNIT	PLACE	DATE/TIME
Hurricane (or Spitfire)	(Pilot) †		Għajn Riħana (between Mosta and Bidnija)	
(Possibly) Hurricane	(Pilot) †		Near Luqa Cemetery	
Hurricane (or Spitfire)			Għajn Riħana, area of Tarġa Battery	
Hurricane (or Spitfire)	(Pilot) †		Wied il-Kbir, l/o Qormi/Luqa	
Ju 87	(Crew) †		Bull Street, Cospicua	
(Probably) Ju 87	(Crew) † ?		Water Mill Street, Kalkara	
Ju 88			Taz-Zokrija, l/o Mosta	
Unidentified fighter (possibly Bf 109)			Sea, just east of Il-Kalanka tal-Gidien (Delimara)	
Unidentified fighter (thought to be Italian)			Wied il-Mielaħ, l/o Gharb (Gozo)	

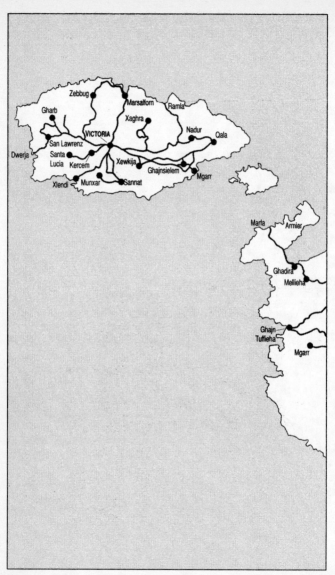

Map 1: Malta, Gozo and Comino

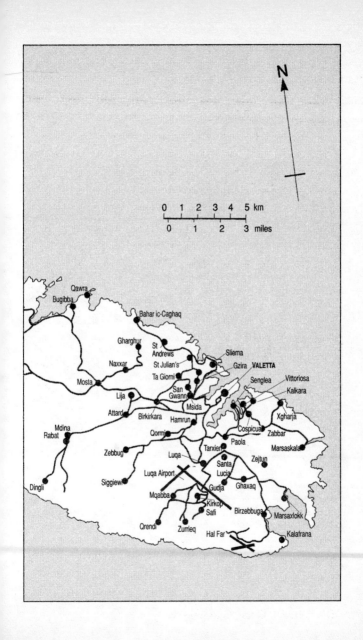

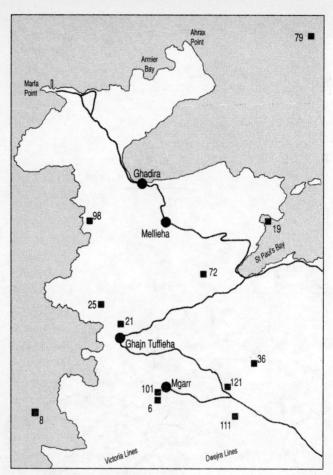

Map 2: North-west Malta

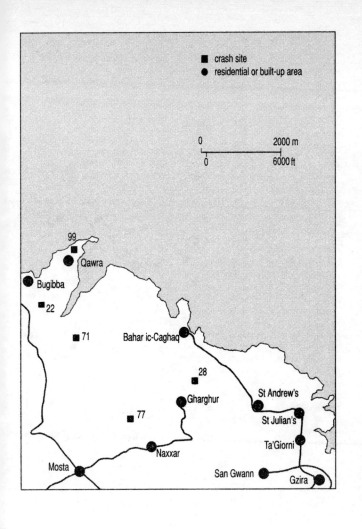

- ■ crash site
- ● residential or built-up area

0   2000 m
0   6000 ft

99
Qawra
Bugibba
■ 22
■ 71
Bahar ic-Caghaq
■ 28
Gharghur
St Andrew's
■ 77
St Julian's
Ta'Giorni
Naxxar
Mosta
San Gwann
Gzira

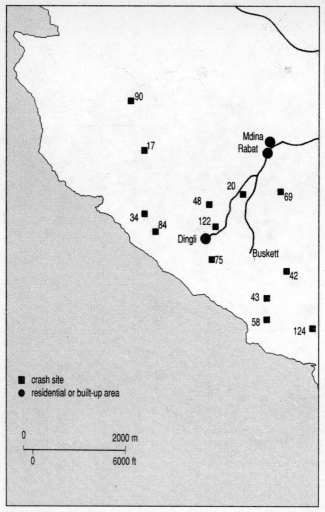

Map 3: South Malta

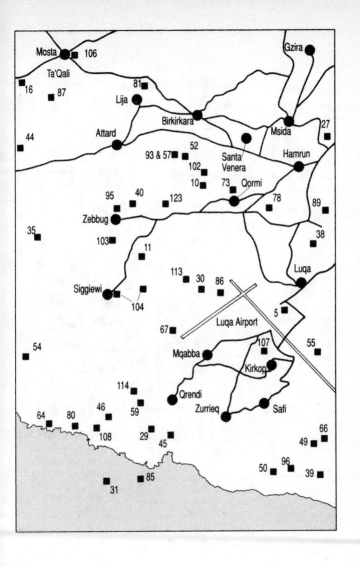

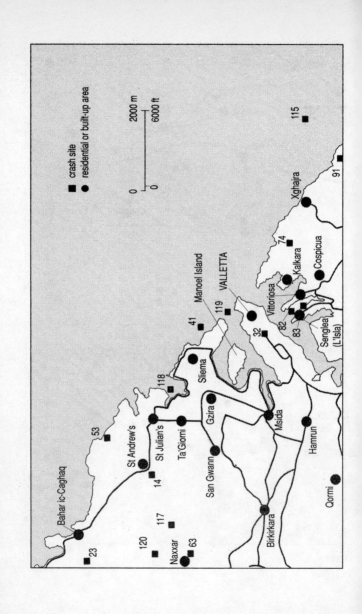

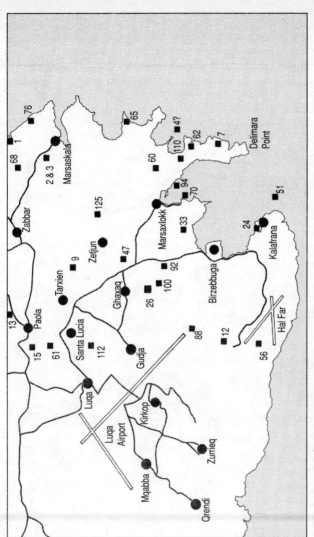

Map 4: East Malta

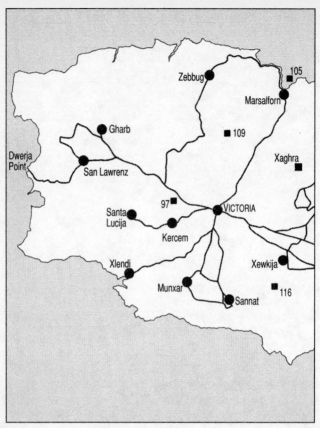

Map 5: Gozo and Comino

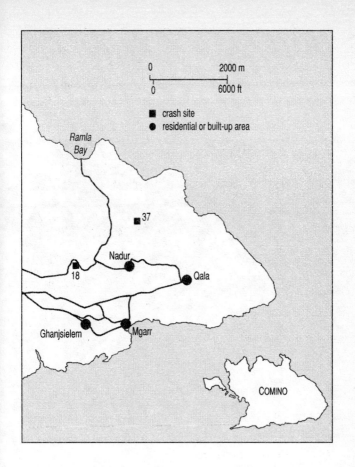

1.   Map 4
AIRCRAFT: Savoia Marchetti S.79
CREW: Sottotenente Felice Filippi (Pilot), Crew believed to have also included:
            Sergente Maggiore Enzo Muratori, Aviere Scelto Cesare Ottavini, Primo
            Aviere Antonio Serafini
UNIT: 195ª Squadriglia, 90º Gruppo, 30º Stormo Bombardamento Terrestre
PLACE: It-Torri Ta'Triq il-Wiesgha, Zonqor
DATE/TIME: 10 July 1940/0800 hours

At approximately 0745 hours on 10 July 1940, the banshee
wail of Malta's air-raid sirens heralded the approach of an
estimated twenty Savoia Marchetti S.79s.[22] Even though
they were behind schedule and had missed the rendezvous
with their fighter escort, the bombers continued with their
mission, concentrating primarily on the Dockyard, Manoel
Island, Tarxien and Zabbar. As the billowing dust clouds
caused by the bomb bursts rolled across the area, the
Italians were intercepted by Hurricanes of the Island's
Fighter Flight. Two S.79s were destroyed and many other
damaged.

One of the bombers, believed to have been piloted
by Sottotenente Luigi Illica Magnani of 192ª Squadriglia,
crashed offshore after it was attacked by Flying Officer
William 'Timber' Woods. Another, flown by Sottotenente
Felice Filippi, is thought to have been credited to Flying
Officer Frederick Taylor.[23] This, the first enemy aircraft to
fall on Maltese soil, came down in flames just behind the
Knights' watchtower east of Fort San Leonardo, severely
damaging Post RA6, which was occupied by personnel of
B Company, 1st Battalion The Dorsetshire Regiment.
Three soldiers suffered extensive burns: Private George
Le Provost and Lance Corporal Maurice Malcolm were
fatally injured and died two days later.

One civilian was also killed during the raid and three
injured. At least one Italian baled out of his stricken aircraft
with his parachute on fire. Neither he, nor any of those
from either of the bombers shot down, are known to have
survived.[24] There were also casualties, including at least one
fatality, among the returning bomber crews.

2.   Map 4
AIRCRAFT: Hawker Hurricane
PILOT: Flight Lieutenant Peter Keeble
UNIT: Fighter Flight
PLACE: Wied il-Ghajn, limits of Marsaskala
DATE/TIME: 16 July 1940/0916 hours

3.   Map 4
AIRCRAFT: FIAT CR 42
PILOT: Tenente Mario Benedetti
UNIT: 74ª Squadriglia, 23º Gruppo Autonomo Caccia Terrestre
PLACE: Wied il-Ghajn
DATE/TIME: 16 July 1940/0916 hours

Shortly after 0900 hours on 16 July a dozen FIAT CR 42 bi-planes of 23º Gruppo appeared over Malta on reconnaissance. Flight Lieutenant Peter Keeble, flying a Hurricane Mk I, and Flight Lieutenant George Burges, in a Gladiator, engaged the enemy. Keeble apparently attacked one CR 42 before being chased by two others, piloted by Tenente Mario Pinna and Sottotenente Oscar Abello.[25]

The Hurricane was eventually hit, and dived out of control towards the south-east of the Island, closely followed by Tenente Mario Benedetti in a CR 42. Both machines smashed into the ground near Wied il-Ghajn. Keeble was the first RAF fighter pilot to be killed in the defence of Malta. The Italian, Benedetti, survived the initial impact of his crash, but died soon afterwards.

Subsequently, it was claimed that the CR 42 was brought down with LMG fire by C Company headquarters, 1st Battalion The Dorsetshire Regiment.[26]

4.   Map 4
AIRCRAFT: Gloster Gladiator (N5519)
PILOT: Flying Officer Peter Hartley
UNIT: Fighter Flight
PLACE: (Probably) in sea off Ras il-Fenek, limits of Marsaxlokk
DATE/TIME: 31 July 1940/0930–0943 hours

'Faith', 'Hope' and 'Charity', the three Gladiator bi-planes that helped to defend Malta against the Regia Aeoronautica, have become part of Maltese folklore. The legend persists, notwithstanding recent findings that, prior to hostilities, HMS *Glorious* had offloaded eighteen Sea Gladiators to be stored in crates in Malta. Three were subsequently taken back on board and three despatched to Egypt. Of the remainder, six were assembled for service in Malta, and six used for spares. Yet, because the public apparently never saw more than three Gladiators in the air at any one time, it was believed that these were all there were. It is not known who christened the machines 'Faith', 'Hope' and 'Charity', or even when. Neither is it certain which aircraft, if any, were actually referred to by name.[27]

Of the operational Gladiators just one is recorded as having been shot down in combat, and while the crash site has yet to be positively identified, it is perhaps fitting that the circumstances of that loss are included here.

During the morning of 31 July 1940, Flying Officers Woods, Taylor and Hartley took off in their Gladiators to intercept an S.79 escorted by between seven and nine CR 42s of 23° Gruppo. In the ensuing action, 'Timber' Woods claimed a CR 42, Capitano Antonio Chiodi being reported missing after his fighter crashed some 5 miles north of Grand Harbour. In turn, Sergente Manlio Tarantino shot down Flying Officer Hartley in Gladiator N5519.[28] The event was witnessed from the ground by South African Flying Officer Roger 'Jock' Barber of the Island's Fighter Flight.

Peter Hartley must have been hit in his centre tank because his Gladiator burnt just like a magnesium flare – an actually brilliant light in the sky, and it was a very lovely day: typical Malta summer day, very hot, clear blue sky, no clouds.

He actually baled out after his aircraft caught fire and he fell into the sea. He was very badly burnt, particularly about the knees and arms and face. In those days, we, of course, flew in khaki shirts and shorts and stockings and it was, of course, the exposed portion of his body that got damaged. He spent a very long time in hospital and was eventually evacuated to UK, but I believe made a good recovery and flew again.[29]

According to at least one report, Gladiator N5519 fell just offshore, close to Ras il-Fenek, in south-east Malta.[30] Hartley was rescued by a boat from Kalafrana and admitted to the Station Sick Quarters suffering from shock and third degree burns. Soon after he was transferred to the military hospital at Mtarfa. He did indeed return to flying duties in the UK and the Middle East, but was eventually reassigned a ground role due to continuing problems with his injuries.

5.	Map 3
AIRCRAFT:	Hawker Hurricane (N2700)
PILOT:	Sergeant Frederick Robertson
UNIT:	418 Flight
PLACE:	Between Ta'Daniel and Ta'Bir Miftuh, limits of Luqa
DATE/TIME:	2 August 1940/0830 hours

Operation 'Hurry' was the first attempt to reinforce Malta with fighters from an aircraft carrier. At dawn on 2 August 1940, twelve Hurricanes of 418 Flight took off from the deck of HMS *Argus*. The aircraft were divided into two groups of six, each led by a Skua. Two hours and twenty minutes and some 380 miles later, the first machine landed at Luqa. The second to approach was Hurricane N2700, flown by Sergeant Fred Robertson. According to Flying Officer 'Jock' Barber:

> He [Robertson] and two Sergeant Pilots arrived in a vic of three over Luqa. He came in very, very low doing a very fast beat-up, followed by a roll off the top by himself and upward Charlies by his Numbers 2 and 3 . . . Robertson made a typical carrier-type, split-arse approach . . . very low and very steep turn and, as he was doing his final turn to line up with the runway, his motor cut – it was very audible to us on the ground – and he flicked over to the right on to his back and ploughed into the ground upside down. I think he went through three . . . stone [field] walls. . . . Well, we were very shattered to say the least. This was our first reinforcement, pilots and aircraft, and we'd been really looking forward to this, and we wrote his off, but fantastic as it may sound, Robertson only had minor concussion and was flying again two days later.[31]

The OC Luqa rushed to the scene, helped the dazed pilot into his car and drove him to the MI Room at Luqa Camp. Robertson subsequently recorded in his logbook that the Hurricane's petrol gauge was faulty. This had presumably misled him into thinking that he had more fuel than was actually the case, and may have contributed to the accident.

The rest of the Hurricanes and a Skua landed without mishap. The other Skua landed heavily on one wheel and slid along on its port wing for about 200 yards before crashing over the air-raid shelter near Luqa's control tower. The crew escaped unhurt.

6.	Map 2
AIRCRAFT:	FIAT CR 42
PILOT:	Sottotenente Francesco Cavalli
UNIT:	70ª Squadriglia, 23° Gruppo Autonomo Caccia Terrestre
PLACE:	L'Iskorvit, limits of Mgarr
DATE/TIME:	17 September 1940/1040–1115 hours

At 1040 on 17 September, the air raid sirens signalled the approach of twelve Ju 87s of the 96° Gruppo Autonomo Bombardamento a Tuffo escorted by at least two dozen fighters. The dive-bombers (some of which were seen to have the *Balkenkreuz* on their wings) concentrated on Luqa aerodrome where a Wellington and a Hurricane were burnt out and considerable damage was caused to a hangar, huts and water supplies.

In the air, a brief but fierce encounter took place as the ground defences and RAF fighters retaliated. A Ju 87 B, flown by Sergente Maggiore Luigi Catani on his first sortie over Malta, was attacked by Flying Officer 'Jock' Barber. Catani, a former fighter pilot, promptly turned towards the Hurricane, the two aircraft firing at each other in a series of head-on attacks that ended with the *Picchiatello* crashing into the sea off Mtahleb, west of the Island. Catani was captured soon afterwards. The gunner, Primo Aviere Francesco Di Giorgi, was killed (as was the gunner of a battle-damaged Ju 87 that returned to Sicily).

Meanwhile, a FIAT CR 42 was reported by ground observers to be in difficulties over the west coast; the pilot, Sottotenente Francesco Cavalli, baled out and landed a few hundred metres north of Fort Bingemma, while his burning aircraft dived into a field near Mgarr and exploded, the wreckage continuing to smoulder for hours afterwards. When he reached the ground the pilot was quickly surrounded by villagers whose anger on discovering the airman's nationality was soon overcome by the plight of the helpless and obviously frightened Italian. He asked for, and was brought, a glass of water before being placed on a stretcher and carried to Mgarr where he was taken into custody by military personnel. Cavalli later told his interrogator, Flight Lieutenant Wyndham Grech: 'I was not hit by AA fire or by a fighter, but my oil feed burst and as I expected a fire at any moment I baled out.'[32]

Notwithstanding Cavalli's statement, the cause of his crash was attributed to the shooting of Flying Officer 'Timber' Woods, piloting a Hurricane, who was duly credited with its destruction.

7.	Map 4
AIRCRAFT:	Macchi C.200
PILOT:	Maresciallo Lino Lagi
UNIT:	79ª Squadriglia, 6º Gruppo Autonomo Caccia Terrestre
PLACE:	It-Tumbrell (Delimara)
DATE/TIME:	25 September 1940/1208 hours

On 25 September, three Hurricanes and two Gladiators were scrambled to intercept a reconnaissance by Italian fighters. Flying Officer Frederick Taylor is thought to have been credited with one destroyed,[33] while Sergeant Fred Robertson claimed: 'One Macchi 200 believed to be shot down into sea', about 1–2 miles north-east of Grand Harbour at 1218.[34]

The Italians actually lost one aircraft; Maresciallo Lino Lagi being shot down near Delimara at 1208. The crash site was inspected by security and intelligence officers, including Squadron Leader H. Thomas-Ferrand of RAF Intelligence, who reported:

The aircraft, a Macchi 200, was burnt out, and pieces were scattered over six fields near Delimara Camp. The machine had numerous .303 bullet holes in it. The aircraft belonged to No 79 Squadron. It did not catch fire until striking the ground.

The pilot who was dead was visited at Ta Silch [Tas-Silg] Camp . . . He was only just alive when dragged from the aircraft. He will be buried at St Andrews Cemetery on 26th September.[35]

8.	Map 2
AIRCRAFT:	Macchi C.200
PILOT:	Tenente Mario Nasoni
UNIT:	(Probably 79ª Squadriglia), 6° Gruppo Autonomo Caccia Terrestre
PLACE:	In sea, (probably off) Fomm ir-Rih Bay
DATE/TIME:	4 October 1940/1015 hours

Soon after 1000 hours on 4 October, there was a reconnaissance raid by between nine and twelve Macchi C.200s. Anti-aircraft guns opened fire, causing the aircraft to break formation, whereupon they were engaged by three Hurricanes and three Gladiators. One of the Macchis was claimed damaged by Sergeant Fred Robertson, and another destroyed, apparently by Sergeant Reginald Hyde.[36] The aircraft together with its pilot, Tenente Mario Nasoni of 6° Gruppo Autonomo CT, fell offshore, various reports naming the crash site as Ghajn Tuffieha Bay or, more specifically, Gnejna Bay. However, the only MC 200 to have been found in the area actually lies slightly further south, half a kilometre off the coast at Fomm ir-Rih Bay..

9.	Map 4
AIRCRAFT:	Macchi C.200
PILOT:	Sergente (or Sergente Maggiore) Abramo Lanzarini
UNIT:	72ª Squadriglia, 17° Gruppo, 1° Stormo Caccia Terrestre
PLACE:	Buleben il-Kbir, limits of Zejtun
DATE/TIME:	2 November 1940/Approximately 1220 hours

At about 1220 on 2 November, the first of several formations of enemy aircraft, comprising twenty S.79s escorted by at least fifteen fighters, were reported high to the north of Malta. Soon afterwards, Luqa and Zabbar were bombed. The RAF managed to scramble six Hurricanes and two Gladiators and, together with AA gunners, made several claims. In fact, one MC 200 was shot down though it is not known whether this fell to air or ground defences. Shortly afterwards, a

reconnaissance party from 2nd Battalion The Devonshire
Regiment was dispatched to the crash site at Buleben il-Kbir,
between Zejtun and Fgura, arriving to find 'the whole
village . . . out in the streets'. The unit War Diary also noted
that the pilot 'was quite dead and the Italian equipment was
very poor indeed'.[37] The unfortunate Sergente (or Sergente
Maggiore) Abramo Lanzarini had baled out of his stricken
72^a Squadriglia machine only to plummet to his death when
his parachute failed to deploy – a not uncommon occurrence
usually associated with the design of the automatic opening
device of Italian parachutes.

10.	Map 3
AIRCRAFT:	Vickers Wellington (R1094)
CREW:	Sergeant Philip Forrester (Pilot?), Sergeant David Rawlings (Second Pilot?), Sergeant Thomas Wood (or Woor) (Air Observer), Sergeant D. Palmer (Wireless Operator/Air Gunner?), Sergeant Arthur Smith (Wireless Operator/Air Gunner)
UNIT:	Wellington Flight
PLACE:	Dun Mario Street, Qormi
DATE/TIME:	4 November 1940/Approximately 0005 hours

Sunday 3 November 1940 was largely uneventful until
shortly before midnight, when a bomb-laden Wellington
departing on a raid from Luqa failed to gain sufficient height
and crashed and burst into flames in the Tal-Handaq area.
Though injured, the pilot, Sergeant Raymond Lewin,
managed to drag and carry clear the second pilot, shielding
him with his own body just before the bombs on board the
aircraft exploded. Nevertheless, Pilot Officer David Allen did
not survive. (Tragically, another of the crew, Sergeant
T. Reay, would be killed in an air raid on 28 January 1941).

At about five minutes past midnight, a second Wellington
Mk IC was lost in similar circumstances when it crashed and
caught fire on the outskirts of Qormi. Rescuers arrived on
the scene to find part of the wreckage on top of some
houses, and the front of the aircraft, together with a seriously
injured crewman, in a nearby quarry. In spite of the danger
from unexploded bombs and detonating ammunition, Police
Constable Carmelo Camilleri volunteered to be lowered into
the quarry whereupon he secured a rope to the airman

(believed to be Sergeant Arthur Smith) enabling him to be pulled clear. PC Camilleri, together with Second Lieutenant Richard Lavington, Lieutenant (Acting Captain) Anthony Flint and Lieutenant P. Buckle, all of The Queen's Own Royal West Kent Regiment, was also instrumental in rescuing several children from one of the houses.

In addition to Pilot Officer Allen, four aircrew perished at Qormi; the sole survivor from Wellington R1094 being a wireless operator/air gunner, Sergeant D. Palmer. Two civilians also died. Among those commended for their courage that night were Sergeant Lewin, who was awarded the George Cross, and PC Camilleri, who received the George Medal.

11.	Map 3
AIRCRAFT:	Hawker Hurricane
PILOT:	Sergeant William Timms
UNIT:	261 Squadron
PLACE:	West end of Wied Qirda, limits of Zebbug
DATE/TIME:	11 January 1941/0745–0848 hours

On 11 January 1941, Sergeant William Timms was scrambled solo from Ta'Qali, probably to intercept a lone reconnaissance machine seeking the recently arrived HMS *Illustrious* (see next entry). It has been speculated that Timms may have blacked out as a result of oxygen failure, and therefore was unable to switch the Hurricane's airscrew setting from fine pitch (required for take-off and to climb), to coarse pitch (used when the required altitude was reached). If Timms did lose consciousness, and his aircraft subsequently went into a dive with the airscrew still set in fine pitch, the engine would have quickly over-revved and blown up. Another 261 Squadron pilot, Sergeant James Pickering, who was watching events from the ground, believes that this is precisely what happened. He recalled that some months earlier Timms had faced a similar problem when he evaded an attacking Italian aircraft by diving his Hurricane in fine pitch, destroying the engine in the process. On that occasion:

He decided to try and get to Luqa instead of baling out. He was undershooting on his approach and opened up the throttle. In spite of one connecting rod having gone through its cylinder wall and other damage, the engine responded enough to drag the aircraft over the boundary.

We decided that when faced with a forced landing in Malta, the correct procedure was to bale out. Luqa then had vehicles and obstructions distributed over the airfield to frustrate a paratroop attack. A line was cleared on the runway into wind, so only a perfect forced landing could be successful . . .

Bill Timms would have been reluctant to lose an aircraft, and after getting one back, he obviously hoped to do it again.[38]

Timms was seen to overfly Ta'Qali towards Luqa when it must have become apparent that the shattered engine would not make it. From Zebbug, John Galea witnessed the demise of the Hurricane pilot.

I was on the roof-top when I heard the sound of an engine coming at speed right over my village. As soon as it passed over, heading to Luqa, it just turned over and dived headlong. The pilot baled out at too low an altitude and his parachute never opened. His body was only a short distance from the aircraft. On his jacket was the name, Timms.[39]

12.	Map 4
AIRCRAFT:	Junkers Ju 87 (5530/A5+JK?)
CREW:	Feldwebel (or Unteroffizier) Richard Zehetmair (Pilot), Gefreiter Heinrich Müller
UNIT:	I/Stukageschwader 1
PLACE:	Wied il-Qoton, limits of Birzebbuga
DATE/TIME:	18 January 1941/1415–1537 hours

13.	Map 4
AIRCRAFT:	(Probably) Junkers Ju 87
CREW:	(Probably) Oberfeldwebel Kurt Zube (Pilot), (and) Unteroffizier (or Feldwebel) Franz Bussek (or Buczek)
UNIT:	(of) I/Stukageschwader 1
PLACE:	South of Corradino and west of Ghajn Dwieli, limits of Paola
DATE/TIME:	19 January 1941/1247–1325 hours

In late December 1940 Operation 'Excess' was launched, primarily to resupply by sea British Forces in Malta and on the Greek Front. 'Excess', comprising a number of convoys originating in Britain and Alexandria, Egypt, would also enable vessels already at Malta to depart under the protection of the escorting warships. In response to British naval activity in the Mediterranean, the Regia Aeronautica dispatched to Còmiso several Ju 87s in early January 1941. Meanwhile, the first units of the Luftwaffe's X Fliegerkorps also began to arrive in Sicily to support Italian efforts to neutralise Malta and the British Mediterranean Fleet.

Operation 'Excess' saw the delivery to Malta of reinforcements and supplies, as well as Hurricanes, but at a heavy cost in manpower and materiel. On 10 January the destroyer HMS *Gallant* had to be taken in tow after her bows were blown off by a mine. She was beached at Grand Harbour the following day. Meanwhile, the carrier *Illustrious*, already severely damaged on the 10th by German and Italian aircraft, was also obliged to seek shelter at Malta. On the 11th two more warships were attacked east of the Island; the cruisers *Gloucester* and *Southampton* were both damaged, the latter so seriously that she had to be abandoned and was later sunk by the cruiser *Orion*. A number of Fleet Air Arm aeroplanes were also lost, most of them on board *Illustrious*.

After berthing at Parlatorio Wharf, in Grand Harbour, *Illustrious* remained a scene of frenzied activity as her dead and wounded were brought ashore and a massive clearance operation began. Except for several aerial reconnaissances, the enemy initially seemed content to leave the ship alone. The only other alerts were for an attack on Hal Far during the morning of the 11th, and a half-hearted effort that began soon after 2140 on the 15th, when a number of bombs were dropped, most of which fell harmlessly offshore. The lull lasted until 1415 on 16 January when Luftwaffe bombers commenced the first in a series of terrifying precision attacks against the *Illustrious* and the Dockyard. The Germans returned two days later, this time concentrating on Luqa and Hal Far. After further attacks on the 19th, when *Illustrious* was again singled out, there was a sudden decrease in enemy aerial activity.

Of more than sixty killed in Malta, most were civilian victims of the first day of what became known as the

'*Illustrious* Blitz'. It cost the enemy four Ju 88s, four Ju 87s, one Z-506B, a CR 42 and MC 200 definitely destroyed. At least three more aircraft crashed/forced landed on return. The RAF lost one Hurricane and its pilot while two FAA Fulmars were shot down with the loss of one of the pilots. In addition, several machines were damaged in combat and five destroyed on the ground. Ships damaged included the merchantman *Essex* and minesweepers *Decoy* and *Beryl*. Although she also sustained further bomb damage, *Illustrious* was able to leave Malta during the night of the 23rd, arriving at Alexandria two days later. The battered carrier later departed for the United States and underwent months of repair before she could again put to sea.

Crash sites have been located of two German aircraft destroyed in the blitz. During a raid between 1415 and 1537 hours on 18 January, dive bombing attacks on Hal Far and Luqa resulted in damage to two hangars and the Officers' Mess at the former location, and two hangars destroyed at the latter. Three Swordfish, one Hurricane and a Wellington were also written off. Two RAF ground personnel and an artilleryman were killed as was Sub Lieutenant Arthur Griffith of 806 Squadron, whose Fulmar was shot down off the coast. Another Fulmar ditched just west of Delimara: Sapper Spiro Zammit of 24 Fortress Company Royal Engineers was awarded the BEM for helping to save the crew, Lieutenant Robert Henley and Naval Airman A.S. Rush. In spite of enthusiastic claims by air and ground defences just two enemy bombers are thought to have been destroyed: a Ju 88 coming down offshore and a Ju 87 at Wied il-Qoton (just inside the perimeter fence of the present-day Lyster Barracks). The pilot of the latter, Feldwebel (or Unteroffizier) Richard Zehetmair, and his radio operator, Gefreiter Heinrich Müller, were killed. It is uncertain whether this aircraft fell to AA fire or was one of those credited to RAF or FAA pilots.

At 1243 on the 19th, the last bombing raid of the blitz began with an estimated forty Ju 87s and Ju 88s again targeting Grand Harbour where further damage was caused to civil and naval property. Allied casualties included Hurricane pilot Sergeant Eric Kelsey of 261 Squadron who was reported missing. One Italian and six German machines are also known to have been destroyed on this date, one of the German bombers falling at Ghajn Dwieli, between Paola and Grand Harbour. This was almost certainly another Ju 87 of I/StG1 crewed by Oberfeldwebel Kurt Zube and Unteroffizier (or Feldwebel) Franz Bussek (or Buczek), both of whom died. Again, it is not known whether this aircraft fell to AA or fighters.

14.	Map 4
AIRCRAFT:	FIAT CR 42
PILOT:	(Probably) Sergente (or Sergente Maggiore) Andrea Baudoni
UNIT:	(Probably 379ª Squadriglia), 156º Gruppo Autonomo Caccia Terrestre
PLACE:	Ta'Gokondu (south-west perimeter of St Andrew's Barracks)
DATE/TIME:	1 February 1941/Approximately 1145 hours

At about 1135 on 1 February, a single S.79 escorted by CR 42s was reported over the north coast of Malta. Anti-aircraft guns and at least two (and possibly as many as ten) RAF fighters engaged, Sergeant Fred Robertson claiming a CR 42 shot down at Gharghur shortly afterwards:

> I was Pink 2 and on patrol with Pink 1 when we sighted the enemy formation coming in over Gozo at about 19,000 feet. Pink 1 peeled off and attacked the S.79 leading the formation – I followed him down about 15 seconds later but was attacked by the CR 42s which were above and behind the S.79. I gave one a good deflection burst as he was turning and caused him to spin. I watched him partially recover but he continued to lose height in a spiral dive until I finally lost sight of him just before he crashed.[40]

According to the War Diary of 2nd Battalion the Royal Irish Fusiliers, one enemy plane was reported to have crashed in the south-west corner of St Andrew's camp (just over a mile east of Gharghur).[41] Flying Officer C.D. Whittingham may also have shot down a CR 42 that fell offshore. If so, the pilot seems to have survived as the Italians acknowledged only the loss of Sergente Andrea Baudoni of 156º Gruppo CT.

15.   Map 4
AIRCRAFT: Hawker Hurricane
PILOT: Flight Lieutenant James MacLachlan
UNIT: 261 Squadron
PLACE: Paola
DATE/TIME: 16 February 1941/0915–0949 hours

Between 0015 and 2359 hours on 16 February, Malta endured ten air-raid warnings, the third sounding at about 0900 as up to a dozen Bf 109s escorted a single Ju 88 to the Island. In his diary, Flight Lieutenant James MacLachlan wrote that 'A' Flight of 261 Squadron had just come on watch when:

> At about 9.15 we were ordered to scramble, and climbed to 20,000 ft. We were still climbing over Luqa when six Me 109s screamed down on us out of the sun. We immediately broke away and formed a rather wide circle. Just as I took my place in the circle I saw four more Messerschmitts coming down out of the sun. I turned back under them, and they all overshot me. I looked round very carefully, but could see nothing, so turned back onto the tail of the nearest Hun who was chasing some Hurricanes in front of him. We were all turning gently to port, so I cut the corner and was slowly closing in on the Hun. I was determined to get him, and must have been concentrating so intently on his movements that, like a fool, I forgot to look in the mirror until it was too late. Suddenly there was a crash in my cockpit – bits and pieces seemed to fly everywhere.

MacLachlan's aircraft had almost certainly been attacked by Oberleutnant Joachim Müncheberg of 7/JG 26, who claimed two Hurricanes over Malta on this date as his 25th and 26th victories.[42] Two more Hurricanes are believed to have been damaged. MacLachlan's diary continues:

> Instinctively I went into a steep spiral dive, furiously angry that I had been beaten at my own game. My left arm was dripping with blood, and when I tried to raise it only the top part moved, the rest hung limply by my side.

Everything happened so quickly that I have no very clear recollection of what actually took place. I remember opening my hood, disconnecting my oxygen and R/T connections and standing up in the cockpit. The next thing I saw was my kite diving away from me, the roar of its engine gradually fading as it plunged earthwards. It was a marvellous feeling to be safely out of it; everything seemed so quiet and peaceful. I could hear the roar of engines above me, and distinctly heard one long burst of cannon fire. I could not see what was happening as I was falling upside down, and my legs obscured all view of the aircraft above me. My arm was beginning to hurt pretty badly, so I decided to pull my chute straight away in case I fainted from loss of blood. I reached round for my rip cord, but could not find it. For some unknown reason I thought my chute must have been torn off me while I was getting out of my kite, and almost gave up making any further efforts to save myself. I remember thinking that the whole process of being shot down, and being killed, seemed very much simpler and less horrible than I had always imagined. There was just going to be a big thud when I hit the deck and then all would be over – my arm would stop hurting and no more 109s could make dirty passes at me behind my back. I think I must have been gradually going off into a faint when suddenly I thought of Mother reading the telegram saying that I had been killed in action. I made one last effort to see if my parachute was still there, and to my amazement and relief found that it had not been torn off after all. With another supreme effort I reached round and pulled the rip cord. There was a sickening lurch as my chute opened and my harness tightened round me so that I could hardly breathe. I felt horribly ill and faint. Blood from my arm came streaming back into my face, in spite of the fact that I was holding the stump as tightly as I could. I could only breathe with the utmost difficulty, and my arm hurt like hell. I could see Malta spread out like a map 15,000 ft below me and I longed to be down there – just to lie still and die peacefully. I was woken from this stupor by the roar of an engine, and naturally thought some bloodthirsty Gerry had come to finish me off. I don't think I really minded what happened; certainly the thought of a few more cannon shells flying past me didn't exactly cheer me up. To my joy, however, I saw that my escort was a Hurricane piloted, as I learned later, by Eric Taylor. He had quite rightly decided that he could do no good by playing with the Huns at 20,000 ft, so came down to see that none of them got me.

For what seemed like hours I hung there, apparently motionless, with Malta still as far away as ever. Once or twice I started swinging very badly, but as I was using my only hand to stop myself bleeding to death, I was unable to do anything about it. At about 1,500 ft I opened my eyes again, and to my joy saw that I was very much lower down. For a little while I was afraid I was going to land in the middle of a town, but I mercifully drifted to the edge of this. For the last 100 ft I seemed to drop out of the sky – the flat roof of a house came rushing up at me, and just as I was about to land on it, it dodged to one side and I ended up in a little patch of green wheat. I hit the ground with a terrific thud, rolled over once or twice, and then lay back intending to die quietly. This, however, was not to be.

MacLachlan's Hurricane is thought to have crashed 200 metres east of the entrance driveway to Addolorata Cemetery, near Paola. According to his log book, MacLachlan himself landed about 2 miles away in a field near Zejtun.

Scarcely had I got myself comfortable and closed my eyes, when I heard the sound of people running. I hurriedly tried to think up some famous last words to give my public, but never had a chance to utter them. I was surrounded by a crowd of shouting, gesticulating Malts, who pulled at my parachute, lifted my head and drove me so furious that I had to give up the dying idea in order to concentrate completely on kicking every Malt who came within range. From what the pongos [army] told me after I believe I registered some rather effective shots.

Eventually two very dim army stretcher-bearers arrived with a first-aid outfit. I told them to put a tourniquet on my arm, and give me some morphia, whereupon one of them started to bandage my wrist, and the other went off to ask what morphia was. In the end I got them to give me the first-aid outfit, and fixed myself up. At last a doctor arrived who actually knew what to do. He put me on a stretcher, had me carried about half a mile across fields to an ambulance, which in turn took me down to the local advanced field dressing station. Here they filled me with morphia, gave me ether, and put my arm in a rough splint. When I came round they gave me a large tot of whisky, another injection of morphia, and sent me off to Imtarfa as drunk as a lord. When I eventually arrived at the hospital I was feeling in the best of spirits and apparently shook the sisters by asking them to have a drink with me.[43]

After three days, it became necessary to amputate the injured arm. Incredibly, this did not end MacLachlan's flying career. Less than three weeks after being wounded, he flew solo in a Magister and 'shot up' Mtarfa Hospital! After being fitted with a prosthetic arm, he continued to fly operationally and as an instructor, but in July 1943, while flying a Mustang, he was fatally injured after crash-landing in northern France.

16.	Map 3
AIRCRAFT:	Messerschmitt Bf 110 (3723?/KB+NC?)
CREW:	Oberleutnant Günther Rudolf (Pilot), Unteroffizier Hans Dittmayer
UNIT:	(Probably) Stab III/Zerstörergeschwader 26
PLACE:	Tas-Sriedak, limits of Mosta
DATE/TIME:	5 March 1941/1710-1805

Shortly after 0700 on 5 March, a single raider, identified as either a Do 25 or a Bf 110, carried out a low-level strafe of the Sunderland anchorage at St Paul's Bay. Neither of the flyingboats there are thought to have been damaged. About an hour later, another aircraft flew over Malta, apparently on a reconnaissance preparatory to a major raid later that day when, at 1710 hours, several plots totalling an estimated forty fighters and sixty bombers began to converge on Hal Far. Within 50 minutes the aerodrome was rendered temporarily unserviceable: four aircraft were destroyed on the ground, and a number of buildings and hangars were damaged.

Among those scrambled for the raid was Flight Lieutenant
C.D. Whittingham:

> A flap on about 5 o'clock. I was up and saw them being
> bombed below. I positioned myself to run down in a
> right-hand dive in case of being chased by 109s. In doing
> so, I blacked out for a bit, but came out at about 1,200
> feet. I soon recovered and attacked one of the many
> enemy aircraft in front of and below me. My first shot was
> at a Ju 87 and the next at a Ju 88. They both fired back at
> me. I then spiralled to ground level for safety and to get
> away from any 109s that might by this time have been
> positioning themselves against me. Making for base I saw
> about five Ju 88s going out to sea. I hadn't much
> ammunition but decided to climb in their direction. This I
> did and pointed my nose at one and gave him a burst. I
> may have hit him but he fairly let me have it from his
> underneath guns. I twisted and was making for land when
> I saw a machine burst into gigantic flames about 100 yards
> from me. It was a Messerschmitt 110 which had been hit
> by ack-ack. It was a stroke of luck for myself, as I learned
> afterwards that he was firing at me just previous to being
> hit. I hadn't seen him. In the engagement the squadron
> got seven confirmed. Poor old M [Sergeant Charles
> McDougal] was killed. A 109 got him just after he had
> bagged an '87'.[44]

Oberleutnant Joachim Müncheberg and Unteroffizier
Kestler each apparently claimed a Hurricane shot down
during this action,[45] as did Leutnant Willi Kothmann whose
unit, I/JG 27, was temporarily in Sicily while en route to
North Africa.

Allied claims included as many as nine aircraft destroyed
and at least four damaged by AA, and up to seven destroyed,
one 'probable' and two damaged by the RAF. The Luftwaffe
acknowledged the loss of one Ju 88, two Ju 87s and two Bf
110s. Another Ju 87 returned with a wounded gunner.

One of the Messerschmitts, probably that seen by
Whittingham, crashed at Tas-Sriedak, just north of Ta'Qali.
Neither the pilot, Oberleutnant Günther Rudolf, nor his
wireless operator, Unteroffizier Hans Dittmayer, survived.

Flight Lieutenant James MacLachlan, who was on a hospital outing in Valletta, was visiting the underground War Rooms at Lascaris when news of the crash came through. He immediately rushed back to Ta'Qali and joined the many spectators at the scene.

> We found the remains still burning in a field just across the road from the NW corner of the aerodrome. The Gerries had come down to machine gun Takali, and had been attacked by a Hurricane and Bofors guns at the same time. It caught fire at about 500 ft, and went in at about 45°. The majority of the machine, including three [sic] horribly burnt and mutilated bodies, were smouldering inthe middle of a small clover field. Both engines, and some of the heavier debris however, had been flung over the road into a field on the other side. As usual on such occasions the air was sickly with the stink of burning flesh, and that peculiar smell that all German aircraft seem to have. I took off the number plate of one of the engines as a souvenir.[46]

17.	Map 3
AIRCRAFT:	Martin Maryland (AR706)
CREW:	Flying Officer John Boys-Stones (Pilot), Sergeant J.M. Alexander (Observer), Sergeant Jack Levy (Wireless Operator/Air Gunner?)
UNIT:	69 Squadron
PLACE:	Wied il-Busbies, limits of Rabat
DATE/TIME:	7 March 1941/1230 hours

At 0955 hours on 7 March, Maryland Mk I AR706 of 69 Squadron took off from Luqa on a reconnaissance of Taormina. Shortly after photographing the objective, the Maryland was attacked by an unidentified fighter. Both aircraft opened fire without noticeable effect before the Maryland was able to escape. A short time later a Cant-Z 506B floatplane was seen and promptly shot up, being claimed as damaged. The Maryland then continued on its way to Malta.

Its return was covered by Hurricanes of 261 Squadron, airborne as a precaution against patrolling Bf 109s. However, the slower, less powerfully armed British fighters were unable to prevent the Messerschmitts from attacking the reconnaissance machine as it crossed the coast. A Hurricane that attempted to intervene was shot down; the pilot, Sergeant F.J. Jessop, baling out into the sea from where he was later rescued.

The Maryland was also hit. One engine was set on fire and the rear-gunner, Sergeant Jack Levy, killed. Flying Officer John Boys-Stones struggled to keep the aircraft steady long enough to allow the observer, Sergeant J.M. Alexander, to bale out, only for him to be mistaken for an enemy airman and shot at by soldiers of 2nd Battalion The King's Own Malta Regiment. Despite his ordeal, Alexander escaped unharmed.

Flying Officer Boys-Stones was less fortunate. By the time he was able to abandon the burning aircraft it was too low for his parachute to deploy fully. He plummeted some 250 feet onto solid rock, and died shortly afterwards.[47]

Both machines fell to 7/JG 26, the Maryland being credited to Leutnant Hans Johannsen, and Sergeant Jessop's Hurricane to Oberfeldwebel Karl Kühdorf.[48]

18.	Map 5
AIRCRAFT:	Messerschmitt Bf 110 (2057/L1+BH?)
CREW:	(Possibly) Oberleutnant Horst von Weegmann (Pilot?), (and) Unteroffizier Wilhelm Banser
UNIT:	(Possibly) 1/Nachtjagdgeschwader 3
PLACE:	West of Nadur, Gozo
DATE/TIME:	9 March 1941/0725 hours

On 9 March 1941, one Hurricane was burnt out and two others damaged during an early morning raid on Ta'Qali by four aircraft reported to be Messerschmitt Bf 110s. During its low-level approach over the island of Gozo, another Bf 110 crashed when it failed to clear a 450 feet rise just west of Nadur. Both crewmen were killed. (Probably, the pilot simply misjudged his approach – a theory supported by the recent discovery of the tip of a propeller blade embedded in rock atop the point of the exposed northern edge of the ridge overlooking the Victoria–Nadur main road).

It has not been possible to positively identify this aircraft, which may have been a 1/NJG 3 machine reported to have flown into the ground during a sortie to Malta, though this is recorded as having occurred on 11 March 1941.[49]

19.	Map 2
AIRCRAFT:	Short Sunderland (L2164)
CREW:	(None aboard at time?)
UNIT:	228 Squadron
PLACE:	In sea, St Paul's/Mistra Bay
DATE/TIME:	10 March 1941/1221 hours

The same raid which resulted in the loss of Maryland AR706 on 7 March also saw a strafing attack by a pair of Bf 109s on the flyingboat anchorage at St Paul's Bay, where Sunderland L2164 of 228 Squadron was badly damaged. The boatguard, Sergeant A.S. Jones, managed to get a Vickers 'K' gun into action and fired a number of rounds before being killed at his post.

At about the same time three days later, Saint Paul's Bay was subjected to another, more concentrated attack. Low-flying aircraft, variously reported as Messerschmitt Bf 109s or Bf 110s, shot up and damaged Sunderland T9046 before redirecting their efforts against L2164, setting it on fire. Personnel quickly boarded the aircraft and temporarily brought the blaze under control, but when the flames again took hold, L2164 was towed into Mistra Bay and abandoned, eventually settling in the shallows just offshore.

20.	Map 3
AIRCRAFT:	Hawker Hurricane (V7495)
PILOT:	Sergeant Frederick Robertson
UNIT:	261 Squadron
PLACE:	Approximately 150 metres south-west of Rabat reservoir (south of Rabat)
DATE/TIME:	23 March 1941/1530 hours

On Sunday morning, 23 March, Convoy 'MW6', comprising the merchantmen, *City of Lincoln*, *City of Manchester*, *Clan Ferguson* and *Perthshire*, arrived under Royal Navy escort at Grand Harbour. At 1145, the Dockyard area was subjected to the first of two bombing raids, neither of which achieved significant results. During the second attack (1540–1620 hours), fourteen or so Hurricanes were scrambled to intercept an estimated thirty Ju 87s escorted by up to twenty fighters. The *Perthshire* and *City of Lincoln* were both slightly damaged, as were a number of buildings in the area.

Claims by AA and the RAF at the end of the day amounted to at least thirteen Ju 87s destroyed, one probable and six damaged: the Luftwaffe acknowledged the loss of four Ju 87s. The RAF lost one Hurricane, from which Sergeant Fred Robertson managed to bale out:

I was on patrol with X-ray Squadron when Blue 1 (S/Ldr Lambert) gave the order to attack, I being Pink 1, and weaving slipped into the line astern formation about fifth and followed into the attack, which owed its success to the excellent positioning and leadership of Blue 1.

I saw Squadron Leader Lambert attack a JU 87 from astern and break away – as he broke off, the tail unit of the enemy aircraft fell away and it crashed into the sea. I then attacked another JU 87 from astern setting it on fire under the starboard wing root and saw it hit the sea. (Blue 1 also fired at this machine after I broke away). I was then attacked by another JU 87 from ahead and got a bullet in my port main petrol tank. I followed the enemy aircraft around in a very steep turn and finally shot it down into the sea; next I found that my aircraft was burning fiercely and so I climbed from 700 feet over the sea to a position about a mile South of Rabat and baled out landing in a field midway between Zebbug and Luqa Aerodrome.[50]

Robertson's Hurricane Mk I V7495 crashed in flames 150 metres south-west of Rabat reservoir and 100 metres south of the Pumping Station on the Rabat–Dingli road, south-west of Rabat.

21.	Map 2
AIRCRAFT:	Hawker Hurricane (V7430)
PILOT:	Sergeant R.J. Goode
UNIT:	274 Squadron attached to 261 Squadron
PLACE:	Pwales Valley
DATE/TIME:	28 March 1941/1726 hours

At about 1720 hours on 28 March, the first of eight Hurricanes was scrambled in response to an impending raid. By the time the all-clear sounded half an hour later, one

Hurricane had forced-landed near Ghajn Tuffieha, the impact tearing off the fuselage just behind the cockpit. The pilot, Sergeant Reg Goode, who had recently arrived from the Western Desert on detachment from 274 Squadron, was conveyed to hospital with shrapnel wounds to the neck and back. The victor was almost certainly Oberleutnant Joachim Müncheberg of 7/JG 26, who claimed a Hurricane destroyed south of Gozo at 1720 hours.[51]

22.	Map 2
AIRCRAFT:	Hawker Hurricane
PILOT:	Sergeant Peter Waghorn
UNIT:	261 Squadron
PLACE:	Erba'Mwiezeb, limits of St Paul's Bay
DATE/TIME:	11 April 1941/1154 hours

On 11 April, Axis fighters shot down or damaged five Hurricanes of 261 Squadron. The RAF claimed at least one Messerschmitt Bf 109 and a Bf 110 destroyed. Pilot Officer Peter Kennett and Sergeant Peter Waghorn are also thought to have attacked a Junkers Ju 88 before both were shot down. Kennett was apparently seen in the sea shortly afterwards, waving to another Hurricane. Tragically, he died before a rescue launch could reach him. Waghorn was also killed. Pilot Officers Douglas Whitney and P.A. Mortimer and Sergeant A.H. Deacon all survived forced/crash-landings as a result of enemy action. The Luftwaffe recorded three losses for II Fliegerkorps on this date, including a Ju 88 of 7/KG 30 and a Bf 110 of 2(F)/123.[52] Three claims for fighters destroyed were submitted by 7/JG 26; Oberleutnant Joachim Müncheberg being credited with a Hurricane south-east of Malta at 1131, and another south-east of St Paul's Bay twenty-two minutes later, and Oberleutnant Klaus Mietusch with a Hurricane north of the Island at 1150.[53]

Ground observers closely monitored the action. A detailed timetable of events was recorded in the War Diary of the 2nd Battalion The Royal Irish Fusiliers:

1126: Air Raid Warning – 1130 Plot +6 – 135° – 3 Miles off coast – 8 Hurricanes up. 1145 AA Fire 240° from A Coy – 1146 – 2 Planes going out 020° A Coy – 2 Hurricanes

following – 1150 – Heavy MG Fire at Sea – 5 Planes
involved in fight – 1134 – 1 plane (Hurricane) crashed near
King's Corner – Guard at once mounted on plane from L49
– 1200 – 1 ME reported in sea – South one down at Hal Far
– 1210 Raiders passed . . .[54]

It may be significant that one of the times – 1134 – fails
to correlate with the rest, and in all probability should read
1154 (which virtually coincides with when Oberleutnant
Müncheberg claimed his second victim). King's Corner
(a place name no longer in use) was less than 1 mile south-
east of St Paul's Bay. Carmen Fenech, then a young girl,
lived nearby at 2 (later changed to 4) Wileg Street. Fifty-seven
years on, she recalled how a Hurricane approached from
the direction of Bidnija to crash in fields opposite the road.
It slid along on one wing before coming to rest against her
house. (Another eyewitness described how the aircraft
went through a carob tree and cartwheeled towards the
building.) According to Fenech, the dead pilot was close
by, still strapped in his seat after having been thrown clear
of the wreckage. (A third eyewitness maintained that the
pilot was extricated by soldiers of The Royal Irish
Fusiliers.)

What is generally agreed is that the Hurricane was shot
down by Bf 109s at about Easter time, and that the pilot,
since identified as Sergeant Peter Waghorn, was killed.

23.	Map 4
AIRCRAFT:	Junkers Ju 87 (5724/J9+BL?)
CREW:	Leutnant Werner Zühlke (Pilot?), Obergefreiter Hans Feldeisen
UNIT:	9/Stukageschwader 1
PLACE:	Near Chapel of St Mary, Maghtab, limits of Gharghur
DATE/TIME:	11 April 1941/2234 hours

After a respite of nearly ten hours, warning was given of an
impending raid at 2155 on 11 April. Eighteen minutes later,
the first of nine Junkers Ju 87 Stukas crossed the coast at
Madliena and shortly afterwards began to bomb Ta'Qali
Siggiewi and Mgarr. Four people were killed and six injured.
Searchlights criss-crossed the night sky in an effort to
illuminate targets for the RAF and ground defences. At

2234, 2nd Battalion The Royal Irish Fusiliers claimed a Ju 87 destroyed; the crew and a young girl lost their lives and another girl was seriously injured when the aircraft crashed into a farmhouse at Il-Maghtab, north of Victoria Lines. The same aircraft was probably also claimed by Pilot Officer Claude Hamilton.[55]

24.	Map 4
AIRCRAFT:	Short Sunderland (L5807)
CREW:	Pilot Officer L.G.M. Rees (Captain), Flying Officer F.M. Goyen, Pilot Officer N.M. Maynard, Leading Aircraftman D.A.J. Taylor
UNIT:	228 Squadron
PLACE:	In sea, off Kalafrana
DATE/TIME:	27 April 1941/1007 hours

During the morning of 27 April, twenty-three Hurricanes flew off HMS *Ark Royal* and were led by three FAA Fulmars towards Malta, some 575 miles to the east. En route, they were met by a Sunderland of 228 Squadron and three Marylands of 69 Squadron tasked with escorting the new arrivals on the final leg of their journey. Eight of the Hurricanes and a Fulmar, which were to rendezvous with the Sunderland, arrived half an hour behind schedule, and eventually reached Malta while an air raid was still in progress. The Sunderland Captain, Pilot Officer L. Rees, decided to land as quickly as possible so that the flyingboat might be brought ashore and placed in a hangar where it would at least be concealed from aerial view. After arriving at Marsaxlokk Bay, Sunderland L5807 was hurriedly moored in the camber at Kalafrana. There was just time to adjust one of the beaching legs before the arrival overhead of enemy aircraft compelled the crew and maintenance party to abandon their task and head for shore. At least two Messerschmitt Bf 109s of 7/JG 26 dived from out of the sun and sped eastward towards the camber. The Sunderland presented an all too easy target. A fuel tank in the starboard wing was punctured and a fire started. This quickly grew out of control until the entire wing broke away and the stricken flyingboat listed to port, before finally sliding beneath the burning, fuel-covered water.

25.	Map 2
AIRCRAFT:	Junkers Ju 88 (2279/LI+BT?)
CREW:	Feldwebel Rudolf Lenzner (Pilot), Feldwebel Wilhelm Heller (Observer), Feldwebel Helmut Hartlich (Wireless Operator), Unteroffizier Paul Kietzmann (Air Gunner)
UNIT:	9/Lehrgeschwader 1
PLACE:	Between the Naval Firing Range and Ix-Xhaghra L-Hamra, limits of Manikata
DATE/TIME:	29 April 1941/Early evening

Grand Harbour was the main target for the Luftwaffe during the evening and night of 29/30 April. Bombs were also dropped at Luqa and Ta'Qali. Shortly after 1835 hours, a Ju 88 of 9/LG 1 was hit by anti-aircraft height control and set on fire. Two of the crew baled out. RAF fighters subsequently attacked the aircraft, which was then abandoned altogether. One of the crew was captured at Pembroke Ranges, and the remainder rescued from the sea. The prisoners' first interrogation was conducted by Assistant Defence Security Officer, Lieutenant J. Harrow:

On the 30th April, 1941, accompanied by Captain JACKSON (General Staff), I accompanied four German aviator prisoners-of-war, whose particulars are attached, at Corradino Prison.

2.   In each case they refused to give the number of their Squadron, and indicated that their Military Identity Card was quite sufficient. All sorts of persuasion was attempted, but they steadfastly refused to disclose the Squadron to which they belonged.

3.   Apart from noting their particulars, I refrained from taking any notes in their presence and have trusted entirely to memory.

4.   The four German airmen were the complete crew of a Junkers 88 which was brought down on the evening of the 29th April.

5.   According to their statement, their machine was damaged by AA fire and there was the danger of the whole plane catching fire when they finally decided to bale out. It will be seen that the crew consisted of three Sergt. Majors and one NCO.

6.   In discussion with Sergt. Major LENZNER, he stated that their target consisted of two cruisers and eleven destroyers which were known to be in the Port of Valletta.

7.   Sergt. Major HELLER stated that the bomb release gear was damaged by AA fire and his bombs did not leave the plane. Whether this is true or not I cannot say, but they were under the impression that their plane crashed into the sea – in fact they were almost certain. They were very surprised when I informed them that a Junkers 88 actually landed on the ground.

8.   Air Gunner KIETZMANN was wearing the Iron Cross (1st Class). He refused to give the details which earned him this decoration – he merely said "Besendere [sic] Leistung" ("Special Performance").

9.   All four were 100% Nazi and were quite confident that the Axis Powers were going to win the war. On being asked how they were going to conquer the British Empire, they admitted they did not know how, but said that Adolf Hitler would accomplish this act as he had others. In spite of many subtle attempts during a four hours conversation, they refused to be drawn into any matter which they thought would assist the enemy. LENZNER maintained that "as sure as the sun rises, so will the Jewish problem develop to a crisis in Great Britain".

10.   All aviators admitted having made many trips over England and at least four over Malta. In one raid over England HELLER said that his target was Andover Aerodrome. This crew took part in the attack on the "ILLUSTRIOUS" whilst it was in Malta, and admitted suffering heavy losses.

11.   From the general discussion, it appears that a German air 'ace' by the name of Capt. Wilhelm DUERBECK, holder of the German decoration 'Ritter Kreuz" (Knights Cross), had been lost in the attack on the "ILLUSTRIOUS".

12.   On being questioned why they had resorted to night flying, they maintained that it was more profitable, and drew my attention to our nocturnal activities over Germany.

13.   I discussed indiscriminate bombing with them and they compared what is happening here with what is

happening in Germany and had the audacity to state that the British started first.

14.   Attempts were made to find out their opinion of the armed forces of their Axis partner, but, although they appeared to agree with some of my derogatory remarks regarding Italian fighting powers, they would not commit themselves to any statement. They knew very little about the battle of Matapan, and when I explained the probability that in the confusion Italian battleships actually fired at each other in the dark, they appeared to agree that this was a 'poor show'. They were most surprised to hear that German naval Officers and ratings were rescued from one of the cruisers.

15.   My talk with Sergt. Major LENZNER lasted some time, and during my interrogation of Sergt. Major HELLER the latter asked if he might see what LENZNER had said. This may indicate that HELLER is what they call "Vertrauensmann" (confidential man) in the party. LENZNER fully expected to be home in Germany again with his family before Christmas. I advised him not to count on it. I asked Sergt. Major HELLER how he liked life at Comiso, and this question immediately startled him and he asked if his comrades had informed me that this was their station. I side-tracked his question but he appeared ill at ease, and stated that it was strictly against all regulations to mention their aerodrome.

16.   I discussed parachute mines with all the prisoners and they pleaded ignorance regarding their existence. They stated that Junkers 88 invariably carry bombs. From my own point of view I do not believe that they could not be aware of the existence of parachute mines.

17.   The whole four hours interview showed to me that their training from a Security point of view leaves nothing to be desired and that their sense of discipline is excellent. Hitler's continued run of successes no doubt helps towards their high morale, but in the case of LENZNER his attitude completely changed when the conversation turned towards the bombardment of German towns, particularly HAMBURG where his parents live. I am quite convinced that it is only after the

Germans have been made to feel the full weight of our RAF that their morale will take a distinct turn – perhaps not so much the German fighting forces outside Germany, as the news is very cleverly concealed from them.
18.   Particulars of prisoners attached, also their personal effects. Please acknowledge.[56]

The report is typed, except for the last item concerning the PoW's personal effects, which was clearly added later, and seems to be linked to a report which includes the following complaint made by the prisoners:

Articles of clothing such as shirts, belts, pullovers; decorations such as 1 Iron Cross, Eagle badges and stripes; personal papers, photographs, postcards; and other minor items found in pockets have been removed from prisoners by someone on their way to internment and have not proceeded with the remainder of P/W's effects to the proper Authority. This is doubly regrettable as not only do we give ourselves a bad name which is bound to get back to Germany for propaganda; but we are also losing very valuable information. At the back of one photograph I obtained the number of the Squadron and on the corner of a postcard I found the Feld post number and proof that the Squadron's Headquarter's in Germany in Munich.[57]

Pilot Officers Anthony Rippon and J.E. Hall of 261 Squadron were both credited with the destruction of the Ju 88[58] which crashed near the Naval Firing Range at Ghajn Tuffieha in north-west Malta and was completely burnt out.

26.	Map 4
AIRCRAFT:	Hawker Hurricane (Z3061?)
PILOT:	Sergeant B.C. Walmsley
UNIT:	'C' Flight, 261 Squadron
PLACE:	Ghaxaq
DATE/TIME:	1 May 1941/Early evening

On 1 May 1941, 'C' Flight, 261 Squadron (retitled 185 Squadron on 12 May) was placed on readiness for the first

time. Based at Hal Far, the nucleus of the new unit consisted of pilots and ground crews from 261 Squadron, with additional ground personnel provided by 251 Squadron and 1430 Flight which arrived shortly afterwards from Egypt.[59] As well as its Operations Record Book, the unit had an unofficial diary, with individual pilots taking responsibility for recording daily 'gen and doings'. The entry for 1 May reads:

> Our first day of operations. During the morning some ME 109s were seen but they had the advantage of height and sun but made no effort to attack.
>
> During the early evening, the Squadron was on patrol and was attacked by 6 ME 109s. These again had the advantage of height and caused us to break up in all directions. Unfortunately Sgt [B.C.] Walmsley didn't move quite fast enough and had to bale out as a result of damage to his aeroplane. P/O [R.A.] Innes was injured in his foot but not seriously. This was not discovered until he started to climb out of his cockpit. As he trod on the injured foot, he gave a loud howl and subsided onto the firing button which had been left to fire position and a hail of lead forthwith projected over to hangars much to the alarm and consternation of all.
>
> Taken all round – not a brilliant start but we hope better may be expected![60]

Both aircraft were attacked by Bf 109s of 7/JG 26, Leutnant Hans Johannsen and Oberleutnant Joachim Müncheberg each claiming a Hurricane destroyed south-west of Luqa aerodrome at 1714 and 1715 hours respectively. Another claim for a Hurricane destroyed over Luqa at 1720 was also submitted by Oberfeldwebel Karl Kühdorf.[61] Müncheberg apparently reported that his victim crashed about a mile north-east of the airfield.[62] This was probably Sergeant Walmsley, whose Hurricane Mk II crashed close to Ghaxaq church, one and a half miles north-east of the then unfinished Safi landing ground that extended south-east of Luqa aerodrome.

27.	Map 3
AIRCRAFT:	Junkers Ju 88 (3199/4D+FS?)
CREW:	Unteroffizier Werner Gerhardt (Pilot?), Unteroffizier Heinz Demmer (Observer?), Obergefreiter Heinz Franke (Wireless Operator?), Obergefreiter Alfred Starke (Air Gunner?)
UNIT:	8/Kampfgeschwader 30
PLACE:	Ospizio (between Gwardamanga and Floriana)
DATE/TIME:	6 May 1941/2020 hours

At about 2020 hours on 6 May, two fighters were scrambled to meet an estimated 36–40 'hostiles' at 10,000 and 15,000 feet. Initially, anti-aircraft gunners refrained from firing, enabling the Hurricanes to close in. AA then engaged by barrage before the fighters returned, Squadron Leader C.D. Whittingham ultimately claiming one bomber destroyed, one probable and another damaged. Light AA (Bofors) also engaged all aircraft below 3,000 feet. As always, the searchlights were in operation, and performed particularly well, illuminating targets for up to three and a half minutes.

Bofors were credited with direct hits on two bombers, one of which came down at the Ordnance Repair Shops, Ospizio. This was almost certainly Ju 88 A-5 4D+FS of 8/KG 30, and may have been one of the bombers attacked and claimed by Whittingham. None of the crew are thought to have survived.

28.	Map 2
AIRCRAFT:	Hawker Hurricane
PILOT:	Sergeant Henry Jennings
UNIT:	261 Squadron
PLACE:	Wied id-Dis, limits of Gharghur
DATE/TIME:	7 May 1941/Approximately 1600 hours

Shortly before 1600 on 7 May, Hurricanes were scrambled to intercept a reconnaissance Ju 88 and its fighter escort. Soon afterwards, two aircraft of 261 Squadron collided. One of the pilots, thought to be Sergeant G.A. Walker, baled out before his stricken machine crashed off the coast. However, Sergeant Henry Jennings was killed when his fighter fell on land.

Records show that on 7 May 1941, two Hurricanes collided and crashed in the area of 2nd Battalion The Royal Irish Fusiliers.[63] Eyewitness accounts and recently found wreckage

indicate that one of the aircraft (evidently that piloted by
Jennings) crashed south-west of Fort Madliena at Wied id-Dis,
a valley east of Gharghur (and formerly part of 2 RIF's sector).

29.	Map 3
AIRCRAFT:	FIAT BR 20M
CREW:	Tenente Sergio Reggiani (Pilot), Sergente Maggiore (or Maresciallo) Guglielmo Mazzolenis (Second Pilot), Primo Aviere Francesco Minuto (Wireless Operator), Primo Aviere Michele Turco (Mechanic), Primo Aviere Giovanni (or Ugo) Bonanno (Air Gunner)
UNIT:	243ª Squadriglia, 99º Gruppo, 43º Stormo Bombardamento Terrestre
PLACE:	Guarena, south of Qrendi
DATE/TIME:	8 June 1941/0330 hours

In the early hours of 8 June, five BR 20s took off at intervals
from Catania to attack Luqa airfield. Over Malta, Tenente
Sergio Reggiani's aircraft was caught and held in the beams of
two searchlights, enabling Hurricane Z3063, flown by Squadron
Leader Robert 'Butch' Barton of 249 Squadron, to close in and
deliver two attacks, from the port then starboard sides. The
bomber's engines caught fire and Barton swept in again, this
time from dead astern. Soon after, four parachutes were reported
over south-west Malta, but only Tenente Reggiani and the
second pilot, Maresciallo Guglielmo Mazzolenis, survived. The
bodies of two crewmen were recovered, including one whose
parachute had caught on the bomber's tail, while the gunner,
Primo Aviere Bonnano, was reported missing, presumed killed.

Various reports confirm that the aircraft crashed on land but
provide conflicting information as regards the location. The
War Diary of 2nd Battalion The King's Own Malta Regiment
states that: 'One Fiat BR20 was shot down in flames by fighters
at Siggiewi, pilot and second pilot taken prisoners. Second
plane engaged by fighters and believed down at sea . . . '[64]
There is a similar entry in the War Diary of 2nd Battalion The
Devonshire Regiment,[65] while those of 3 KOMR[66] and
1st Battalion The Hampshire Regiment[67] record the crash site
as, '400 YARDS south of GUARENA', and, 'between QRENDI
and Hagar QIM', respectively. Where, then, did the BR 20
actually come down?

Tenente Reggiani was captured near the Blue Grotto, and
Maresciallo Mazzolenis at Wied Bassasa, both within a mile

and a half of Guarena, where there is still evidence of a
crashed Italian aeroplane on farmland about 200 metres south
of Guarena Tower, near Qrendi. In spite of the inconsistencies
in available records, this is now known to have been the
aircraft shot down by Squadron Leader Barton. The location
corresponds to the only detailed reference of the crash site:
'400 yards SOUTH of GUARENA', that is, south-west of
Qrendi and east of Hagar Qim. Local Police reports, which are
usually accurate, also record an 'Enemy bomber shot down on
outskirts of Qrendi' during the hours of 0249 and 0424.[68]

30.	Map 3
AIRCRAFT:	Hawker Hurricane (Z4317?)
PILOT:	Sergeant Robert MacPherson
UNIT:	260 Squadron
PLACE:	Near dam just west of Hal Farrug, limits of Luqa
DATE:	14 June 1941

During Operation 'Tracer' on 14 June, forty-seven Hurricanes
of 238 and 260 Squadrons were flown off the carriers HMS
Victorious and *Ark Royal*, with four Hudsons from 200 Squadron
in Gibraltar escorting the fighters to Malta, from where
most were to continue to North Africa. Four Hurricanes were
lost, including a 260 Squadron machine which arrived at Malta
short of fuel and crashed at Wied il-Kbir, north-west of Luqa
airfield. The pilot, Sergeant Robert MacPherson, was killed.

31.	Map 3
AIRCRAFT:	Hawker Hurricane (Z3055)
PILOT:	Sergeant Thomas Hackston
UNIT:	126 Squadron
PLACE:	In the sea at Hamrija Bank (south coast)
DATE/TIME:	4 July 1941/Morning

Until recently, very little was known about the circumstances of
the death of Sergeant Thomas Hackston of 126 Squadron,
whose Hurricane was lost off Malta on 4 July 1941. On 16 July
and 19 September 1995, information provided by a local scuba
diver led to the Malta Aviation Museum Foundation recovering
an aircraft from a depth of 42 metres off Malta's south coast. The
wreck was soon identified as Sergeant Hackston's Hurricane Mk

II Z3055. While the Merlin engine was being cleaned, the probable cause of the crash also became apparent, with signs of overheating on one of the cylinder banks indicating engine failure. It is presumed that after ditching the fighter, Sergeant Hackston drowned in rough seas. His body was never found.

His aircraft is currently being reconstructed by the Malta Historic Aircraft Preservation Group at the Aviation Museum workshops at Ta'Qali.

32.	Map 4
AIRCRAFT:	Macchi C.200
PILOT:	Sottotenente Francesco Liberti
UNIT:	98ª Squadriglia, 7º Gruppo, 54º Stormo Caccia Terrestre
PLACE:	Near the Church of St Francis, Valletta
DATE/TIME:	25 July 1941/1059 hours

Twenty-two Hurricanes were scrambled by 185 and 249 Squadrons in response to an Italian aerial reconnaissance late in the morning of 25 July. The RAF claimed to have destroyed one Savoia Marchetti S.79 and a FIAT BR 20, though it would appear that only one tri-motor, a Cant Z-1007 Bis, was lost.[69] 249 Squadron also shot down two of the escorting fighters. One of the Macchi C.200s was attacked over Valletta by Pilot Officer Robert Matthews. The event was witnessed by many, including Second Lieutenant J. Quentin Hughes of 26 Defence Regiment Royal Artillery, who recorded in his diary:

> [In] the morning, we were shopping in Valletta during an air raid when a Macchi 200 hit by the Hurricane's cannon power dived to earth. As she approached the roar of her engine grew into a scream and the Maltese in the street shouted, running hither and thither not knowing how to escape. The roar ended with a dull thud as the plane fell into the ruins of a bombed house . . .
>
> Half a mile away the pilot glided serenely down little guessing the commotion he had caused.[70]

The pilot observed descending was evidently that of the other Macchi shot down; Tenente Silvio De Giorgi was rescued from the sea about six miles north-east of Grand Harbour. Pilot Officer Matthews' victim, Sottotenente

Francesco Liberti of 98ª Squadriglia, also abandoned his aircraft but 'was killed because his parachute failed to open properly'.[71] His aircraft crashed in the cellar of a bombed building between Strait Street and the city's main thoroughfare, Strada Reale (now Republic Street), close to the Church of St Francis.

33.	Map 4
AIRCRAFT:	Junkers Ju 87 (MM7072 or MM7074?)
CREW:	(Probably) Sottotenente Vittorino Bragadin (Pilot), (and) Sergente Maggiore (or Maresciallo) Angelo Gatti
UNIT:	238ª Squadriglia, 101º Gruppo Tuffatori
PLACE:	Il-Fiddien (between Birzebbuga and Marsaxlokk)
DATE/TIME:	5 November 1941/2132 hours

A *Picchiatello* of 238ª Squadriglia was destroyed by AA during the night of 5 November, the diarist of 185 Squadron recording: 'We were treated to a grand display of fireworks this evening when the A/A guns engaged some enemy raiders, they brought one down – a Ju 87.'[72]

Records and eyewitness accounts confirm that this aircraft crashed at Il–Fiddien, between Birzebbuga and Marsaxlokk. The crew is thought to have been Sottotenente Vittorino Bragadin and Sergente Maggiore (or Maresciallo) Angelo Gatti, both of whom were killed.[73]

34.	Map 3
AIRCRAFT:	Macchi C.202 (MM7736 or MM7746?)
PILOT:	Capitano Mario Pluda
UNIT:	73ª Squadriglia, 9º Gruppo, 4º Stormo Caccia Terrestre
PLACE:	Wied Qasrun, limits of Dingli
DATE/TIME:	8 November 1941/1210–1220 hours

35.	Map 3
AIRCRAFT:	Hawker Hurricane
PILOT:	Sergeant Alan Haley
UNIT:	126 Squadron
PLACE:	400 metres west of XHC 14 HAA gun position, Halq Dieri, limits of Zebbug
DATE/TIME:	8 November 1941/1210–1220 hours

Four Cant Z-1007 Bis bombers escorted by eighteen of the latest Macchi C.202 fighters approached the Island late in the

morning of 8 November, the Cants dropping bombs
between Rinella and Luqa. Six Hurricanes of 249 Squadron
failed to intercept the enemy, but four of 126 Squadron
sighted the bombers at between 21,000 and 23,000 feet. As
the RAF fighters climbed to attack, they were engaged by
the escorting Macchis.

In the ensuing action, Flight Lieutenant John Carpenter
and South African Pilot Officer Henry 'Pat' Lardner-Burke
each attacked a Macchi, the former claiming in his combat
report to have observed two unidentified aircraft crashing
into the sea.[74] The latter was then wounded, but managed to
land his Hurricane at Ta'Qali. Sergeant Worrall was credited
with damaging a fighter, and Australian Sergeant Alan Haley
claimed one probably destroyed before colliding head-on
with another, his combat report stating:

Dived on to top cover fighters who were diving on to
P/O [sic]Carpenter and as they broke away fired from
50 yards at nearest Macchi giving him a total of six
seconds. Observed first white smoke changing to black.
Turned away and saw a second Macchi coming straight at
me and kept firing at him at 300 yards range and my
bullets were going into him the whole time until we
collided. I pulled cover back and found myself in the air
and after some time found rip cord and pulled it. I
dropped at first to sea but eventually inland and landed on
a roof top on top of a dog.[75]

The RAF Daily Intelligence Summary records that Flight
Lieutenant Carpenter and Pilot Officer Lardner-Burke were
each credited with a Macchi shot down off the coast. It also
states that both aircraft destroyed in the collision came down
on land. Haley's Hurricane crashed near the Heavy AA gun
position at Halq Dieri, west of Zebbug, and 'The Macchi
and dead pilot . . . near Dingli'.[76] In fact, the Italian aircraft
slammed into the ground at Wied Qasrun, one mile north-
west of Dingli, the impact 'throwing up a cloud of dust and
debris several hundred feet into the air'.[77]

Subsequently, an Italian aircraft dropped on Malta a canister
containing a message addressed 'TO THE COMMAND OF
THE ROYAL AIR FORCE – MALTA'. It read:

During the attack on one of our fields, at november 12th, Lieutenant Colonnel Henry Brown [Ta'Qali Wing Leader, Wing Commander Mark Henry Brown] crshed fighting and was burried with the highest military honour.

Sergent Peter Shabbar Simpson [Sergeant Peter Sharrah Simpson of 126 Squadron] went down on the sea, with parachute. He was taken a little after; he is in perfect health, not even blessed.

Other pilots of yours went down on the sea, but we were not able to find them.

Will you pleae, give us notices of two pilots that we lost on Malta, november 8th: Cpitano Pilota Mario Pluda and Sergente Maggiore Pilota Luigi Taroni.

Address, please, the answer to the Comando Aviazone da Caccia della Sicilia.

Thank you very much.

The RAF responded with:

Your message received and appreciated. In reply: Capitano Pilota Mario Pluda was killed in action. His body was found and buried with all honours in a military cemetery. With regret we have no other news about Sergente Maggiore Pilota Luigi Taroni. Probably he fell in the sea but could not be traced notwithstanding several searches.[78]

Evidently, at least two Macchis were lost, together with Sergente Maggiore Taroni of 96ª Squadriglia, and Capitano Mario Pluda, commander of 73ª Squadriglia – the latter after colliding with Sergeant Haley's Hurricane.

36.	Map 2
AIRCRAFT:	Hawker Hurricane (Z3495?)
PILOT:	Flight Lieutenant Donald Stones
UNIT:	Malta Night Fighter Unit
PLACE:	Between Hal Dragu and village of Zebbieh
DATE/TIME:	9 November 1941/Approximately 2200 hours

There were six alarms during the night of 9/10 November. At about 2200 hours, Flight Lieutenant Don Stones of the

Malta Night Fighter Unit was among those scrambled to intercept the second raid:

> I had just got my wheels up when the engine stopped dead. I was at about 400 feet and just past the perimeter of the airfield. I knew instantly that there was no possibility of putting the Hurricane down in the dark on any of the little fields ahead of me, enclosed with stone walls as they all were. Instinctively disconnecting my helmet and straps, and heaving the stick back, I stepped out on the wing. Facing aft I pulled my rip-cord, as another Hurricane flew over my head. A moment of panic as I saw my auxiliary 'chute, which pulls out the main canopy, appear between my legs. I frantically pushed it back behind me, as I thought it would spoil everything. The canopy cracked open above me . . . and I landed almost at once on a stone wall, cushioned by a thorn bush. My poor Hurricane was burning brightly in the next field about 50 yards away. [The Hurricane Mk II had crashed one kilometre north-east of the little village of Zebbieh.] Getting out of my parachute, I started to walk towards the fire when I was surrounded by some Maltese rustics waving sticks at me, convinced that I was the German for whom the air-raid sirens had sounded. I tore off my 'Mae West' and opened my overalls to reveal my RAF uniform and wings. This partially convinced the Maltese, but just then my Hurricane's full load of ammunition started exploding in the inferno, followed by the oxygen bottles, which sounded like bombs to the Maltese, and certain lynching for me. The area was brightly illuminated by now and mercifully there appeared a British Gunner-Officer from one of the airfield defence batteries and he saved my bacon. The Maltese disappeared, and with them my silk parachute, but that was a small price to pay. The splendid Gunner took me to his hut and we sat down in its welcome warmth on this chilly November night. I suppose the scene which followed could only be enacted by Englishmen. After thanking him warmly for his timely arrival, which he airily dismissed as all part of the job, he said 'I think we should open the bar. I happen to have a decent bottle of Scotch. Shall we see if it's any good?' It

was a straight malt and, after a few sips, we decided that it
was most acceptable. By the time I had got through to the
dispersal hut on his field-telephone via inter-service link-
ups, the malt was imposing its authority and I felt very
well. [Flight Lieutenant Ernest] Cassidy, my fellow flight-
commander, answered and said: 'I can't speak now, I'm
afraid. The other flight-commander has just been killed on
take-off.' Before he could ring off, I yelled: 'It's me you
bloody fool! I baled out.' He simply could not believe me
and stammered idiocies like 'What! Impossible! Is this a
joke?' etc. I put the Gunner on the line who told Cass
where I was and he collected me in the truck. His was the
Hurricane which had taken off through the flame and
smoke of my poor aircraft. There wasn't much left of that
excellent Gunner's malt and we departed for our hut,
about a mile away.[79]

37.	Map 5
AIRCRAFT:	Junkers Ju 88 (0564?/R4+HH)
CREW:	Leutnant Wilhelm Brauns (Pilot), Gefreiter Johannes Matuschka (Wireless
	Operator), Obergefreiter (or Unteroffizier) Erwin Heese (Flight Engineer)
UNIT:	1/Nachtjagdgeschwader 2
PLACE:	Bin Gemma (Gozo)
DATE/TIME:	19 December 1941/1058–1148 hours

R4+HH was one of three Ju 88s which departed Catania
during the night of 19 December. Essentially a night fighter,
it carried no bombs other than a few incendiaries. The pilot's
orders were to fly to Malta, remain there for about an hour,
and attack any enemy aircraft seen in the vicinity.

Upon reaching the Island, the raiders were spotted by four
Hurricane pilots on patrol over a convoy off the south coast.
They promptly attacked the German machines, whose crews
took evasive action by heading into cloud. Nevertheless,
R4+HH was hit (possibly by Squadron Leader Stanley Norris
of 126 Squadron, or Squadron Leader Edward Mortimer-
Rose of 249) and crashed in terraced fields on the east side of
San Blas Valley at Bin Gemma, in north-east Gozo. (Other
casualties may have been a Ju 88 of 1/NJG 2 that crash-landed
in Catania on this date, and American Pilot Officer Edward
Steele of 126 Squadron, who was killed when his Hurricane

came down in the sea.) Of the crashed Junkers' three-man crew, the W/T operator, Gefreiter Johannes Matuschka, was killed while manning the aft dorsal machine-gun. The pilot, Leutnant Wilhelm Brauns, and his flight engineer/air gunner, Obergefreiter Erwin Heese, were both wounded. According to the date on his interrogation report, Brauns remained unconscious for several weeks before recovering sufficiently to answer his captors' questions.[80]

A substantial amount of information was obtained from the shooting down of this aircraft, an unusual characteristic of which was its Italian markings! In addition to maps, Intelligence recovered a diary belonging to Gefreiter Matuschka. From this and other papers it was established that he and Brauns had flown together intermittently since 3 July 1941. Early in August, all three crew members joined 10/KG 51 based initially at Lechfeld and Illesheim in Germany. In mid-September, they transferred to I/NJG 2 at Breda in the Netherlands; Brauns, Matuschka and, probably, Heese, joining the unit's 1 Staffel. All three were based at Gilze-Rijen from 25 September, operating over England on two occasions. Following leave, the unit returned to Breda on 20 October, and after another break moved to München-Riem and then to Sicily, arriving at Catania on 18 November. During the next month, the crew flew a number of missions over the Mediterranean before being shot down on their fourth sortie over Malta.

Until quite recently, the front canopy of Ju 88 R4+HH could still be found *in situ*, and even today, pieces of alloy and other fragments litter the area, especially along the rubble walls of the tiny fields in which the aircraft crashed.

38.	Map 3
AIRCRAFT:	Hawker Hurricane
PILOT:	Pilot Officer Robert Matthews
UNIT:	249 Squadron
PLACE:	West of Addolorata Cemetery, limits of Paola
DATE/TIME:	22 December 1941/1429–1522 hours

According to Malta's RAF Daily Intelligence Summary, fourteen Hurricanes were scrambled between 1429 and 1522 hours on 22 December 1941, for a raid involving approximately thirty-three enemy fighters.[81] Two civilians were wounded. The RAF also reported one loss. It is uncertain whether this was due to AA fire or enemy action although German sources indicate that JG 53 was credited with at least one Hurricane destroyed over Malta on this occasion. Whatever the cause, Pilot Officer Robert Mattews of 249 Squadron was probably seriously wounded or already dead when his aircraft began its almost vertical descent from high above the Island before it crashed and exploded near M33, a defence post just west of Addolorata Cemetery, on the outskirts of Paola.

39.	Map 3
AIRCRAFT:	Junkers Ju 88
CREW:	Leutnant Wilfried Babinek (Pilot), Gefreiter (or Obergefreiter) Heinrich Schwarz (Wireless Operator), Gefreiter (or Obergefreiter) Wilhelm Gutt (Air Gunner)
UNIT:	3/Nachtjagdgeschwader 2
PLACE:	West perimeter of Hal Far aerodrome
DATE/TIME:	28 December 1941/2030 hours

Soon after 1940 hours on Sunday 28 December, a single Ju 88 began to circuit the Island before crossing the south coast and dropping its bombs on Qrendi landing strip.[82] Searchlights caught and held the raider on three occasions, enabling both heavy and light AA to engage. The pilot, twenty-year-old Leutnant Wilfried Babinek, was undeterred and continued to harass those on the ground. The courage of this officer and his crew, however admirable, was hardly appreciated by those at the receiving end of the bombs and bullets. Stanley Fraser, a Gunner in 4th Heavy Anti-Aircraft Regiment Royal Artillery, kept a diary throughout his war service, which included two and a half years in Malta. Of this episode he wrote:

> Mounting guard that night . . . was a really cold and soaking wet business. The rain was pelting down on the guard room roof [when] we heard a bomber flying exceedingly low and its engines sounded just like a Wellington . . .
> We were soon disillusioned when half a dozen 'crumps' shook the place. The plane circled round and again flew

over only a few hundred feet up. The sentry shouted to us as a searchlight caught the plane in its beam and the tracers began to stream towards it.

We ran out into the rain just in time to see the display, but it was all over in about half a minute. The tracers went right into the plane and, circling sharply, it dived straight to earth, still held in the beam, until it crashed with a loud explosion and the flames leapt upward illuminating the low clouds and the ground for quite a distance.

Another to our score![83]

The Ju 88 (tentatively identified by the RAF as a modified A-5)[84] came down between Il-Mizieb and Hal Far, smashing through stone boundary walls and leaving wreckage spread across several fields as far as the western perimeter of the aerodrome. None of the crew survived

40.	Map 3
AIRCRAFT:	Junkers Ju 88 (1346?/M7+AK)
CREW:	Oberleutnant Viktor Schnez (Pilot), Feldwebel (or Oberfeldwebel) Ulrich Arnold (Observer), Obergefreiter Gerhard Hoppe (Wireless Operator), Feldwebel Heinrich Freese (Air Gunner)
UNIT:	2/Kampfgruppe 806
PLACE:	Ta'Srina, limits of Zebbug
DATE/TIME:	3 January 1942/0925 hours

On Saturday morning 3 January 1942 at least two Ju 88s escorted by Bf 109s arrived over Malta where they were intercepted by twenty-two Hurricanes of 126, 185 and 249 Squadrons. Anti-aircraft guns also engaged, claiming Unteroffizier Werner Mirschinka's Bf 109 F, which was observed by Pilot Officer A.J. Reeves of 185 Squadron to blow up alongside his own aircraft at 8,000 feet. (What is assumed to be the crash site of this Messerschmitt has been located on farmland 125 metres south-west of the Chapel of Santa Agata, near Bubaqra.) AA apparently also shot down Sergeant J.A. Westcott of 185 Squadron, who baled out over Kalafrana (his aircraft crashing near the Officers' Mess), while Pilot Officer Howard Coffin of 126 Squadron crash-landed at Ta'Qali after being shot up by a pair of Messerschmitts.

In addition to the 4/JG 53 Bf 109 destroyed, AA claimed a Ju 88 damaged and the RAF one bomber destroyed and another probably so. Pilot Officer G.K. Hulbert of 249 Squadron reported firing at a Ju 88 with its port engine already on fire, possibly following an attack by Canadian Sergeant Garth Horricks of 185 Squadron, who noted in his log book: 'I attacked JU 88 from quarter astern and set its port engine on fire. It crashed near Takali. Rear gunner put 10 bullets in my plane. Saw Westcott bale out okay.'[85]

The same aircraft, M7+AK of 2/KGr 806, was also attacked by 126 Squadron's Pilot Officers John Russell and American Edward Streets, the former's combat report stating:

On patrol as Yellow 2 at about 18,000 feet sighted two Ju 88s over Luqa. Attacked one steering West at about 12,000 feet with full beam shot, broke away and returned to attack from beam following to a quarter from above. Broke away because of Me 109 on tail. One engine caught fire and one parachute left A/C. Fired 300 rounds. After evasive action followed but did not engage again A/C which steered towards Ta Qali. Sighted Wombat Red 1 delivering attacks. A/C crashed near Ta Qali after three more parachutes left A/C. Return fire on just one attack only.[86]

Pilot Officer Streets reported:

On patrol as Red One – at about 18,000 feet. Saw one Ju 88 over Luqa – 3 or 4 109s attack one (88) immediately after Yellow 2 delivered attack – Followed enemy until all types bailed out firing all the time from ¼ to stern until it spun in and burned up – Followed it down to 0 feet. 250 rounds of ammunition fired – Return fire from Rear Gunner until he bailed out.[87]

The resolute gunner was probably the W/T operator, 22-year-old Obergefreiter Gerhard Hoppe, whose responsibilities included manning the dorsal gun position. The combat was witnessed from the ground by John Galea:

I spotted a Ju 88 coming towards Zebbug, smoking and getting lower and lower. I counted three aircrew bale out. The pilot still controlled the aircraft – It was nearing my village but luckily just clear of the buildings. The plane turned over, the pilot came out and his parachute opened almost at once as otherwise he would not have survived – he was very low . . .

Galea watched as a Hurricane, obviously that of Pilot Officer Streets, pursued the Ju 88 A-4, 'very low over the village with guns blazing . . .', before it crashed in a field near Zebbug and burst into flames. A hostile reception awaited Oberleutnant Viktor Schnez as he floated to earth: 'Soldiers and policemen arrived with the crowd which was not in a friendly mood. The pilot was brought along the narrow streets surrounded by the soldiers. A woman had some hot coffee in a tin and threw the stuff at the German but hit a couple of soldiers instead.'[88]

All four crewmen survived to become prisoners of war. The pilot and the W/T operator were slightly wounded. The observer, Feldwebel (or Oberfeldwebel) Ulrich Arnold and gunner, Feldwebel Heinrich Freese, both escaped injury.

41.	Map 4
AIRCRAFT:	Martin Maryland (AR721)
CREW:	Wing Commander John Dowland GC (Pilot), Pilot Officer Arnold Potter (Observer), Pilot Officer Robert Gridley (Wireless Operator/Air Gunner)
UNIT:	69 Squadron
PLACE:	In sea off Tignè
DATE/TIME:	13 January 1942/1245 hours

During the morning of 13 January 1942, Maryland AR721 of 69 Squadron departed Luqa on a special reconnaissance sortie to the Pantellaria–Cape Bon–Kerkennah Island area. Six merchant vessels escorted by three destroyers were sighted 12 miles off Keliba after which the Maryland pilot, Wing Commander John Dowland GC, set course for Malta, arriving while an air raid was in progress. Before long, the aircraft was seen and attacked by a pair of Messerschmitts. The action was witnessed by Battery

Sergeant Major F.G.R. Packington of 74th Light Anti-Aircraft Regiment:

> A Maryland came in chased by two ME 109s and they fought him just over our heads. The Maryland pilot shewed wonderful skill turning his plane all ways and the AA guns dare not fire. Round and round they [went and] put burst after burst into him and at last one member of the crew baled out [and] although very low his parachute opened. [The observer, Pilot Officer Arnold Potter, survived.] The pilot made desperate efforts to evade and at last came down over the hill to our rear.[89]

Critically short of fuel, the aircraft ditched just off Cambridge Battery, Sliema. Both the gunner, Pilot Officer Robert Gridley, and the pilot died. The body of Wing Commander Dowland was subsequently recovered and buried in Malta. Sadly, Gridley has no known grave. The latter had been on the Island throughout much of the siege and had a Maltese wife. She gave birth to a son soon after her husband's death.[90]

42.	Map 3
AIRCRAFT:	Lockheed Hudson (V9126)
CREW:	Sergeant Alan Story (Pilot), Sergeant Colville, Sergeant Noel Wouldes (Observer), Sergeant Percy Hankins (Air Gunner)
UNIT:	59 Squadron
PLACE:	Ghajn il-Kbira, limits of Rabat, Dingli and Siggiewi
DATE/TIME:	18 January 1942/0620 hours

A 59 Squadron Hudson Mk III was lost in transit early in the morning of 18 January when it crashed into high ground west of Luqa airfield. The pilot, Sergeant Alan Story, was killed together with Sergeants Noel Wouldes and Percy Hankins. The only survivors were Sergeant Colville and, according to Private T.C. (Charlie) Savage of The King's Own Royal Regiment (who was stationed at the nearby Inquisitor's Palace), a pet Spaniel![91]

43.	Map 3
AIRCRAFT:	Junkers Ju 88 (0149/R4+MM?)
CREW:	Leutnant Felix-Dieter Schleif (Pilot), Gefreiter (or Obergefreiter) Rolf Wiegand (Wireless Operator), Gefreiter Karl-Heinz Bülow (Flight Engineer?)
UNIT:	I/Nachtjagdgeschwader 2
PLACE:	Ghar Mundu, limits of Rabat, Dingli and Siggiewi
DATE/TIME:	18 January 1942/0645 hours

Within half an hour of Hudson V9126 crashing (see previous entry), a Junkers Ju 88 of I/NJG 2 flew into the same rise no more than 800 metres from the wrecked RAF machine. It is uncertain why either aircraft crashed, although according to RAF Intelligence the Ju 88, believed to be a modified A-1, 'apparently lost its bearings in 10/10 cloud',[92] while the War Diary of Headquarters Royal Artillery Malta records:

> 9 Bombers approached from the North – only two crossed the coast. The remainder patrolled South of the Island. 1 Raid crossed over St Paul's Bay and was engaged by Immediate Barrage (4324) at 8,000 feet.
> Second raid crossed coast at Madalena (4330) at 700 feet and crashed into hillside near Inquisitor's Palace (3720) – this aircraft was not barraged.[93]

Private Charlie Savage recalled that he and a number of other soldiers were on their way from the Inquisitor's Palace to relieve the overnight guard near Ta'Zuta when:

> [The Ju 88] came over from the direction of Gebel Cantar on our left, about 20 feet above us and about 50 yards in front of us flying toward Dingli-Sicily. We could see the pilot. We automatically dived down behind a wall [and] it crashed about 100 yards to our right. It was smoking heavily when it passed over us. Our training had taught [us] not to approach too quickly in case of exploding bombs and, rightly or wrongly, a fuse set to destroy the plane. Debris lay all around. We closed in. No sign of life. Then sent a runner back to Company Office at Inquisitor's Palace.[94]

The Junkers, which was thought to have been carrying eight 50 kilogramme bombs, was totally destroyed and the crew killed. Only the identity of the pilot, 22-year-old Leutnant Dieter Schleif, could be established.[95]

44.	**Map 3**
AIRCRAFT:	Hawker Hurricane (BE346?)
PILOT:	Sergeant Donald Neale
UNIT:	242 Squadron
PLACE:	Hemsija area, limits of Mdina
DATE/TIME:	22 January 1942/1130–1200 hours

There were two alerts on Thursday morning, 22 January. During the second, at 1130, at least sixteen Hurricanes from 126, 242 and 249 Squadrons were scrambled to intercept three Ju 88s escorted by up to five fighters. Among those involved in the ensuing action was Flight Lieutenant Nigel Kemp of 242 Squadron.

> I was . . . Blue 1, leading Blue, Green, Black sections at 18,000 feet about 10 miles East of Kalafrana. Whilst flying toward Luqa I saw two e/a (fighters) coming out of the sun. They broke away in a steep dive, and I began to follow them. At 14,000 feet after having previously given "Tally ho", we were fired at by AA causing us to break up into wide formation. At this moment 3 Ju 88s were seen just below us on our starboard side on the same course. Blue 2 and Green 2 attacked. Green 1 had to return to base owing to loose gun panels, and Black 2 was badly hit by AA . . .[96]

All three squadrons became involved in the action, with Kemp claiming to have probably destroyed a MC 202, and other pilots to have damaged two bombers and probably destroyed another.[97] Of the two Hurricanes hit by AA, one flown by Sergeant Ray Harvey force-landed at Luqa minus one elevator and with the back of the fuselage stripped of fabric. The other spun in between Mdina and Ta'Qali, killing the pilot, Sergeant Donald Neale, who had been flying in spite of having an injured leg as a result of being shot up and crash-landing nearly four weeks earlier.

45.   Map 3
AIRCRAFT: Hawker Hurricane
PILOT: Pilot Officer Albert Anderson (or) Pilot Officer C.A. Blackburn (or) Pilot
                 Officer C.F. Sluggett
UNIT: 126 (or) 242 Squadron
PLACE: Il-Hotba, limits of Qrendi
DATE/TIME: 25 January 1942/1025–1115 hours

46.   Map 3
AIRCRAFT: Hawker Hurricane
PILOT: (As above)
UNIT: (As above)
PLACE: South-west perimeter of Qrendi airfield
DATE/TIME: (As above)

47.   Map 4
AIRCRAFT: Hawker Hurricane
PILOT: (As above)
UNIT: (As above)
PLACE: Ta'Marianu, limits of Zejtun
DATE/TIME: (As above)

As the Operations Record Book of 249 Squadron records, Sunday 25 January 1942 was to prove particularly costly for the RAF in Malta:

> 4 Hurricanes of the Squadron scrambled with 5 of 126 and 6 of 242 Sqdn. 3 returned early with mechanical trouble. 185 SQDN from HAL FAR were leading with 242 Sqdn behind and 249 and 126 Sqdns acting as top cover. An attempt was made to vector them on to some incoming fighter bandits, but they were jumped by the ME 109s first. F/LT [E.H.C.] KEE of 242 SQDN shot all his ammunition into an ME 109 W of RABAT and chased it 20 miles N, but made no claim. No one else fired his guns.
>
> F/SGT [CHARLES] ALPE (126) and P/O [C.R.] MORRISON-JONES (242) were shot up and successfully 'belly-landed' at TA KALI sustaining only minor injuries.
>
> P/Os [ALBERT] ANDERSON and [C.A.] BLACKBURN (126) and P/O [C.F.] SLUGGETT (242) all baled-out. The

first landed safely at LUQA, the other two were taken to IMTARFA Hospital with injuries.

P/O [JOHN] RUSSELL] (126) was missing – believed killed.

4 machines of 185 or 605 Sqdns landed at TA KALI.

F/LT [PETER] THOMPSON of 185 SQDN baled out near DINGLI and was safe.

No claims were made, but our losses were 7 Hurricanes and P/O RUSSELL missing.[98]

In all, twenty-two Hurricanes are reported to have taken off at about 1030 to cover the departure of two merchantmen, when Major Freiherr Günther von Maltzahn led Stab/JG 53 into the attack and shot down the first Hurricane. He recalled:

How did it happen? Initially, I was concerned that they would see us, therefore I led my five machines away to the rear in order to begin the first attack against the five Hurricanes, approaching in a wide arc out of the sun. This was successful. We came in unnoticed, and I attacked the Hurricane flying on the extreme left. She was hit, went down immediately, and hit the sea in flames. [This was probably Pilot Officer John Russell; his body was never found.] I assembled my *Schwarm* and began the second attack. The Hurricanes changed direction towards land and tried to climb above us. I allowed a little time to allow my machines to attack together. As I did so, I saw that two of the higher flying 12 Hurricanes were lingering, apparently to place themselves behind us. However, they didn't do that, on the contrary, they flew towards land. As a result, I was able to commence the second attack unhindered. Again, I had a go at the machine flying on the outside left to allow my comrades a chance to shoot as well. Again, the Hurricane received a direct hit. The pilot baled out. I saw him falling frightfully close to my cabin roof. At the same time another two Mes attacked two enemy machines which were also shot down and crashed in flames on land. So that was another three shot down.

I then started the third attack on the large *staffel* of 12 [sic] Hurricanes, two of which had already headed inland. Once again I approached from behind with my machines homing in on the left [aircraft]. It went down trailing black smoke. Now a real hurly-burly broke out, in the course of which I was no longer able to follow the fate of the machine that was shot down. For sure though, another Hurricane was brought down by Leutnant L. [Joachim Louis]. The other machines turned away while diving in order to get away from us. They succeeded in this, unfortunately they had the bad luck to come into contact with our fighters escorting the bombers which were just then flying a mission against Malta. Again, two Hurricanes were shot down, and again plunged burning into the sea. Two more went down in a spin, trailing black smoke, however their impact could not be observed. On the other hand, Leutnant P. [Karl-Heinz Preu] pursued a Hurricane almost to the coast, where he hit her at a height of 600 metres and finished her off. That was the eighth shooting down.

The fact that we came out of this encounter completely unharmed, without a hit, is down to good luck – it was a tremendously successful Sunday.[99]

Luftwaffe claims for eight Hurricanes destroyed are closely in line with recorded losses of five shot down and two crash-landings as a result of battle damage. Contrary to the account in the ORB of 249 Squadron, there was one claim by Flight Lieutenant Peter Thompson of 185 Squadron who remembered 25 January as

a complete shambles from the very beginning. The enemy plots were estimated at being between 20+ and 30+ and the Controller decided to scramble every available Hurricane on the Island . . . I was elected wing leader . . .

We finally got together as a Wing and then I think the Controller got the two plots mixed up. Certainly he put us down sun with the incoming plot above and behind us. Then my RT packed up and I looked at my Number 2 to indicate my problem, but to my surprise his place had been taken by an Me 109!

I took immediate avoiding action and hopefully set course for home when I saw bomb bursts on [Hal Far] airfield running from east to west. It was therefore easy to spot the bombers and they were at about 3,000 feet. With a height advantage I was able to catch them up. I had a go and was subsequently credited with a 'probable'. It was only a few seconds after I opened fire that I was severely clobbered. I had no option but to go ahead as the engine had been hit, as also was I. I was then hit a second time and the aircraft caught fire. I baled out at very low altitude and the aircraft and I ended up very close to each other.

I must add that the Ju 88 probable was claimed for me by someone who apparently saw the action. For my part, I was in hospital and had lost all interest in the day's happenings.[100]

The battle was witnessed by many on the ground including recently promoted Lance Bombardier Stan Fraser:

This morning the sun is shining brightly and, with some HQ chaps, I am manning No 2 gun when a formation of 11 Hurricanes flying at about 15,000 feet in close formation are surprised by some ME 109s which burst into them from the rear. What a dog-fight! Right above our gun site too! Droning, zooming, twisting, intermittent rattles of machine gun fire and then two parachutes open and one fighter streaks straight down to earth a quarter of a mile west of the site, another fighter gliding gracefully in circles, although upside down, crash lands ¼ mile east of us. Unfortunately they were both Hurricanes but the pilots landed safely.[101]

Wreckage still evident in a field at Hal Tartarni, near Dingli, is probably that of Peter Thompson's Hurricane Z5147. The two aircraft seen to crash by Stan Fraser were those of Pilot Officers Albert Anderson, C.A. Blackburn or C.F. Sluggett. The first came down near the south-west perimeter of Qrendi airfield, while the other smashed through rubble walls before coming to rest in a field at Il-Hotba, just south of Qrendi village. Another Hurricane crashed near Zejtun, in a field known locally as 'Ta'Marianu'.

48.	Map 3
AIRCRAFT:	Hawker Hurricane
PILOT:	Pilot Officer Alexander Mackie
UNIT:	1435 Flight
PLACE:	Southern outskirts of Santa Katerina
DATE/TIME:	27 January 1942/1735-1754 hours

At 0910 on Tuesday 27 January, the *Breconshire* was escorted into Grand Harbour by the Royal Navy's Force 'K', one destroyer transporting a company of 1st Battalion The Durham Light Infantry, and the merchantman carrying supplies and more troops. (Other members of the unit arrived from Egypt by sea over the next few weeks.) At 1017, warning was given of an impending raid. Fifteen Hurricanes were scrambled, but none of the enemy aircraft crossed the coast. The sirens sounded again shortly before midday, as the soldiers were disembarking. This time the harbour was targeted by the Luftwaffe in an unsuccessful attempt to strike at the shipping gathered there. The raiders encountered no aerial opposition but were clearly dissuaded by AA fire, many of the bombs falling wide and damaging buildings in Vittoriosa and Cospicua.

The next raid did not appear until 1735 with an alert lasting nineteen minutes when three Messerschmitt Bf 109s surprised three Hurricanes of 1435 Flight on intruder raid air tests. Pilot Officer Alexander Mackie was shot down and critically injured; he died later in hospital. Records indicate that he fell to Oberleutnant Helmut Belser of 6/JG 53 (who apparently misidentified the aircraft as a Battle).[102]

49.	Map 3
AIRCRAFT:	Messerschmitt Bf 109 (7463/Yellow 4?)
PILOT:	Oberfeldwebel Otto Göthe
UNIT:	6/Jagdgeschwader 53
PLACE:	North-east of Post HF5, Hal Far
DATE/TIME:	7 February 1942/1120 hours

During the twenty-four hours to midnight on 7/8 February, there were at least thirteen air-raid warnings. At 1031 on the 7th, the sirens heralded the approach of four Ju 88s and an estimated seventeen Bf 109s. After the Junkers had bombed

Hal Far, two of the fighters swept past and strafed a 69 Squadron Beaufighter as it landed at Luqa. Both the pilot of the Beaufighter, Flight Lieutenant Benjamin White, and the observer, Leading Aircraftman Norman Shirley, were wounded. Although the aircraft was set on fire during the attack, LAC Shirley was able to extinguish the flames and salvage reconnaissance photographs taken that morning over Sicily. For his actions he was immediately awarded the Distinguished Flying Medal.

After crossing Safi, the Messerschmitts continued towards Hal Far where Pilot Officer Oliver Ormrod of 605 Squadron was watching events with Pilot Officer Philip Wigley. Ormrod described what happened next:

They reappeared over the ridge just beyond the Albacore dispersals. One bore to his port and disappeared from view, passing the other side of the camp towards Binga Booga [sic: presumably Birzebbuga]; but the other swung right, straightened out and came straight for us. He could now have opened fire on us with his cannon, and I supposed he would do so, so I stepped behind the building with Wigley. Some airmen remained in the open (rather unnecessarily, as they would have no warning before his shells and any bullets arrived) and they gave cheers of joy. Bofors had hit the Messerschmitt and I saw his remains smoking on the slope to the left of the Albacore dispersals – he must have pulled right as he crashed. [Bofors had blown off the tail of the Bf109, causing it to crash in fields north-west of Hal Far aerodrome]. I was rather irritated that he'd "gone in", because it shook my faith in ground strafing a little. On the other hand he should have kept lower; there is probably a bigger concentration of Bofors guns on Malta than I am likely to meet, and the Maltese guns have now had a great deal of practice. I did not visit the remains, but I understand that there was little left of either pilot or aircraft. I have heard gruesome descriptions – of an instrument panel, or rather its remains, coated with flesh and blood; of a pulped corpse with one foot sticking out; of a thumb stuck to the control column; of a flying helmet with its owner's ears still inside. Such are the

effects on the pilot of a high speed crash. Low flying
offers quick death for a mistaken judgement.[103]

The remains of Oberfeldwebel Otto Göthe are thought to
have been buried close to where they were found, not far
from observation post HF5 (now a farmhouse).

50.	**Map 3**
AIRCRAFT:	Junkers Ju 88 (8581/3Z+FP?)
CREW:	Leutnant Waldemar Stadermann (Pilot), Oberfeldwebel Walter Heese (Observer?), Oberfeldwebel Albert Stahl (Wireless Operator?), Unteroffizier Martin Knobloch (Air Gunner?)
UNIT:	6/Kampfgeschwader 77
PLACE:	Tal-Qortin, limits of Bubaqra
DATE/TIME:	15 February 1942/0800-0910 hours

Except for a twenty-two minute respite at 0738, Malta was
on continuous alert from 0200 to 1836 on Sunday 15
February 1942. Between 0800 and approximately 1000, a
number of Ju 88s approached the Island with Luqa as the
primary objective; one aircraft, hit by heavy AA, crashed in
flames at Tal-Qortin, south-east of Bubaqra. Subsequently,
two bodies were identified as Leutnant Waldemar Stadermann
and Unteroffizier Martin Knobloch. Lance Bombardier Stan
Fraser's diary records:

Today we had much more encouraging results with our
defences, and the AA gunners brought down 3 Junkers
bombers, while the fighters got 2 ME fighters. The first
bomber to come down was one of a formation of seven
which dropped their bombs across the harbour and then
flew across towards out site. A terrific barrage went up and
then a cheer went up also, for dense smoke began to pour
out from one of them; a parachute was the next thing to
come out of the plane as it circled back across the coast
diving steeply to its doom only a couple of miles from our
site.[104]

51.	Map 4
AIRCRAFT:	Martin Maryland (AR714)
CREW:	Squadron Leader W.E.M. Lowrey (Pilot), Flying Officer J.E. Bosley (Observer), Sergeant N.E. Rasmussen (Wireless Operator/Air Gunner?), Sergeant Durant (Wireless Operator/Air Gunner?)
UNIT:	69 Squadron
PLACE:	In sea, off Benghisa
DATE/TIME:	15 February 1942/1700 hours

At midday on 15 February, as Malta endured one of its longest alerts to date (see previous entry), the crew of a 69 Squadron Maryland Mk I were enjoying a comparatively idyllic time some 80 miles north-east of the Island. At 1245, three Italian cruisers and nine destroyers were located whereupon the Maryland pilot, Squadron Leader W. Lowrey, set course for home. Soon afterwards events took a turn for the worse when the port engine failed. Fifteen minutes later, there was further trouble when the reconnaissance aircraft was spotted by the pilots of four Bf 109s, one of whom proceeded to attack from below. The ventral gunner, Sergeant N. Rasmussen, promptly opened fire, causing the fighter to dive sharply. It was not seen again. A second Messerschmitt then approached from the port beam. The Maryland made a feint turn to port, followed by a starboard turn towards cloud cover just as the other two 109s swept in from astern. By the time Lowrey reached the clouds, his aircraft's aerial mast and starboard elevator had been shot away. The Bf 109s waited for the Maryland to reappear before recommencing their attacks from above and below. This time the dorsal gunner, Sergeant Durant, was able to claim hits on one of the fighters, which was last seen in a vertical descent at 2,000 feet. One of the remaining pair attacked again, its cannon shells thudding into the starboard wing, ailerons and engine. The petrol tank was hit, the starboard window shot away, the gunner's cockpit was smashed, and a fire started when rounds ignited some vereys cartridges. The aircraft now went into an almost uncontrollable spin, creating difficulties for the two gunners as they desperately struggled to bring the blaze under control.

Once more, Lowrey managed to reach cloud cover, and when he next emerged into clear sky the Messerschmitts had gone. The Maryland continued to within 12 miles of

Malta when it again came under fighter attack. Cannon and machine-gun fire tore into the aileron flaps, engine and instrument board. Lowrey's helmet was hit and his goggles knocked off and yet the pilot still managed to escape injury!

The arrival of Hurricanes, scrambled to cover the returning Maryland, now forced the Bf 109s to break off their engagement, enabling Lowrey to concentrate on his pre-landing checks. As the undercarriage was lowered, the fuel-starved starboard engine stopped, leaving the pilot with no option but to attempt a ditching just off the coast. The undercarriage was hurriedly retracted, whereupon several feet of the starboard wing, the aileron and rudder fell off. Leading Aircraftman Philip Chandler, who was watching events from Kalafrana, recalled how the Maryland, 'limped pitifully along the bay, skimming the water. She pancaked about 100 yards from where I stood . . . A launch dashed out and rescued all three [sic] of the crew just after the plane went down. 109s then attempted to attack but were driven off by Hurricanes and ground defences'.[105]

Of the four-man crew, only the observer, Flying Officer J. Bosley, was injured, having broken an arm when the aircraft ditched. However, one of the covering Hurricanes was shot down into the sea, taking Pilot Officer Peter Lowe of 605 Squadron to his death. The victors, in both cases, are thought to have been pilots of JG 53.

After a number of exploratory dives in 1969 by members of Malta's RAF Sub Aqua Club, Maryland AR714 was identified as lying some 400 metres east of Benghisa Point. It remains there to this day.

52.	Map 3
AIRCRAFT:	Messerschmitt Bf 109 (7541/+10?)
PILOT:	Unteroffizier Walter Schwarz
UNIT:	9/Jagdgeschwader 53
PLACE:	Il-Hotob, limits of Qormi and Birkirkara
DATE/TIME:	22 February 1942/1325–1355 hours

Malta was on alert for much of 22 February, with bomber and fighter attacks made against all three aerodromes where a number of aircraft were damaged or destroyed. At 1325, seven Hurricanes of 185 Squadron were scrambled at the approach of the first of an estimated ninety Ju 88s and Bf 109s that were to target the airfields until well after nightfall. Sergeant J.R. Sutherland, who was credited with a Bf 109 destroyed, recorded:

On the 22nd, the Squadron came to Readiness at midday, with W/Comm "Ragbags" [Alexander Rabagliati] leading. Three 88s and some 109s were intercepted over Hal Far on a scramble. We jumped the 88s as they were pulling out of their dive, but only one is claimed as damaged (by self). I managed by a lucky shot to fix up a 109 who was about to tackle Sgt [J.A.] Westcott, who later observed his late attacker spin down minus a wing. Sgt [D.E.] Eastman had quite an enjoyable time as the attached newspaper clipping will show.[106] P/O [B.J.] Oliver was very indignant when he landed after being attacked by a 109 as his one and only good pair of trousers were ruined by glycol. He put up an excellent performance in bringing back safely his much damaged aircraft. S/Ldr [Ronald] Chaffe did not return, but nobody knows why. It is with sorrow that I record his death as, though he had been with us for so short a time, we had admired him as a leader and a man, little though we knew him. He was rather quiet, though that may have been because he was still feeling his way on the island, but what he did say or do had a very definite purpose behind it, and we were happy in having such a man as our leader.[107]

Feldwebel Heinz Hipper and Unteroffizier Max Nairz of JG 53, who were each credited with a Hurricane destroyed, were both probably responsible for shooting down Squadron Leader Chaffe.[108] He was spotted in his dinghy four to five miles south of Delimara, but a subsequent search failed to relocate him.

The body of Sergeant Sutherland's victim, Unteroffizier Walter Schwarz of 9/JG 53, was found with the wreckage of his Bf 109 at Il-Hotob, near Qormi.

53.	Map 4
AIRCRAFT:	Messerschmitt Bf 109 (8649/Black 3?)
PILOT:	Unteroffizier Benedikt Wegmann
UNIT:	5/Jagdgeschwader 3
PLACE:	Pembroke Ranges
DATE/TIME:	4 March 1942/1250 hours

Malta was on continuous alert from 1938 on Tuesday 3 March, to 0618 the next morning. During the following thirteen hours, there were at least seven more air-raid warnings. At 1224, Hal Far was the main objective in an attack that lasted just over an hour and involved eleven Ju 88s and Bf 109s. No Hurricanes were airborne, but one Messerschmitt was claimed by AA, the aircraft crashing on the rocky shore at Pembroke Ranges, just north of St Andrew's Barracks.[109]

Unteroffizier Benedikt Wegmann of 5/JG 3 baled out into the sea and swam ashore, where he was captured by B Company, 11th Battalion The Lancashire Fusiliers. During interrogation, Wegmann appeared doubtful as to whether he had, in fact, been hit by AA and seemed inclined to believe that his machine may instead have suffered engine failure.[110]

54.	Map 3
AIRCRAFT:	Junkers Ju 88 (1392/7T+JK?)
CREW:	Unteroffizier Albert Degenhardt (Pilot?), Unteroffizier Friedrich Engelmann (or Engelbert) (Observer?), Unteroffizier Hermann Gessele (Wireless Operator?), Unteroffizier Werner Rehschütz (Air Gunner?)
UNIT:	2/Küstenfliegergruppe 606
PLACE:	Gebel Cantar, limits of Siggiewi
DATE/TIME:	5 March 1942/0237–0625 hours

Except for a nine minute respite, Malta was again subjected to a continuous alert, from 1912 hours on Wednesday 4 March, to 0632 the next day. During a raid in the early hours of the 5th, a Ju 88, believed to have been 7T+JK of 2/KüFlGr 606, was observed firing at a searchlight by Sergeant James Wood of 1435 Flight who was flying a two-cannon Hurricane. Approaching from behind, Woods quickly closed to about 300 yards, but the bomber's slipstream prevented him from taking aim until he was just 50 yards from the target. There was time for a brief twenty to thirty round burst before Woods disengaged; his fighter narrowly missing the tail and port wing of the enemy machine. Notwithstanding the relentless fire from its rear gunner, Woods had succeeded in seriously damaging the Ju 88. A series of coloured lights – probably flares – were seen moments before the aircraft fell in flames to the south-west of Siggiewi. There were no survivors, and only the identity of Unteroffizier Engelmann could be established.[111] Anthony Busuttil, who was then no more than ten years of age, visited the scene soon after daybreak:

> In the morning I met my friend and he told me that he knew of a Junker crashed at Gebel Cantar (near an area also known as Il-Gibjun). It was nearly 8.00 am and we immediately decided to go and see the crash. Gebel Cantar is not more than two miles away from Siggiewi, so within three quarters of an hour we were on the spot of the crash . . . big parts of the Junker were scattered all over the area. About eight soldiers were collecting parts of the bodies in sandbags. My friend and I found a foot with the big toe missing. We left it on the ground as the soldiers sent us away because they said that there may be some ammunition which may have been dangerous.[112]

Twisted scraps of alloy, shattered perspex, exploded cartridges and other fragmented debris still litter the rocky plateau of Gebel Cantar. The remains of the Ju 88 crew are said to have been buried beneath a carob tree at the edge of the crash site.

55.	Map 3
AIRCRAFT:	Hawker Hurricane
PILOT:	Pilot Officer Howard Coffin
UNIT:	126 Squadron
PLACE:	Between Safi airfield and Gudja
DATE/TIME:	9 March 1942/1520 hours

On 7 March 1942, Malta was reinforced with fifteen Spitfires flown off the carrier HMS *Eagle*, the first of several deliveries. Their arrival was to make a distinct impression on the air battle, finally providing the Island's fighter pilots with a machine that could compete with the Messerschmitt

Bf 109, though it would be another three days before the Spitfires were combat-ready.

The last action prior to the Spitfires' introduction to the battle took place on Monday 9 March, yet another day of virtually continuous enemy air activity. Eighteen Ju 88s and twenty-six Bf 109s, some of them bomb-carrying *Jabos*, were reported over the Island between 1221 and 1550 hours. The airfields were the main targets, and a number of aircraft were damaged on the ground.

Twenty-one Hurricanes are reported to have been scrambled during the raid. At about 1500, six Hurricanes of 126 Squadron and four of 185 joined the fight. Claims include a Ju 88 destroyed by Flying Officer Albert 'Andy' Anderson of 126 Squadron; a Bf 109 destroyed and another damaged by Pilot Officer William Hallett of the same unit; and a Messerschmitt destroyed and a Ju 88 damaged by Sergeant 'Archie' Steele of 185 Squadron. However, Luftwaffe records fail to show any combat losses over Malta on this date, the RAF apparently coming off worse when two Hurricanes were damaged by pilots of III/JG 53.

After a determined attack on a Ju 88, Sergeant Gordon Tweedale of 185 Squadron was set upon by at least three fighters and wounded in the heel by a cannon shell. On returning to Hal Far, he was again targeted by a Messerschmitt but was able to crash-land because of the timely intervention of Armourer, Sergeant Baines, who was manning a twin-Brownings post, and the prompt action of Sergeant Steele, who opened fire while landing with wheels and flaps down! Pilot Officer Howard Coffin of 126 Squadron also managed to attack a Ju 88 before being shot-up and force-landing his Hurricane between Safi airstrip and the nearby village of Gudja. He, too, was fortunate and escaped with slight head injuries.

56.	Map 4
AIRCRAFT:	Junkers Ju 88 (8680/3Z+JP or 3Z+LP)
CREW:	Oberleutnant (or Hauptmann) Gerhard Becker (Pilot), Unteroffizier Arnulf Thiemann (Observer), Unteroffizier Walter Kunzi (Wireless Operator?), Unteroffizier Anton Schwäger (or Schweiger) (Air Gunner)
UNIT:	II/Kampfgeschwader 77
PLACE:	Hal Far
DATE/TIME:	9 March 1942/Approximately 1800 hours

Savoia Marchetti S.79, believed to be that piloted by Sottoten Felice Filippi of 195ª Squadriglia moments before it crashed into a beach post just east of Fort San Leonardo on 10 July 1940. (National War Museum Association – NWMA)

FIAT CR 42 (MM4368) in which Tenente Mario Benedetti of 74ª Squadriglia was fatally injured after crashing at Wied il-Ghajn on 16 July 1940. The Stemma di Stato has been cut from the rudder, and presumably taken as a souvenir. (NWMA)

Flight Lieutenant George Burges of Malta's Fighter Flight in Gladiator N5519, which was shot down off the south-east coast on 31 July 1940. (After the Battle)

Personnel of the three Services at the crash site of an unidentified Junkers Ju 87. (NWMA)

Sunderland L2164 of 228 Squadron in Mistra Bay after low-level attack by Messerschmitts on 10 March 1941. (NWMA)

Wing Bombardier George Dale of 10th HAA Regt RA guarding the wreckage of a Stuka at Ghar Hanzir, north-west of Luqa aerodrome. This is probably one of several Ju 87s of II/StG 1 destroyed over Malta on 26 February 1941. (George Dale)

Two views of a Hurricane V7430, in which Pilot Officer R.J. Goode (274 Squadron attached to 261) was shot down at Pwales Valley on 28 March 1941. (Author's Collection)

27 April 1941: Sunderland L5807 of 228 Squadron on fire at Kalafrana after being strafed by Bf 109s of 7/JG 26. (Ted Eaborn)

Burnt-out Ju 88 of 2/KGr 806 after being shot down by Hurricanes at Ta'Srina, near Zebbug, on 3 January 1942. (Author's Collection)

9 March 1942: A crewman descends by parachute (centre, to left of smoke) above the burning wreckage of his II/KG 77 Ju 88, shot down by AA at Hal Far. (via Mrs Joan Broad)

Afterwards: the tail section of Ju 88 Werk Nr 8680 at Hal Far. (via Mrs Joan Broad)

An unidentified Bf 109 burns itself out on Maltese soil.
(Author's Collection)

Curious onlookers examine a Bf 109 – almost certainly the II/JG 3
machine piloted by Unteroffizier Pilz (or Pelz), who survived a
forced-landing after being hit by AA on 1 April 1942.
(Phil Francis)

Subject of much controversy: Rhodesian, Pilot Officer Douglas Leggo of 249 Squadron (seen here before his commission) was killed after baling out of his Spitfire over the south coast of Malta on 20 March 1942. (via Gavin Cooper)

The victor may have been Leutnant Hermann Neuhoff of 6/JG 53, who was captured when he baled out near Luqa on 10 April 1942. His Bf 109 fell nearby on Luqa/Safi airstrips. (Hermann Neuhoff)

During the same action in which Leutnant Neuhoff was shot down, two pilots of 185 Squadron also had to abandon their fighters: Sergeant Ernie Broad (right, with Australian, Jack Yarra) came down near Naxxar. (via Mrs Joan Broad)

Pilot Officer Phil Wigley (left, with Pilot Officer Ron Noble) landed alongside his crashed Hurricane near Ghar Lapsi. (via John Wigley)

Some of the dismantled wreckage of the Bf 109 F flown by Hauptmann Karl-Heinz Krahl, Gruppenkommandeur of II/JG 3, who was shot down by AA and killed near Hal Far on 14 April 1942. (NWMA)

Flight Lieutenant Rhys Lloyd of 185 Squadron with a wing panel from Hauptmann Krahl's Bf 109. (via John Wigley)

*8 May 1942: Unteroffizier Heinrich Becker's 8 JG 53 Bf 109 F
at Marsa Sports Club just after being shot down by AA.
(Author's Collection)*

*Afterwards, jubilant British and Maltese pose with the wreckage.
(Author's Collection)*

Flight Lieutenant Denis Barnham of 601 Squadron in the Spitfire he flew on 14 May 1942 when he took part in the destruction of a Ju 88 of KGr 806. (Author's Collection)

The bomber mentioned above crashed at Ta'Qali. None of the crew survived. (Author's Collection)

Reggiane Re 2001, piloted by Tenente Remo Cazzolini of 152ª Squadriglia, after being moved from Fort San Leonardo, where it crashed on 18 May 1942. (NWMA)

S.84 Bis of 4° Gruppo Aut BT destroyed by Spitfires of 249 Squadron near Ta'Garda on 4 July 1942. (NWMA)

At 2346 hours on 20 July 1942, Stan Fraser, a Gunner in 4th HAA Regt RA, took this photograph of a Ju 88 of 8/KG 77 crashing at Kirkop (flash right of centre). Searchlights illuminate another raider (top left) and heavy anti-aircraft guns – probably XHE 24H at Il-Marnisi – can also be seen firing (far right). (Stan Fraser)

One of four 3.7 inch AA guns at XHB 8, near Benghisa. XHB 8 was credited with the destruction of two out of three Ju 88s brought down during the night of 20/21 July 1942. (Stan Fraser)

40mm light anti-aircraft (Bofors) guns also took their toll.
(Author's Collection)

A number of low-flying raiders were also claimed by LAA machine gun
posts, such as this at Benghisa. (Stan Fraser)

Canadian 'ace' Sergeant George 'Screwball' Beurling of 249 Squadron with the rudder and 'cat and mice' emblem of 378ª Squadriglia, removed from the Macchi C.202 piloted by Sergente Maggiore Faliero Gelli, whom he shot down near Zebbug, Gozo, on 27 July 1942. (Peter Watson)

Pilot Officer Philip Wigley of 605 Squadron recalled that on
9 March 1942:

> I was duty officer at Hal Far and one of my responsibilities
> was supervising the filling-in of bomb craters after a raid to
> enable the airfield to become serviceable again . . . a Ju 88
> was shot down and crashed at Hal Far some time after
> 1615 hours. I was with the crater-filling personnel at the
> time near the south side of the airfield. Two crew members
> of the Ju 88 baled out at low altitude and landed about 100
> yards from me. They were only a few yards from each
> other. A machine gun with a circular bullet-proof glass
> screen was lying nearby . . . Both men were unconscious
> but showed no outward signs of wounds . . . They were
> taken to Station Sick Quarters before they could become
> victims of the unfriendly intentions of local people![113]

The bomber was part of a raid involving a dozen Ju 88s,
including a reconnaissance aircraft, and eleven Bf 109s, some
of which carried bombs. Hal Far, Luqa and Safi were all
targeted. Although the raiders encountered no aerial
opposition, they faced both light and heavy anti-aircraft fire,
the gunners ultimately destroying the II/KG 77 machine
over Hal Far.[114] The men seen to bale out by Phil Wigley
were the W/T operator, Unteroffizier Walter Kunzi, and the
observer, Unteroffizier Arnulf Thiemann. The latter died in
hospital. The pilot, Oberleutnant (or Hauptmann) Gerhard
Becker, and the rear gunner, Unteroffizier Anton Schwäger
(or Schweiger) also perished.

57.	Map 3
AIRCRAFT:	Hawker Hurricane (Z5140?)
PILOT:	Sergeant John Mayall
UNIT:	126 Squadron
PLACE:	Mriehel, limits of Qormi and Birkirkara
DATE/TIME:	10 March 1942/1020 hours

58.	Map 3
AIRCRAFT:	Supermarine Spitfire (AB343?)
PILOT:	Pilot Officer Kenric Murray
UNIT:	249 Squadron

PLACE: Ta'Zuta, limits of Rabat, Dingli and Siggiewi
DATE/TIME: 10 March 1942/1640–1842 hours

After their arrival on 7 March, Malta's first Spitfire Mk VBs were allocated to 249 Squadron. Ready to take to the air again on the 10th, seven Spitfires were scrambled for the first time at about 1020 together with eight Hurricanes of 126 Squadron and four of 185 for a bombing raid in which three Ju 88s escorted by Bf 109s targeted Luqa. The Spitfires immediately made their presence felt when Flight Lieutenant Philip Heppell was credited with shooting down Feldwebel Heinz Rahlmeier, who was killed when his 8/JG 53 machine crashed into the sea. In turn, Australian Sergeant Jack Mayall of 126 Squadron died when his Hurricane was shot down at Mriehel. Another pilot who crash-landed his Hurricane escaped without injury.

In the afternoon, there were four more alerts; one for a fighter patrol and three for bombing raids. The last, at 1632, numbered an estimated forty enemy aircraft, and was intercepted by four Spitfires together with eight Hurricanes of 242 Squadron and three from Hal Far. Although one Ju 88 was claimed as destroyed and two others as damaged, it appears that none were, in fact, lost on this occasion. However, Pilot Officer Ken Murray of 249 Squadron was fatally injured when his parachute failed or, as some thought at the time, was collapsed by the slipstream of a Bf 109, after he baled out of his Spitfire above Ta'Zuta, south-west of Siggiewi.

German sources credit Unteroffizier Hans Schade of 8/JG 53 with being the first of his unit to destroy a Spitfire over Malta at 1110 on 10 March.[15] The evidence suggests that he had, in fact, shot down Sergeant Mayall. Pilot Officer Murray, it seems, actually fell to the Kommandeur of II/JG 3, Hauptmann Karl-Heinz Krahl.

59.	**Map 3**
AIRCRAFT:	**Supermarine Spitfire (AB337?)**
PILOT:	**Pilot Officer Douglas Leggo**
UNIT:	**249 Squadron**
PLACE:	**Midway between Ta'San Niklaw reservoir and Guarena Tower, limits of Qrendi**
DATE/TIME:	**20 March 1942/0805–0840 hours**

The first daylight raid of Friday 20 March began soon after 0800 and lasted five hours as about twenty Ju 88s arrived at intervals under fighter escort to bomb Valletta, Sliema, St Julian's Bay, Hamrun and Zejtun. Six civilians and two soldiers were killed and two more soldiers and many civilians injured.

Sixteen fighters were scrambled with four Spitfires, led by Flight Lieutenant P.B. 'Laddie' Lucas of 249 Squadron, providing top cover for twelve Hurricanes. While patrolling at 11,000 feet, the 249 Squadron quartet observed six Bf 109s heading north over Filfla. The Spitfires, with a height advantage of some 2,000 feet, attacked. AA also engaged, claiming one Ju 88 and a Bf 109 destroyed and four bombers damaged, while Pilot Officer Robert 'Buck' McNair was credited with shooting down a Bf 109 which was thought to have crashed south of Delimara. In fact, 7/JG 53 lost one fighter, the body of the pilot, Unteroffizier Josef Fankhauser, being washed ashore in Sicily nearly seven weeks later.[116] A Spitfire VB, flown by Rhodesian Pilot Officer Douglas Leggo, was also shot down. As Laddie Lucas saw it:

> After combat and separation, pilots were looking for another to join up with in line abreast . . . It was the best recipe for survival, given the odds stacked against us.
>
> In my section, we spotted, far away to port, a single Spitfire obviously looking for a mate. As we turned to go to his aid, a lone 109, diving steeply and very fast out of the sun, pulled up, unseen, under the Spitfire. From dead astern, the pilot, who plainly knew his business, delivered a short, determined burst of cannon and machine gun fire, sending his victim rolling on to his back and spiralling down to earth or sea. It was a clinical operation. Relieved, we saw a parachute open.
>
> As we watched the silk canopy floating down in the distance, with the pilot swinging on its end, another single 109, diving out of broken cloud, made a run at the 'chute, squirting at it as he went and collapsing it with his slipstream as he passed by. The canopy streamed, leaving the pilot without a chance. The next thing we knew, the 109 was diving away for Sicily with never a hope of catching it.[117]

Pilot Officer Leggo is believed to have been shot down by Leutnants Hermann Neuhoff and/or Ernst Klager, both of

III/JG 53, who claimed a Spitfire within three minutes of each other.[118] The victor was then pursued by Pilot Officer Raoul Daddo-Langlois, who shot off all his ammunition without apparent result.

The demise of 'Douggie' Leggo was witnessed by members of 4th Heavy Anti-Aircraft Regiment Royal Artillery, from their gun position near Hagar Qim. Lance Bombardier Stan Fraser subsequently entered in his diary:

Before breakfast we witnessed a dog-fight above our site, which resulted in a rather sickening start to the day's activities, for one of our Spitfires had one of its tail fins practically shot off and the pilot lost control of the plane. It fell like a falling leaf, describing small circles, with its nose downwards, and several times it seemed as though the pilot had managed to straighten out into a glide, but no – on it came until, just over 100 feet from the ground, the pilot baled out.

He was too late; his parachute just billowed until the cords were taut when he reached the ground about the same time as the plane which just pancakes in the next field only a couple of hundred yards from our camp.

When we picked the pilot up he was grasping the harness of the parachute with both hands – dead; we placed him on a stretcher covering him up with the parachute, and carried him into our MI room. I thought at the time of his family in Rhodesia somewhere, just having breakfast maybe, oblivious of the horrible shock which awaited them, depriving them of the pride which they felt in having a son so young, in his early twenties, and a pilot officer in the RAF.[119]

The episode remained in the minds of other gunners who were at Hagar Qim. Fifty-three years after the event, former SNCO George Lord remembered:

The pilot of a Spitfire which had sustained bad damage ejected from his plane but was too low for his 'chute to properly open. He dropped between the gun-position and a line of hills, known to us as Jebel Chanter [Gebel Cantar] . . . Several of us ran to see if we could be of assistance . . . On arriving at the scene it was obvious the young man was quite dead. On his shoulders was the word 'RHODESIA'.[120]

Howard Bell, then an Acting Bombardier, recalled:

His body was brought in on a stretcher by our medical orderly, Lance Bombardier Jimmy Corr . . . and placed on the floor of the MI Hut. I saw him there and noticed he was dressed in blue battledress with one shoe missing and a large hole in his sock, which somehow seemed to make the whole incident more tragic. Later, the RAF came and took him away.[121]

There is one obvious and important discrepancy between what was perceived by Laddie Lucas and witnessed by those on the ground. Lucas was the last survivor of those who flew with Douglas Leggo on 20 March 1942. He died exactly fifty-six years later, having always insisted that he saw the Rhodesian being deliberately targeted after abandoning his aircraft. Yet, according to George Lord: 'There were no enemy aircraft in the immediate vicinity'.[122] He and the other ex-gunners felt convinced that Leggo's parachute simply did not have time to deploy.

On the German side, Hermann Neuhoff could no longer distinguish between his many combats, but was adamant that, 'none of my men attacked a pilot in his parachute. A pilot in a parachute was taboo. It was the same as someone raising his hands or showing the white flag'.[123]

Today, one can only speculate but if, after he baled out, a Bf 109 had passed behind and above Leggo, might it not have seemed to a distant observer to have over-flown his parachute canopy, apparently collapsing it in the process? Or did Lucas unknowingly witness Unteroffizier Fankhauser being mistakenly shot down by one of his own countrymen? Questions which, today, only the dead can answer.

60.	Map 4
AIRCRAFT:	Hawker Hurricane (Z5302?)
PILOT:	Sergeant Archibald Steele
UNIT:	185 Squadron
PLACE:	Approximately 200 metres west of Tas-Silg Battery, limits of Marsaxlokk
DATE/TIME:	31 March 1942/1000 hours

There were eleven alerts recorded for Tuesday 31 March, with the Luftwaffe carrying out small-scale raids throughout much of the day. Two Hurricanes of 185 Squadron were ordered up at 0950, Sergeant Garth Horricks recording:

> Sergeants Steele and [Charles Ernest] Broad were scrambled after some Ju 88s hiding in the clouds. While flying at cloud base four Me 109s suddenly appeared behind them. Steele, it appears, was a bit slow in turning, and one of the Me 109s shot him down. Broad had a quick squirt at one of the 109s but observed no results. Sergeant Steele's death came as a great blow to the Squadron. He was one of the most skilful and keenest pilots on the Island. He can be ill spared during these hard times. Steele was just getting into his stride, having destroyed two Me 109s as well as having some probables and damaged to his credit.
> I knew Archie Steele in private life, and I know everyone agrees with me when I say he was a damn good fellow.

Sergeant Steele's Hurricane crashed three miles north-east of Hal Far, in a field just west of Tas-Silg Battery.

Shortly after Steele and Broad encountered the 109s a Mosquito, in fact the only one on the Island, appeared over Hal Far with two Me 109s on its tail. The results were disastrous. With one engine on fire, the Mosquito crashlanded on our drome and was burned to a cinder. The crew of two, fortunately, escaped unhurt.[124]

The Mosquito was W4063 of 69 Squadron, crewed by Pilot Officer Philip Kelley and Sergeant Pike, which had been recalled minutes after departing on a photographic reconnaissance of Tripoli.

61.	Map 4
AIRCRAFT:	Messerschmitt Bf 109 (8668/Black 11?)
PILOT:	Unteroffizier Hans Pilz (?)
UNIT:	II/Jagdgeschwader 3
PLACE:	Off Luqa Road, limits of Paola
DATE/TIME:	1 April 1942/Approximately 1820 hours

62.	Map 4
AIRCRAFT:	Junkers Ju 87 (2147/T6+FN?)
CREW:	Unteroffizier Winfried Günther (Pilot), Gefreiter Wilhelm Neubauer
UNIT:	8/Stukageschwader 3
PLACE:	Il-Qali, limits of Marsaxlokk
DATE/TIME:	1 April 1942/1825 hours

Heavy raids on 1 April resulted in extensive damage to vessels in the harbour area: the minesweeper/drifter *Sunset* and submarines *P36* and *Pandora* were all sunk, the latter with much loss of life. During the day's seventh alert (1710–1858) an estimated seventy Ju 87s, Ju 88s and Messerschmitt Bf 109s approached the Island, some of the fighters patrolling off the coast while the bombers proceeded inland towards Hal Far, the Dockyard area and Cospicua. The RAF was able to scramble fourteen to fifteen Hurricanes and Spitfires between 1700 and 1835 and these, together with AA, probably accounted for two Ju 87 Stukas. The gunners also shot down a Messerschmitt.

Unteroffizier Pilz (or Pelz) of II/JG 3[125] crash-landed his damaged fighter in a wheat field close to Rahal Gdid (Paola), the aircraft finally tipping over and coming to rest in an inverted position. Locals rushed to free the trapped pilot. Somewhat surprisingly, he was even offered a tot of whisky, which he declined. Within minutes, the Air Raid Police arrived accompanied by a doctor who also offered the German a drink. This time it was accepted. The prisoner was then taken away to be treated for his injuries.[126]

Those credited with a Ju 87 destroyed include Pilot Officer Peter Nash and Rhodesian Flying Officer George 'Buck' Buchanan, both of 249 Squadron, and Canadian Flight Sergeant Jack Fletcher of 185, though a number of 'probables' may later have been upgraded to 'confirmed'.[127] Another 249 Squadron pilot, Sergeant Ray Hesselyn from New Zealand, apparently also claimed a Ju 87 that, 'dived straight into the drink'.[128] Certainly one such aircraft came down on land, close to the shore at Il-Qali, in the Delimara area. The gunner, Gefreiter Wilhelm Neubauer, was killed, while Unteroffizier Winfried Günther baled out into the sea and was later taken prisoner. Interrogation revealed that the Ju 87 had been hit by AA at 12,000 feet, just before the pilot began the dive to attack a warship.[129]

That night, as military personnel inspected the crashed Ju 87, a bomb on board exploded with deadly result, killing Lance Bombardier John Scarborough-Taylor and Gunners Thomas Burfield, Ernest Smith and Thomas Richardson of 4th Heavy Anti-Aircraft Regiment Royal Artillery. Other fatalities included Corporal William Foote, Lance Corporal Charles Pearce and Private Ernest French, while Private R. Garrett and Lance Corporal John Bell were wounded, the latter dying of his injuries more than three months later. All were in 1st Battalion The Dorsetshire Regiment. Other army and air force personnel listed as killed on this date may also have been victims of this tragic incident.

63.	Map 4
AIRCRAFT:	Hawker Hurricane
PILOT:	Sergeant Charles Broad
UNIT:	185 Squadron
PLACE:	Is-Simblija, limits of Naxxar
DATE/TIME:	10 April 1942/Approximately 1800 hours

64.	Map 3
AIRCRAFT:	Hawker Hurricane
PILOT:	Pilot Officer Philip Wigley
UNIT:	185 Squadron
PLACE:	Hagra s-Sewda (Ghar Lapsi)
DATE/TIME:	10 April 1942/Approximately 1800 hours

The seventh alert recorded for Friday 10 April began at 1744 and lasted a little over an hour as some sixty-five Ju 88s and twenty Ju 87s escorted by fighters targeted Grand Harbour, Hal Far and Ta'Qali. This powerful force was engaged by AA, ten or eleven Hurricanes of 185 and 229 Squadrons and three Spitfires of 249 (one Spitfire having returned with oil on the windscreen and at least two Hurricanes returning early, one with an overheated engine and another with a faulty air speed indicator). Afterwards, Flight Sergeant Garth Horricks of 185 Squadron described events in his own inimitable style:

Squadron came to readiness at 1300 hours with eight serviceable aircraft. 229 at other end of the field had four. Just after tea we were scrambled for approximately 100 bombers and 50 Me 109s. Twelve took off. By the time we were at 15,000 there were 9 [sic] left. Things suddenly happened and every Hurricane found himself surrounded by seven 109s. Then more things happened. We tried to get to the bombers but the 109s didn't think we should. A great argument ensued, resulting in too many private dog-fights to count. The first section led by F/L [Rhys] Lloyd and with P/Os [Oliver] Ormrod and [Philip] Wigley got at the bombers while Yellow section led by F/Sgt [D.E.] Eastman with Sgts [Colin] Finlay, [Charles] Broad and myself more than contacted the Me 109s. In the first few minutes of the fight Sgt Broad was forcibly ejected from his aircraft by anywhere from one to fifteen 109s. However his parachute opened as planned and he landed at Naxxar suffering from "superficial lacerations", in other words, "cuts". [Sergeant Broad's Hurricane crashed on the south-east side of Naxxar.] F/L Lloyd had a whack at the bombers but was set upon by some 109s. He played with them for a while, and after shaking off his allotted ten Mes he landed at Luqa with only a few holes in his plane.

P/O Ormrod also landed at Luqa but in a much different manner. He was cruising around in between 109s when he suddenly spied five or six Ju 87s in line astern diving on a target. He thought they were playing so he got in behind the third one and played too. Only he played with .303 and probably got one of the 87s. Meanwhile the boys flying the 87s behind him thought he was rude butting in like that, so proceeded to shoot at his Hurricane till it caught fire. P/O Ormrod thought his plane would burn much better on the ground than in the air, and knowing that all good fires are at Luqa, he landed there and jumped out of his now fairly warm aircraft while it was still running along the ground. We congratulate him on getting his fire down okay on Luqa.

Braving enemy fire, several of the fire tender crew and a flight sergeant rushed to assist Pilot Officer Ormrod, unaware that he had already abandoned the Hurricane. Shortly afterwards, its petrol tank exploded. For their efforts, Corporal Hugh Clawson and Leading Aircraftman Edward Mitchison were both awarded the George Medal. Horricks' account continues:

While this was going on P/O Wigley put a lot of lead in an 87 and turned around to look for some 109s to play with. But he looked the wrong way because the 109s were all behind him.[130]

Phil Wigley described what happened next:

After about 30 minutes, and many attacks by Me 109 Fs on me, and several by me on them and the bombers, my Hurricane was hit in the coolant system and hot liquid sprayed about the cockpit, probably from the damaged header tank. Of course, the engine over-heated and so I tried to land, first at Hal Far, but was attacked by a 109 F, then at Luqa where the same thing happened. I therefore thought my best action would be to bale out as the engine was losing power and flames were beginning to appear.

As the German fighters had complete control of the air over Malta that evening, I did not want to risk being shot up while hanging below my parachute – That happened to several pilots in the Malta battle. I considered a low bale-out over the sea to be the best option – Ditching a Hurricane is not recommended because of the prominent radiator under the fuselage.

I headed south towards the sea, but the engine had almost completely lost power and the fire situation was now becoming a problem. The last altitude I noticed on the altimeter before I jumped was 700 feet. This would have been set at zero at Hal Far, so I would have been about 900 feet above sea level.[131] However, I was losing height gradually and also lost valuable seconds getting rid of the cockpit hood. Also, I hung onto the radio mast behind the cockpit before I finally let go, pulling the rip-cord when clear of the rudder and tail-plane, probably at about 400 feet above the ground.

The parachute opened perfectly, although the shroud lines briefly entangled my feet, and I landed on rock after about 10–20 seconds. I heard the aircraft hit the ground, or it may have been the fuel tanks exploding in the air, very soon after I pulled the rip-cord. The remains of the Hurricane were only about 20 yards away from my point of landing. [This was in a shallow gorge overlooked today by the reverse osmosis plant near Ghar Lapsi.]

A corporal of the Maltese Army arrived with a Tommy gun in case I was German or Italian and led me up a rocky slope to a path which led to a RAF RDF station. On the way I met the oldest Maltese lady in the world who was charming and shook my hand for about five minutes!

I was well looked after at the RDF station and later taken in a truck to Siggiewi to await collection from Hal Far. By then it was dusk. I was taken into the little police station and treated very kindly.

However, some local people thought I was an enemy airman and I was obliged to go to the door and show them my wings. If I had been German or Italian anything could have happened.[132]

In addition to the Hurricanes shot down, at least one other crash-landed as a result of battle damage. All were victims of JG 53. Meanwhile, Horricks had claimed a Bf 109 destroyed, Wigley a Bf 109 damaged, Ormrod a Ju 87 damaged and Lloyd a Ju 88 damaged. A Bf 109 destroyed was also credited to Flying Officer 'Buck' Buchanan; a Ju 87 probable and a Bf 109 damaged to Pilot Officer Peter Nash; and a Ju 88 destroyed (in conjunction with AA) and another damaged to Flying Officer Norman Lee (all of 249 Squadron). Sergeant N. Vidler of 229 Squadron claimed one Ju 88 damaged. AA seems to have claimed one more Ju 88 probably destroyed and another damaged. Actual losses included Unteroffizier Paul Böger of 8/KG 77, who was killed when he reportedly fell from, or was blown out of his Ju 88; a Ju 87 of III/StG 3 (the crew of which are thought to have been saved by Axis air-sea rescue); and a Bf 109 of 6/JG 53, Leutnant Hermann Neuhoff baling out of his fighter and being taken prisoner. The evidence suggests that he fell to Sergeant Horricks and/or Flying Officer Buchanan, though Neuhoff himself later subscribed to the German view that he was shot down by another Bf 109:

On 10 April, 1942, I was flying with my *Schwarm* over Malta. Suddenly, my second *Rotte* disappeared. Instead, three Spitfires appeared. I shot at one aircraft as it flew in front of me. At the same time I was hit. Leutnant [Werner] Schöw reported his first victory – unfortunately it was me! He had mistaken me for a Hurricane.

I stayed in my aircraft because I knew that if I came down in the drink I would be fished out again. However, when the fire spread I jettisoned the cockpit hood. Shortly afterwards the 109 exploded. It was lucky for me that I had released my harness and got rid of the cockpit hood. I ejected from the aircraft at 2,500 metres altitude and deployed my parachute at about 400 metres and 'belly-landed' near Luqa.[133]

Neuhoff's Bf 109 came down between Luqa and Safi airstrips, probably in the area of the present-day airport terminal car park.

65.	Map 4
AIRCRAFT:	Junkers Ju 88 (5520/3Z+HS?)
CREW:	Unteroffizier Harry Müller (Pilot?), Obergefreiter Peter Dressen (Observer?), Unteroffizier Fritz Haas (Wireless Operator?), Unteroffizier Karl Geilenkirchen (Air Gunner?)
UNIT:	8/Kampfgeschwader 77
PLACE:	Tal-Munxar (east coast)
DATE/TIME:	11 April 1942/Afternoon

The entry for 15 April 1942 in the diary of Second Lieutenant Quentin Hughes of the Royal Artillery reads:

I stood on the cliff near Schirop and watched a Ju 88 crash and burst into flames about 25 yards from our 18 pr [field gun] at Munsharr. The undercarriage shot forward and landed in the sea, while the rest of the plane hit the cliff head and burned itself out.[134]

The account clearly refers to the shooting down, four days earlier, of a Ju 88 of 8/KG 77 which was engaged by LMG fire from The Dorsetshire Regiment Battalion Headquarters and D Company locations after flying through the AA barrage over Grand Harbour. None of the crew is thought to have survived.

66.	Map 3
AIRCRAFT:	Messerschmitt Bf 109 (8784?/Double Chevron)
PILOT:	Hauptmann Karl-Heinz Krahl
UNIT:	Stab II/Jagdgeschwader 3
PLACE:	North-east of Post HF5, Hal Far
DATE/TIME:	14 April 1942/1130 hours

On 14 April, Hauptmann Karl-Heinz Krahl, Kommandeur of II/JG 3, was killed when his Messerschmitt Bf 109 F was hit by AA and crashed in fields between observation post HF5 and the present-day Lyster Barracks. Among those who witnessed the event was Pilot Officer Phil Wigley:

I was not flying at the time and, as most of us did, was manning a Vickers .303 machine gun in the vain hope of shooting down a low-flying aircraft! I saw two Me 109 Fs overhead at about 5–10,000 feet and thought little about it until suddenly one came down and streaked across Hal Far from east to west, at ground level and incredibly fast. Then I saw it hit by Bofors gun fire from just west of the airfield, blowing off its port main-plane – of course, it immediately hit the ground, the wreckage being scattered between the western edge of Hal Far airfield and the village of Safi. The other Me 109 F circled above briefly but wisely did not try the same trick as his late friend![135]

Another eyewitness was Pilot Officer Ian McKay:

This morning the Air Officer Commanding Middle East [Air Marshal Sir Arthur Tedder] gave us a pep talk and told us we were doing a magnificent job here. We all wished he would go up in one of our Hurricanes against ME 109Fs that outnumbered us at least ten to one.

There was a raid just after the talk and then the 109s started ground strafing. One was firing on its way over the aerodrome when it was hit by ack ack and it went straight in. There was a terrific explosion and huge sheet of flame. The engine rolled at least two hundred yards away from the wreckage. The pilot was more or less swept up.[136]

RAF Intelligence apparently failed to recognize who the deceased 'Oberleutnant' actually was, recording somewhat ironically that:

A Hauptmann Heinz KRAHL, who may conceivably be a brother of the pilot of this aircraft, was acting Gruppenkommandeur of II/JG 3, having previously been in JG 2. He is the holder of the Ritterkreuz.[137]

A wing section with its *Balkenkreuz* marking was salvaged from the crash site and afterwards displayed on a wall of the pilots' dispersal hut.

67.	Map 3
AIRCRAFT:	Supermarine Spitfire
PILOT:	Pilot Officer Hiram Putnam
UNIT:	126 Squadron
PLACE:	Ta'Kandja valley, limits of Siggiewi and Mqabba
DATE/TIME:	20 April 1942/1800 hours

The occasional deliveries of Hurricanes and Spitfires had barely been sufficient to sustain Malta's fighter defence, and for the RAF to remain a potent force it urgently needed more reinforcements. On 20 April, forty-seven Spitfires were flown off the carrier USS *Wasp* by pilots of 601 and 603 Squadrons. All but one aircraft (whose American pilot defected to North Africa) arrived safely (though an RAF Sergeant of the Aircraft Servicing Party was killed in an accident during the take-off procedure). No sooner had the Spitfires landed, than the Luftwaffe launched the first in a series of attacks against the Island's airfields.

Luftwaffe aircrew demonstrated their usual skill and courage, and it is due entirely to the heroism and determination of Malta's defenders that relatively few aircraft were destroyed on the ground, but in the air there were losses on both sides. Among the casualties was American Pilot Officer Hiram 'Tex' Putnam of 126 Squadron. He was critically wounded by cannon fire in an attack by a Bf 109 of JG 53, his Spitfire flying into a steel radio mast near Ta'Salvatur before crashing in Ta'Kandja valley, between Luqa aerodrome and Siggiewi.

68.	Map 4
AIRCRAFT:	Hawker Hurricane
PILOT:	Sergeant John Fullalove
UNIT:	229 Squadron
PLACE:	San Leonardo, limits of Zabbar and Marsaskala
DATE/TIME:	21 April 1942/0735–1020 hours

At 0722 on 21 April, an estimated thirty-four Bf 109s escorted as many as thirty-seven Ju 88s towards Malta, the bombers targeting Luqa, Ta'Qali and the Grand Harbour area. At Luqa aerodrome, an unserviceable Maryland was further damaged, while at Ta'Qali, four Spitfires were apparently written-off and five others damaged. Houses at nearby Mosta also suffered, though there were no reports of any casualties.

During the course of the raid, six Hurricanes and between eight and eleven Spitfires were scrambled. There were claims by both sides. Actual Luftwaffe losses cannot be substantiated; however, the RAF lost two fighters together with Pilot Officer Stanley Brooker of 126 Squadron (who was reported missing), and Sergeant John Fullalove of 229 Squadron. According to the Operations Record Book of 229 Squadron, Fullalove was, 'shot down over Ft Leonardo. The aircraft was seen to fall to pieces in the air.'[138]

An ex-infantryman who served in 1st Battalion The Dorsetshire Regiment recalled that he was part of a patrol that found Sergeant Fullalove, looking as though he were asleep, in the cockpit of his crashed, but otherwise intact, Hurricane. This account clearly contradicts that recorded by 229 Squadron. Had the former soldier somehow confused the event with the shooting-down four weeks later of Tenente Remo Cazzolli, who crash-landed his Reggiane Re 2001 just 600 metres away (see pages 168–71).

Wartime records which provide the precise locations of aircraft crashes in Malta are limited, to say the least. Often, the loss of an aircraft is given scant mention, if at all. In this instance, the only significant clue is provided in the ORB of 229 Squadron. If Sergeant Fullalove's Hurricane broke up over San Leonardo, then it is reasonable to assume that the wreckage fell nearby. However, there is evidence to suggest that one of two Spitfires shot down on 20 July 1942 also crashed in the area: Sergeant Hugh Russel of 185 Squadron was posted missing (indicating that he came down off the coast), while Flight Lieutenant James Lambert of the same unit was rescued after parachuting into the sea, apparently off Fort San Leonardo.

In October 1997, aircraft fragments were located in a field about 450 metres south-west of the fort, midway to the main Zabbar–Marsaskala road. Local eyewitnesses maintain that this is where a fighter met its end in or around April. The pilot, who by all accounts was burned beyond recognition, lay nearby. This tends to rule out Flight Lieutenant Lambert. In September 1998, an RAF OR's cap badge, showing signs of fire damage, was also found at the site, suggesting that whoever crashed here was highly unlikely even to have been an officer.

Of the eighteen fighter pilots killed while operating from Malta in April 1941 and 1942, just two or three fell at unidentified locations on the Island: Sergeant John Fullalove; Pilot Officer Oliver Ormrod, who was lost a day later in somewhat different circumstances (and whose aircraft probably crashed offshore – see page 133), and Warrant Officer Douglas Corfe, who was shot down on 25 April 1942, but in another sector altogether (see pages 134–5) – leaving little doubt about the identity of the body found at San Leonardo.

69.	Map 3
AIRCRAFT:	Supermarine Spitfire
PILOT:	Pilot Officer Frank Jemmett
UNIT:	126 Squadron
PLACE:	Tal-Virtu, limits of Rabat
DATE/TIME:	22 April 1942/1725–1838 hours

The last air raid on 22 April began at 1725 and lasted an hour and a quarter, during which time some fifty Ju 88s and twenty Ju 87s escorted by Bf 109s dropped bombs in the Dockyard area and at Luqa, Safi, Ta'Qali and Hal Far. Four gun positions suffered direct hits or near misses, and a number of men were killed or wounded. There was further damage to civilian property. On the airfields, three Spitfires were destroyed and a Blenheim, Hurricane and at least two Wellingtons were damaged.

In the air, six Spitfires of 126 Squadron and two
Hurricanes of 185 intercepted several enemy aircraft, with
claims later submitted for a Bf 109 probably destroyed and
four aircraft damaged. However, on this occasion the RAF
came off worse: one Hurricane was shot down with the loss
of Pilot Officer Oliver Ormrod, who almost certainly fell to
Hauptmann Wolf-Dietrich Wilcke, Kommandeur of III/JG 53.
Ormrod is assumed to have baled out only for his parachute
to malfunction. His body was found on a rooftop several
months later. Two Spitfires were also claimed destroyed
soon after 1800 by Feldwebel Walter Recker of 4/JG 53
and Oberfeldwebel Rudolf Ehrenberger of 6/JG 53.[139]
Both were probably responsible for shooting down Pilot
Officer Frank Jemmett. His Spitfire crashed at Tal-Virtu,
south-east of Rabat, and burst into flames. Personnel of
11th Battalion The Lancashire Fusiliers, manning a nearby
observation post, were quickly on the scene. They
extricated the burned and seriously wounded pilot but in
spite of their efforts Jemmett died later that evening in
hospital.

70.	Map 4
AIRCRAFT:	Junkers Ju 87 (2180/S7+CM?)
CREW:	Unteroffizier Jürgen Schwengers (Pilot?), Gefreiter Franz Netelnbeker
UNIT:	III/Stukageschwader 3
PLACE:	In sea, Marsaxlokk Bay
DATE/TIME:	23 April 1942/1054–1202 hours

Between 1054 and 1202 hours on 23 April, approximately
forty-two Ju 88s and fifteen Ju 87 Stukas with the usual Bf
109 escort crossed the coast and proceeded to bomb the
airfields and Dockyard. Up to twelve fighters were scrambled,
including three Spitfires of 601 Squadron and four
Hurricanes of 185, the latter unit's Sergeant Gordon
Tweedale managing to shoot down a Ju 87 of III/StG 3
which crashed in the north-east of Marsaxlokk Bay. Among
the many spectators was Pilot Officer Philip Wigley:

The pilot was probably wounded and tried to ditch in the
bay. His aircraft hit the water, turned over immediately
and sank, leaving some wreckage on the surface. I went

out in a motor boat with an airman, from Kalafrana I
believe, to look for survivors, but there were none. All I
saw was a tyre floating on the sea. I remember that,
although there were many light and heavy AA guns in the
area, not one fired on the 87 as it glided down.[140]

The pilot, Unteroffizier Jürgen Schwengers, remained
trapped inside the wreck, which was clearly visible on the
seabed and provided a source of idle curiosity for anyone
interested in paddling the short distance to take a look. The
diary of Pilot Officer Peter Nash of 249 Squadron records
the apparent fate of the gunner, Gefreiter Franz Netelnbeker:
'An 87 was shot down off Kala this afternoon. One of the
crew baled out and 2 109s shot him up in his brolly and
4 109s killed him in his dinghy. This time they blundered.'[141]

71.	Map 2
AIRCRAFT:	Supermarine Spitfire (BP973?)
PILOT:	Pilot Officer Kenneth Pawson
UNIT:	601 Squadron
PLACE:	Il-Qadi, limits of Bur Marrad
DATE/TIME:	25 April 1942/1250–1354 hours

At about 1250 on 25 April, there was a raid lasting just over
an hour by approximately eighty Ju 87s and 88s plus fighter
escort. Twenty-seven people were reported killed and
twenty-three wounded, many of them seriously, when
bombs fell at Luqa, Ta'Qali, St Paul's Bay, Ghajn Tuffieha and
the St George's Barracks/Pembroke area where, on this date,
Number 39 General Hospital was attacked on more than one
occasion.

At least eleven Hurricanes and Spitfires were scrambled.
There were a number of claims including one Bf 109
destroyed by Sergeant Gordon Tweedale of 185 Squadron
and another by Sergeant Paul Brennan of 249. Certainly, one
such aircraft was lost; the pilot, Unteroffizier Heinrich
Becker of 8/JG 53 baled out to be picked up by Axis air-sea
rescue. Hurricane pilot Warrant Officer Douglas Corfe of
229 Squadron, and 601's Pilot Officer Kenneth Pawson,
flying a Spitfire, were also shot down, the former probably
falling to Hauptmann Wolf-Dietrich Wilcke of III/JG 53 and

the latter to Oberfeldwebel Josef Kronschnabel of 9/JG 53.[142]
(Hurricane wreckage recently recovered from below the
rocky headland at Ras il-Qammieh, in north-west Malta,
may be from Corfe's aircraft, while Pawson is known to have
crashed on a hilltop just east of Bur Marrad). Flight
Lieutenant Denis Barnham of 601 Squadron later recounted:

> Pawson was the first of our Squadron to be killed – on his
> first flight – Parry [Flight Lieutenant Hugh Parry] and I
> were walking back across Naxxar market place, and talking
> of the last raid. "The dreaded Pawson may be an ace by
> now", he said. "Things happen so suddenly here – he may
> have shot four down." Then we reached the doorway of
> the mess just as the 'B' Flight car drew up and we learned
> the news – yes, he may have destroyed four; he stayed
> with the bombers too long and was attacked mercilessly by
> the 109s as he tried to get back to the island. He most
> certainly destroyed 1 Ju 88. He crash-landed at Salina and
> died on his way to hospital from wounds and injuries.[143]

72.	Map 2
AIRCRAFT:	Hawker Hurricane
PILOT:	Flight Sergeant Lucien Brooks
UNIT:	229 Squadron
PLACE:	Bajda Ridge (just west of Victory Chapel), limits of St Paul's Bay
DATE/TIME:	25 April 1942/1741–1907 hours

The last bombing raid on 25 April began at 1741 and, like
the two that preceded it, was directed at Malta's airfields and
army installations. Of an estimated fifty-seven Ju 88s,
twenty-four Ju 87s and an undisclosed number of Bf 109s
that took part, at least one Messerschmitt and two Ju 88s
were claimed destroyed and another Ju 88 damaged by the
RAF, while AA gunners were credited with damaging two
Bf 109s and a Ju 87. Of the ten or so RAF fighters airborne,
one was shot down with the loss of Flight Sergeant Lucien
Brooks of 229 Squadron, and at least one crash-landed.
There were two claims by returning German pilots:
Hauptmann Walter Spies of II/JG 53 was credited with a
Spitfire destroyed at 1759 and Oberleutnant Friedrich Below
of the unit's III Staffel with a clearly misidentified P-40 one

minute later.[144] Flight Lieutenant Denis Barnham was among those observing events from the RAF rest camp at St Paul's Bay:

4 109s had appeared on the hill on the opposite shore of the bay – a lazy note of their engines. The leading two climbed suddenly and turned out to sea, the second pair followed. A machine roared out from a fold in the hills, it turned violently to the right and disappeared back from where it had come – there was a burst of machine gun fire – a pause then I saw the machine again – it appeared from round the side of the hill, its left aileron breaking away, it turned upside down then it struck the ground. A bubble of crimson flame seared up where it struck and a smoking shape bounced on down the hill, then it stopped and burst into flames also. Two large fires were now burning on the opposite hillside and thick black smoke was rolling back from the flames. Was it a Hurricane or a Messerschmitt? I think it was a Hurricane. "I think so too," said a Squadron Leader – the fires gradually were dying out, the first had stopped completely but black smoke still oozed from the second fire. Little flames were still dancing among the rocks, and through the field glasses we could make out several figures running down from a scarlet building further up the hill. The sea was a peaceful deep blue and lapping quietly on the rocks; the hillside was yellow and white – the noise of engines had now died away and the silence was broken by the sudden impetuous scream of the siren – some Maltese barkeeper giving the all-clear.

Some Army officers were coming down the paths from the house; they came through the archway where the honeysuckle was, onto the terrace. "We brought these along," they said. "They are all the things we could get from the pilot. He was badly burned about the head and he had a cannon shell through the pelvis." They produced a torn fragment of battle dress burnt on all sides but the wings were intact, and a letter badly charred, but from which we could establish his identity . . . he was a Canadian, we could see that from his khaki battledress. His name was F/Sgt Brooks.[145]

73.	Map 3
AIRCRAFT:	Supermarine Spitfire
PILOT:	Pilot Officer Walter Cripps
UNIT:	601 Squadron
PLACE:	High Street, Qormi
DATE/TIME:	26 April 1942/1425-1534 hours

Malta was subjected to yet another major bombing raid between 1425 and 1534 on 26 April, as approximately fifteen Ju 87s and fifty-five Ju 88s proceeded under fighter escort towards the Dockyard, airfields and individual searchlight and gun positions. Substantial damage resulted, and a number of civilians and military personnel were killed or injured. Six Spitfires and at least two Hurricanes were airborne, the pilots claiming between them one Ju 87 probably destroyed and four aircraft damaged while AA claimed one Ju 88 destroyed and another damaged. Four RAF fighters were also damaged and one, a Spitfire, shot down – the latter, which crashed in the main street of Qormi, having probably fallen to Hauptmann Helmut Belser of 8/JG 53.[146] Denis Barnham and Flying Officer Cyril Hone of 601 Squadron watched the action from Naxxar, the former recording:

> Over came the waves of bombers, the noise of the shells shrieking out into space was the same as before, the barrage of black smoke smeared as the planes passed. Clouds of dust and smoke had risen from where the bombs had burst near Valletta and were drifting westwards towards Luqa when we saw something . . . Hone saw it first. "There's a parachute coming down", he remarked quietly. "Where?" I shouted. He pointed it out to me, about 4,000 feet and above the drifting dust . . . It seemed to be coming down very fast – Was it going to pass behind the smoke or fall in front of it? But it was already there, a white silhouette against the drifting redness. It was falling appallingly fast, something must be wrong. Yes, one side of the chute was flapping loosely but the man hanging there was not struggling; as far as I could see he was just suspended looking down at his feet, or perhaps past them at the earth which must

be rushing up to meet him . . . "Oh God, he won't survive that", I said to Hone. His parachute appeared suddenly in front of a sunlit square house and he disappeared from sight behind one of the stone walls in the valley beneath us.

The pilot, as Barnham soon learned, was Pilot Officer Walter Cripps, a Canadian from his own Squadron:

He landed with one foot shot away by a cannon shell and had broken his other ankle on landing. Later we learned that Cripps had died in hospital from spinal concussion and shock.[147]

74.	Map 4
AIRCRAFT:	Junkers Ju 88 (5717/L1+GM?)
CREW:	Leutnant Hans-Georg Witt (Pilot), Sonderführer Doktor Eduard Perertil (or Petertil) (Observer?), Unteroffizier Josef Mirlenbrink (Wireless Operator?), Oberfeldwebel Hans Steus (Air Gunner?)
UNIT:	4/Lehrgeschwader 1
PLACE:	Santu Rokku, limits of Kalkara
DATE/TIME:	27 April 1942/1055–1150 hours

Forty-six Ju 88s and sixteen Ju 87s, escorted by a dozen Bf 109s, were reported over Malta between 1055 and 1150 on Monday 27 April. Bombs were dropped on various targets in the centre of the Island. At Luqa, an unserviceable Wellington was burnt out, while a Beaufort and a Maryland sustained further damage. A bus and a building were also hit. Elsewhere, seven houses were demolished and nine others damaged. A minesweeper was also slightly damaged.

Light AA accounted for two Ju 88s shot down, one of which crashed alongside beach post L42 before careering towards Fort Saint Rocco, coming to a stop just south of this location. The remains of two of the crew were identified by the RAF as Leutnant Hans-Georg Witt and Sonderführer Leutnant Edward Petertil of 4/LG 1.[148]

75.	Map 3
AIRCRAFT:	Hawker Hurricane
PILOT:	Pilot Officer John Fletcher
UNIT:	185 Squadron
PLACE:	Approximately 250 metres east of Dingli reservoir
DATE/TIME:	28 April 1942/0745–0850 hours

On Tuesday 28 April 1942 there were six alerts, the first major raid beginning shortly before 0800 and continuing for more than an hour with Bf 109s escorting an estimated forty-three Ju 88s and twenty Ju 87s towards their targets. Military equipment and many buildings were destroyed or damaged, and in the harbour area four vessels were sunk. At least three civilians were killed, and four more and a soldier wounded.

At 0740, as the raiders approached Malta, three Spitfires were scrambled from Luqa, followed five minutes later by three Hurricanes of 185 Squadron and, at 0830, by three Spitfires of 603 Squadron. Flight Lieutenant Hugh Johnston of 126 Squadron and Pilot Officer Jack Slade of 603 were each credited with damaging a Ju 87 and a Bf 109 respectively, and AA with one Ju 88 destroyed and two damaged. However, Pilot Officer Jack Fletcher of 185 Squadron was obliged to bale out. He apparently deployed his parachute too soon, the canopy becoming entangled with the tail plane of his Hurricane before tearing free and causing the pilot to plummet to his death. He landed about 500 metres from the burning wreck of his fighter, which crashed in a field south-east of Dingli.

76.	Map 4
AIRCRAFT:	Junkers Ju 87
CREW:	Gefreiter Karl Haff (Pilot), Gefreiter Fritz Weber
UNIT:	9/Stukageschwader 3
PLACE:	Zonqor, limits of Marsaskala
DATE/TIME:	3 May 1942/1815 hours

At 1742 hours on 3 May Malta was attacked by twenty-two Stukas, eight Ju 88s and a number of Bf 109s, including *Jabos*. The raid lasted less than an hour. At Hal Far, three soldiers were wounded and a Hurricane was damaged, as were a PRU

Spitfire, a Wellington and a hangar at Luqa. A farmhouse was damaged at Zabbar, where one civilian was also wounded by AA splinters. Nine Spitfires were airborne. 603 Squadron's Flight Lieutenant William Douglas damaged a Ju 87, and Pilot Officer Jack Slade destroyed another by machine-gun fire after stoppages in both 20mm cannon. The latter Stuka, piloted by Gefreiter Karl Haff, was attacked when approximately 2,000 feet over the Island; the engine seized and the pilot decided to attempt a forced-landing. As the aircraft descended over Zonqor, it must have become horribly apparent to Haff that the area was strewn with rocks and hardly suitable for any kind of landing, but by then it was too late. The aircraft touched down near iz-Zellieqa, flipped over and broke up. The pilot was killed in the crash, while the W/T operator/gunner, Gefreiter Fritz Weber, somehow escaped with minor injuries. He was captured by soldiers of 1st Battalion The Dorsetshire Regiment, and admitted to Mtarfa hospital. Miss G.M. Bates, a nursing sister, subsequently recorded in her diary: 'Had a German prisoner admitted to G Upper (he hated the raids!) You cannot stop our men from treating people as they find them! They loved Weber and his bed was usually surrounded!'[149]

The 21-year-old airman apparently also got along with his interrogators, who reported:

> *UNIT* – WEBER refused to give this but papers found on the aircraft suggest the presence in Sicily of a Ju 87 Wing consisting of Squadrons 7, 8 and 9 and a Staff Section probably of three aircraft. The prisoner probably belonged to the 9th Squadron.
>
> *SERVICE HISTORY* – WEBER had been 2½ years in the Luftwaffe and said that he volunteered for the Air Force because the living and rate of pay were better than in the other Services. He wanted to become a pilot but was evidently rejected and finally allocated as a W/T Operator in a Ju 87 Unit. His rate of promotion was slow, probably as a result of his lack of keenness, and he was not due to become an Unteroffizier (on completion of a year as a Gefreiter) until 1st May, 1942.
>
> *UNIT MOVEMENTS* – In November, 1941, he was posted to Salonika where for four months he was engaged

in practice flights but did not fly operationally. The Greeks were starving and unfriendly. Germans there were offered as much as 20/- for a loaf of bread. He then returned to Germany for a few days and was thence posted to Sicily (probably as a replacement for one of the Ju 87s lost when operating over Malta), where he made his first operational flight. Before he was shot down he had made six operational flights against Malta, most of which were directed against A/A Positions.

INVASION – The prisoner was ignorant, and had evidently not considered the possibility of this.

When attacking A/A Positions they normally dived to approximately 1,800 feet but the depth of dive was determined by orders given before they took off.

The prisoner's Ju 87 was equipped with two machine guns firing forward and one in the rear but he said that some Ju 87s had two coupled machine guns in the rear position (NB Guenther, shot down 1/4/42, said that his Ju 87 had two machine guns firing forwards and two firing from the rear position).

The normal bomb load was 1 × 500 kilo bomb carried under the fuselage and 2 × 250 kilo or smaller bombs stowed under the wings. These could be released together or separately but if separately the 500 kilo bomb was always released first.

The high rate of serviceability of Ju 87s at Biscari largely resulted from the fact that replacements of aircraft from Germany only took one or two days to arrive. They were flown by fresh crews so that the number of crews at Biscari exceeded the number of aircraft.

MORALE – WEBER's security is average but his morale is poor. He is ill informed, apathetic, resolved never to fly again and does not care how the war finishes provided it finishes. Before the war he was a member of the Hitler Youth Movement and is still impressed by Hitler's achievements but is now war weary. At home the Germans were not short of food but were anxious for (a German) peace.[150]

77.	Map 2
AIRCRAFT:	Supermarine Spitfire
PILOT:	Flight Lieutenant Norman MacQueen
UNIT:	249 Squadron
PLACE:	San Pawl Tat-Targa, limits of Naxxar
DATE/TIME:	4 May 1942/1745–1820 hours

One pilot was shot up by a 109 – a very great loss, but he had already hit them hard, at least seven destroyed. We saw it happen from the Mess verandah. He was going straight with his No 2 and the two 109s slunk up behind. He turned in time to warn the other one but did not respond in time and a streak of smoke came from his a/c. He called up on R/T that he was going to land; he circled a few times then dived straight into the deck. Conclusion: "He must have passed out".[151]

So died Flight Lieutenant Norman MacQueen of 249 Squadron, as described in the diary of 603 Squadron. MacQueen was one of seven or eight Spitfire pilots scrambled between 1740 and 1820 on 4 May to intercept a raid by five Cant Z-1007s escorted by fighters. It is thought that he fell victim to Unteroffizier Walter Manz of III/JG 53, who claimed a Spitfire, his first victory, at 1800.[152] Another (601 Squadron) machine landed with a shot-up radiator. Australian Sergeant Paul Brennan of 249 Squadron, the only Spitfire pilot to claim, later described the action:

Almos [Pilot Officer Fred Almos] and Linny [Pilot Officer Ossie Linton] were rather slow getting off the ground, and when the fighter sweep came in we were only at 8,000 feet. The Huns caught us as we headed up sun, a little south of Gozo. The 109s were everywhere. Linny and I were at once separated from Mac and Almos. The two of us mixed it with eight 109s in a hell of a dog-fight. We went into violent steep turns, dived down, and pulled up again at them. But the Hun fighters came at us from every direction – from the beam, underneath, astern and head-on. We were separated in a twinkling. The last I saw of Linny was when he was in a vertical dive, skidding and twisting like blazes, with four 109s hotly pursuing him. It seemed to me as if

I had been throwing my aircraft about for an hour, although probably it was less than five minutes, when a Hun blundered. He made a belly attack on me, missed and overshot. He pulled straight up ahead of me. He was a sitting target. I gave him four seconds. He went into a spin, pouring glycol. During the next few minutes, by manoeuvring violently, I succeeded in shaking off the other 109s.

I called up Linny, and learning he was over Ta-Kali I joined him there. Woody [Group Captain A.B. Woodhall, Senior Controller] reported that some 109s, low down, were off the harbour, and we went out to meet them. As we crossed the coast, however, Almos called up that Mac was in trouble and wanted to land. Followed by Linny, I turned back to give Mac cover. We were approaching Ta-Kali when I saw him. He was gliding across the aerodrome at 5,000 feet, and seemed to be under control. As I watched his aircraft gave a sudden lurch, side-slipped about 1,000 feet, and then seemed to come under control again. I did not like the look of things. I called up: 'Mac, if you're not okay, for God's sake bale out. I will cover you'. There was no reply. A couple of seconds later his aircraft gave another lurch, went into a vertical dive, and crashed at Naxxar, a mile from the aerodrome. Almos and Linny landed while I covered them in, but it was some time before I was able to get in myself.

Everybody was down in the dumps over Mac. We felt his loss very keenly. He was one of the finest pilots, and had shot down at least eight Huns. He had been one of the first Spitfire pilots awarded the DFC for operations over Malta, and he had richly earned his gong. At the time of his death he was acting CO of the squadron, but neither that nor the fact that I was merely a sergeant-pilot had prevented us from being the best of cobbers. We had made many plans against our return to England.[153]

A particularly harrowing account is provided by Flight Lieutenant Denis Barnham, who was watching events from a vantage point near Naxxar:

Cyril's [Flying Officer Cyril Hone] seen something: two dots curving downwards, two fighters swinging round over the bomb dust heading towards us, Spitfires, but they're too late, the bombers have gone.

Approaching our hillside the Spitfires start to turn: I'm not particularly impressed by the way they are crossing over. Look out! A black shape is hurtling upon them; swerving, but it's going too fast: it can't bring its guns to bear. Its engine howls as the 109 passes low in front of us; it wavers as the pilot twists in his seat to see if he's being followed, then, with sudden power, it bounds forward, behind Naxxar's square buildings, reappearing above the skyline in the distance, a tiny dot streaking away northwards.

A 109 by itself? Never. Where's its number two? We all search the sky. The two Spits are climbing in vic formation much too close together, tactically vulnerable; why doesn't the second Spit take up its wide line-abreast formation for mutual protection? If there is a second 109, watching, these Spits are asking for trouble; there's nothing we can do to help them. They circle left, still in tight vic formation, and with their engines murmuring lazily they pass above us. The second German! With horror we watch a black dot dive vertically down the blue just this side of Valetta; it eases out of its dive about two miles away, and now, low behind the grain store, it's rushing towards us. The Spitfires haven't seen its angled shape growing larger and larger; they can't hear its roaring engine. Turn, you fools, turn . . . turn . . . The 109, making for the second Spitfire, lifts gently over our heads, then, swerving towards the leader, opens fire. Although the second Spit breaks violently right, the leader continues straight and level for that critical instant longer: a flash of a shell striking below its cockpit before a 109 streaks upwards and away.

The Spitfire circles to the left, wobbling a little, trailing a wisp of smoke, but now, as both machines level out and pass slowly over our heads, the smoke has stopped, the leader's engine is running smoothly, it flies steadily while its companion, after making an inquisitive turn towards it, moves out into wide line abreast where it should have been all the time. The section heads towards Naxxar, lucky to have escaped; but no, the leading machine trembles as if an uncertain hand is holding the controls. It steadies itself again. It's turning. It's nose is dropping. It is plunging straight down. Pull put . . . pull out . . . With engine roaring it seems to hang for an instant between the twin towers of Naxxar church, then drops out of sight. Scotty [Pilot Officer T.W. Scott] puts his fingers in his ears: wuump, a sprout of black smoke is mounting higher and higher above the buildings.

I turn to my pilots: 'Have you learned the lesson from that?' I demand angrily. 'Number two's fault, he was too damned close. If you fly like that in our Squadron, I'll shoot you down myself.'

The second Spitfire is circling the smoke pillar. We run – but what is the use of running? As we pass the church we are joined by a crowd of small boys. I find myself leading a strange party through the narrow streets and out along the road beyond the town, for the plane has crashed near the army camp. Although a platoon of soldiers is called to attention as I pass, I know they salute the officer who has just died. Nearing the place I send back the children; I also tell my pilots that there's no need for them to see the wreck, but they follow me; over the stone walls towards a gulley where a dark red flame fringed with black smoke gushes up. It is a place of humped rock, disturbed red earth and burnt grass; there are a few pieces of telescoped metal; everyone looks very tall; a Sergeant Major and a Corporal are shovelling earth on to flames near a flat disc which may have been a wheel; two other soldiers are searching among scattered fragments, while a private next to me with a rifle slung round his shoulders stares down at a twisted piece of propeller mechanism. My pilots are climbing back towards the road, but I am sketching this scene in my diary. It is silent but for the fire which crackles and spurts. As I stare down at the wreckage, drawing unrecognisable pieces, I seem to feel someone I know, I seem to be in the presence of Mac, Peter's [Pilot Officer Peter Nash] friend. Quietly, in inner silence I bid him farewell.

A car has drawn up on the road above us: the short plump figure of Gracie, now a Wing Commander at Takali, is climbing over the rocks towards me. Two Army

officers have joined him and now all four of us stare down
at the pieces. As Gracie prods a large lump of earth, the
soldiers hand him their finds: a wallet, a photograph of a
girl, two postcards from England, and a ring which have
miraculously been thrown clear. Again Gracie prods the
lump with his foot; with horror I realise I could have been
standing on what is unrecognisably Mac's body.

'What do you want us to do with it?' asks the Army
Officer.

'Dig it in', says Gracie.

'No. Don't dig it in', I interrupt hotly; an air battle is
waging but invasion has not yet started, the soldiers must
have plenty of time to bury him. 'His girl in England', I
continue, 'or his family may want to visit his grave one
day'.

'Any monument in a cemetery will do', replies Gracie.

'Don't dig it in – give him a proper burial', is my only
retort. I am much junior to Gracie, I don't know if I will
be obeyed or not. Gracie's only concern is with the efforts
of the living to save Malta, and he's magnificent at that;
Mac's body is now irrelevant. I know it is a discarded
thing, empty of essence, but for the sake of those who
come after us please God let a stone or a cross mark the
actual spot where this moist earth is finally laid to rest.[154]

Flight Lieutenant Laddie Lucas remembered Norman
MacQueen as a close Squadron friend who

was universally liked with his sunny and modest
personality which bore ill to no man. Life was a game to
be played to the full until the final whistle. For Norman,
'no side' had come cruelly early.

There was a revealing sequel to this depressing end. A
few weeks before, I had had a fine Kodak camera stolen
from my room in the Xara Palace which I shared with
[Pilot Officer Raoul] Daddo-Langlois and others. I had
bought it in America a year before the war and prized it
greatly. Photography was a hobby and the loss cast me
down. Norman, with his generous, feeling heart, knew
how I felt. He, too, was a keen photographer and
possessed an equally treasured, German-made Kodak-

Retina camera with a Schneider Kreuzmach f3.5 Xenar lens and Compur-Rapid shutter. He always flew with it tucked inside his battle-dress pocket.

'Look here', he said to me one evening, 'I can't forget the loss of your camera. If I should ever get bumped here and not survive, I want you to have my camera. We'll find the adjutant and tell him so he can be a witness to my wish.'

I never felt that Norman ever had a premonition that he might not see out the battle. He was much too happy and jolly to harbour any such maudlin thoughts. The gesture was simply a manifestation of the natural goodness and generosity which adorned his mind.

The camera was found on his dead body, apparently undamaged. The adjutant passed it to me . . .

I still have it in use today, one of life's treasures, but ever a poignant reminder of a much-loved friend's sacrifice.[155]

78.	Map 3
AIRCRAFT:	Messerschmitt Bf 109 (7513/Black 3?)
PILOT:	Unteroffizier Heinrich Becker
UNIT:	8/Jagdgeschwader 53
PLACE:	Marsa Sports Club
DATE/TIME:	8 May 1942/Approximately 0900 hours

79.	Map 2
AIRCRAFT:	Junkers Ju 87 (2151/S7+HN?)
CREW:	Feldwebel Walter Obermeiländer (Pilot), Unteroffizier Albert Westphalen
UNIT:	III/Stukageschwader 3
PLACE:	In sea, east of Ahrax Point
DATE/TIME:	8 May 1942/0930 hours

South-east Malta was targeted during a one and a half hour raid commencing at 0835 on 8 May, and involving half-a-dozen Ju 88s and fifteen Ju 87s escorted by numerous fighters. Eleven Hurricanes and four Spitfires were scrambled between 0900 and 0910. Two claims were submitted by 126 Squadron for a Messerschmitt damaged; 229 claimed one Ju 88 damaged and 185 (whose Hurricanes would be replaced by Spitfires the next day) one Bf 109 and two Ju 88s destroyed and a Bf 109 and MC 202 probably destroyed. Anti-aircraft gunners were also credited with shooting down a Ju 87 and a Bf 109. Two Hurricanes of 185 Squadron were damaged, Sergeant Colin Finlay having to force-land at Luqa, and Sergeant John 'Tony' Boyd belly-landing at Ta'Qali.

Actual enemy losses include one Ju 88, a Ju 87 and a Bf 109. The Ju 88 A-4, which ditched off Sicily with the loss of its crew, almost certainly fell to Australian Sergeants Boyd and/or Gordon Tweedale of 185 Squadron[156] (both of whom, together with Sergeant Finlay, would also be dead within a week). The Bf 109 F-4, flown by Unteroffizier Heinrich Becker of 8/JG 53 (shot down for the second time in less than a fortnight), crashed in the north-west area of Marsa Sports Club. The pilot was captured and later told his interrogator that he had baled out of his aircraft after it was hit by AA.[157] LAA also accounted for a Ju 87 D-1 which crashed in the sea east of Ahrax Point in north-west Malta. Neither the pilot, Feldwebel Walter Obermeiländer, or the gunner, Unteroffizier Albert Westphalen, survived.

Scuba divers may have unknowlingly found the remains of this Stuka at Sikka il-Bajda, a reef east of Ahrax Point. On Sunday 12 September 1993, a Junkers Jumo 211 engine was recovered from the wreck, identified as a Ju 87 D, and is now displayed in Malta's National War Museum.

80.	Map 3
AIRCRAFT:	Supermarine Spitfire
PILOT:	Pilot Officer Harry Milburn
UNIT:	249 Squadron
PLACE:	Wied Maghlaq (south coast)
DATE/TIME:	9 May 1942/1055–1150 hours

On Friday 8 May 1942 Wing Commander E.J. Gracie addressed personnel of infantry units supplying working parties at Ta'Qali. He informed them that some sixty Spitfires were due to arrive on the Island and that it was imperative that air supremacy be obtained. Aircraft were to be serviced and bomb craters filled in at all costs; every available machine was to be put in the air, and working parties were to carry on regardless of air raids. Similar preparations were also in hand at Luqa and Hal Far.

Early the next morning, 650 miles west of Malta, the carriers HMS *Eagle* and USS *Wasp* flew off sixty-four Spitfires. One landed back on the *Wasp* with a faulty fuel system; another crashed into the sea during take-off, taking the pilot to his death, and two pilots were lost, possibly when their aircraft collided after being fired on by a FIAT RS 14 floatplane.[158] Yet another machine crashed at Hal Far, the pilot dying of his injuries soon afterwards. Fifty-nine Spitfires were thus delivered during Operation 'Bowery', the latest effort to reinforce beleaguered Malta.

On the same day, anti-aircraft ammunition restrictions (introduced as a result of shortages) were lifted in anticipation of the expected enemy onslaught. So far, during May, AA had fired 591×4.5 inch HE, $3,633 \times 3.7$ inch HE, 428×3 inch HE, 140×3.7 inch shrapnel, 36×3 inch shrapnel and $4,067 \times 40mm$ rounds. In just two days, until ammunition restrictions were reimposed on the 11th, the number of rounds expended would amount to 492×4.5 inch HE, $5,716 \times 3.7$ inch HE, $1,010 \times 3$ inch HE, 115×3.7 inch shrapnel, 57×3 inch shrapnel and $6,036 \times 40$ mm![159]

The Luftwaffe and the Regia Aeronautica were determined to destroy the new arrivals, and the Island's AA guns and fighters were in action even as the first aircraft approached to land. One German and three of Malta's fighter pilots would lose their lives on this date.

At 0924, there was a two and a half hour raid as an estimated forty-five to fifty-three fighters escorted at least five machines, apparently Cant-Z.1007s, towards targets in the Marsa and Floriana areas. At 0940, nine Hurricanes took off from Luqa and Hal Far, followed minutes later by six Spitfires of 603 Squadron; the former to escort the first of the delivery Spitfires, and the latter to provide high cover. At about 1050, 249 Squadron joined the fray with eleven Spitfires. There were claims by both sides. Unteroffizier Helmut Schierning of 6/JG 53, who was reported missing, almost certainly fell during one of these actions, while a number of British fighters were damaged and two Spitfires lost, together with the pilots: Flight Lieutenant John Buckstone of 603 Squadron crashing offshore, and Pilot Officer Harry 'D'Arcy' Milburn of 249 Squadron coming down on the eastern edge of Wied Maghlaq, on the south coast. Both were probably victims of JG 53.

81.   Map 3
AIRCRAFT: Supermarine Spitfire (BR248)
PILOT: Sergeant Gordon Tweedale
UNIT: 185 Squadron
PLACE: Saviour Street, Lija
DATE/TIME: 9 May 1942/1609–1656 hours

At 1609 hours on 9 May, the fifth alert since dawn began with
the approach of approximately twenty Bf 109s and eighteen Ju
87s, the latter bombing the Luqa and Grand Harbour areas.
There were a number of casualties. At Luqa, an unserviceable
Wellington was also burnt out and a Spitfire slightly damaged.
The raiders were engaged by both AA and the RAF, with
twenty-one Spitfires reported airborne from 185, 249 and 603
Squadrons. Seven pilots were credited with damaging or
probably destroying eight enemy aircraft, yet available German
records for 9 May 1942 confirm only the loss of Unteroffizier
Helmut Schierning of 6/JG 53. At least one RAF fighter was
also damaged, while Sergeant Gordon Tweedale of 185
Squadron was shot down and killed in his first sortie in a
Spitfire. Possibly, the victor was Hauptmann Helmut Belser of
8/JG 53.[160] A Gunner in the Royal Malta Artillery also died
when Spitfire Mk VC BR248 crashed in Lija, where the still-
damaged wall of a building on the corner of Saviour Street
remains as a poignant reminder of the deaths of these two men.

82.   Map 4
AIRCRAFT: Junkers Ju 87 (2149/S7+GN? or 2057/S7+FM?)
CREW: (Probably) Unteroffizier Gerhard Nikolai (Pilot?) (and) Unteroffizier Walter
                 Kern (or) Unteroffizier Christian Appmann (Pilot?) (and) Unteroffizier
                 Heinrich Schäfer
UNIT: III/Stukageschwader 3
PLACE: In sea, Dockyard Creek
DATE/TIME: 10 May 1942/1040–1135 hours

83.   Map 4
AIRCRAFT: Junkers Ju 87 (2051/S7+EM?)
CREW: Unteroffizier Walter Rastinnes (Pilot?), Unteroffizier Walter Rauer
UNIT: III/Stukageschwader 3
PLACE: Senglea
DATE/TIME: 10 May 1942/1900 hours

The attacks of Saturday 9 May continued into the following day, by which time, however, the bombers had another target. Early on Sunday morning, the fast minelayer-cruiser HMS *Welshman* reached Grand Harbour and disembarked 117, mainly RAF, personnel. She also brought a cargo of supplies including ammunition, aero engine parts and 15 tons of smoke-producing generators. After two alerts in the early hours, when bombs were dropped mainly in the Luqa area, on Tignè and off the coast, the alarm was again sounded, at 0554 and 0750, for enemy reconnaissance and/or fighter aircraft before the first of three bombing raids on the harbour area. In Malta there were already seven tons of smoke contained in ninety-two generators. Prior to the first major raid at 1020, these were positioned around the ship at distances of between 100 and 200 yards. On a signal from Fighter Control, half were ignited, providing a screen that effectively shielded the vessel from the air for twelve minutes, whereupon the other half were ignited. By 1300, unloading of the *Welshman* was complete, and the used generators replaced in time for the next bombing raid at 1339. The smoke-screen, formidable anti-aircraft barrage and much-improved fighter force cost the enemy dearly, and enabled HMS *Welshman* to depart that night.[161] Lance Bombardier Stan Fraser described the first attack on Grand Harbour:

> The siren sounded at about 9.30 am and everybody was keyed up with expectancy, for large formations of Spitfires and Hurricanes were airborne, a smokescreen already enveloped the harbour area, and a special "Ship" barrage had been prepared, the restriction on ammunition being cancelled.
>
> Telephonist reported "Tally-ho" which means that fighters have sighted and are about to engage the enemy.
>
> "Stand by for Ship barrage" was the order given, as all eyes scanned the sky in the direction of the harbour. Then, before we could see the bombers, the order came: "Ship's barrage – Fire". The original arrangement for the barrage was 5 rounds rapid fire from each gun on pre-arranged co-ordinates, and then, if necessary, repeated.
>
> Whilst we watched the sky over the harbour it became clouded with AA bursts within a few seconds, until it

developed into a thick dense haze with Stukas diving
through one after the other, many of them never
straightening out and crashing to earth together with their
bomb load. For two and a half minutes the guns blazed
away at the rate of one round every 5 seconds. Never had
there been such a barrage fired over this island! The noise
was terrific and over all the gun positions on the island
there hung a thick pall of cordite smoke.

Our fighters pounced upon the enemy after they came
through the barrage and made quick work of those which
did manage to straighten out. What a scene! What a din!
What a tonic![162]

Sergeant Paul Brennan of 249 Squadron was among those
scrambled to counter the first attack:

There were already many 109s above the island, and the
bombers were due to arrive any minute. We managed to
reach 14,000 feet when 109s attacked us over Filfla. As
they came in I could see more 109s above, waiting the
opportunity to jump us. All five of us started turning with
the 109s attacking us. Woody [Group Captain A.B.
Woodhall] called up and told us the 87s were diving the
harbour. While Buck [Flying Officer, believed to be
Acting Flight Lieutenant, George 'Buck' Buchanan] and
his pair held off the Hun fighters, Johnny [Pilot Officer
John Plagis] and I beetled over the harbour. The barrage
was the heaviest I had seen so far in Malta. The flak puffs
were so numerous that they formed a great wall of cloud,
contrasting oddly with the Bofors shells shooting up like
huge, glowing match heads. We dived through the barrage
to get at the 87s on the other side. I looked down as we
went through the flak, and the ground seemed to be on
fire with the blaze of guns. My aircraft was not hit, but it
rolled and yawed, and almost got out of control. I came
out of the barrage suddenly. The sky seemed to be filled
with aircraft. The first thought that struck me, so
numerous were the aircraft, was that there was a great risk
of collision, and that I would have to watch out carefully.
Spitfires were coming in from all points of the compass,
and there were plenty of 109s about as well. Three

thousand feet below me, sharply silhouetted against the blue sea, a couple of fellows in parachutes were floating downwards. The thought occurred to me that I might be joining them shortly. As I watched a 109 crash into the sea I thought that at any rate there was one less with which to contend. Tracers started to whip past my port wing. I turned to starboard. An 87 was right in front of me. It was in the act of pulling out of its dive. I gave it a quick squirt, but overshot it, and found a 109 dead ahead of me. I had a quick squirt at him, but again overshot. Buck was yelling: "Spits over the harbour, for Christ's sake climb! They're up here." I pulled up my nose to gain height, giving the motor all she had. As I shot up, climbing 5,000 feet in a few seconds, I had another quick squirt – this time into the belly of an 87. I saw cannon-shells go into his motor, but had no time to see what effect they had on him. Then I was above the 87s, and went into a steep climbing turn, waiting to pick out one.

Spits seemed to be everywhere, weaving beside the barrage, ready to pounce on the 87s as they pulled out of their dive. It was not long before the Spits were getting on the tails of the 87s. Wherever I looked I could see only 87s with Spits already on their tails. It was several seconds before I saw one which I reckoned was my meat. Diving on to his tail, I opened fire, noticing an 87 crash into the sea and start to burn as I did so. My fellow went into a hell of a steep turn, and I followed him round, firing all the time. I had given him three seconds when the thought flashed through my mind, "This damn '87 should blow up." But, to my surprise, he didn't, so I kept firing. There came no return fire: either the barrage or my fire had got the rear-gunner. The 87 continued in his steep turn, climbing all the time. I hung to him grimly, and kept on firing. I could see all my stuff going into his cockpit and motor. Suddenly he went to pieces. He literally flew apart – an awesome but satisfying sight for a fighter-pilot. His radiator fell off, the air scoop broke away, the pilot's hood whirled off in one piece, and bits of fuselage scattered in every direction. Black smoke poured from him. Rather dumbfounded, I was watching him spinning down when Johnny called up: "Spit attacking 87, there's something firing at you." I looked round quickly. I saw the big yellow spinner of a 109 about 50 yards from my tail. Flashes were coming from his guns. I got a hell of a fright, and pulled the stick back to turn. By this time my speed had fallen away. My aircraft gave a hell of a shudder, flicked over on its back, and started to spin. The suddenness of events so confused me that I did not realise I was spinning. I imagined the 109 had got me, and I prepared to bale out. Subconsciously I must have applied corrective control. My Spit stopped spinning to the left, and I was so surprised that I almost let it go into a spin to the right. The 109, probably deciding that he had shot me down, had left. Johnny told me later that the Hun had been firing at me for about 10 seconds.

I put my nose down to gather speed. Right beneath me, about 100 yards from the bomber I had seen crash earlier, my 87 was plunging into the sea. Having no ammunition left, I went home . . . I did not take off again. I was so tired out that, despite all the noise and excitement, I slept throughout the afternoon.[163]

A preliminary assessment of the day's tally was put at 15 enemy aircraft destroyed by the RAF, 20 probably destroyed and 22 damaged. AA gunners were credited with four destroyed.[164] At least two Italian and nine German machines actually failed to return. Another two Bf 109s were lost in unknown circumstances. There was equally enthusiastic overclaiming by Axis pilots, but just two Spitfires fell to enemy action, with one pilot (Pilot Officer George Briggs of 601 Squadron) killed. Another Spitfire was shot down by AA over Grand Harbour. The next morning, the headlines of *The Times of Malta* proclaimed: "BATTLE OF MALTA AXIS HEAVY LOSSES", the sub-heading declaring: "SPITFIRES SLAUGHTER 'STUKAS'", and, "BRILLIANT TEAM WORK OF AA GUNNERS AND RAF". After listing enemy losses, came the opening paragraph:

The last two days have seen a metamorphosis in the Battle of Malta. After two days of the fiercest aerial combat that has ever taken place over the Island the Luftwaffe, with its Italian lackeys, has taken the most formidable beating that has been known since the Battle of Britain two and a half

years ago. Indeed, in proportion to the numbers of aircraft
involved, this trouncing is even greater than the Germans
suffered at that time.[165]

Complimentary messages sent by exultant commanders
included the following on 11 May, from His Excellency the
Governor and Commander in Chief Malta, Field Marshal
Lord Gort VC: 'I congratulate all the fighting services on
their magnificent team work over the week-end and
I particularly congratulate the Royal Air Force and the Anti-
Aircraft defences on their notable success. The Luftwaffe has
seen that wounded Malta can hit back gamely'.[166]

Although there would be several more months of hard
fighting before the siege was finally raised, 10 May 1942 is
considered as the turning point in a battle that had already
lasted nearly two years. Among Luftwaffe casualties on that
eventful day included a Stuka, claimed in the morning by
Royal Marines LAA. Still carrying its bomb load, the III/StG 3
machine splashed into Dockyard Creek, opposite the Marines'
Bofors position at Fort Saint Angelo. No balers-out were seen.
In the evening, another Ju 87 crashed on the shore nearby. This
was almost certainly a III/StG 3 aircraft crewed by Unteroffizier
Walter Rauer, who was killed, and Unteroffizier Walter
Rastinnes, who was taken prisoner. It was apparently one of at
least three such aircraft claimed by AA between 1810 and
1947.[167] In the same raid, Squadron Leader John Bisdee of 601
Squadron claimed a Cant-Z.1007, the 211ᵃ Squadriglia aircraft
falling on land near Kalkara. Two of the crew who baled
out did not survive. The remainder were killed in the crash.

84.	Map 3
AIRCRAFT:	Savoia Marchetti S.84
CREW:	Tenente Vinicio Vego Scocco (Pilot), Aviere Scelto Francesco Carabellese, Primo Aviere Lino Conte, Aviere Scelto Sergio Orsingher, Primo Aviere Gustavo Petrai, Sergente Eugenio Rivolta
UNIT:	14ᵃ Squadriglia, 4° Gruppo Autonomo Bombardamento Terrestre
PLACE:	Tal-Pitkal, limits of Dingli
DATE/TIME:	12 May 1942/1730–1918 hours

At 1730 on Tuesday 12 May Malta's fifth alert since dawn
heralded the approach of three S.84s and four Ju 88s,

heavily escorted by Italian and German fighters. The main target was Ta'Qali, where one airman and a soldier were wounded and two Spitfires and a vehicle were damaged. The raid was intercepted by three Spitfires of 603 Squadron and several of 126. As the raid developed, these were joined by eight Spitfires of 249, five of 185, at least ten of 601 and six Hurricanes of 229 Squadrons. Later still, after the first aircraft had landed to refuel and re-arm, 603 and 601 Squadrons continued to maintain the defence, scrambling two Spitfires each. RAF losses amounted to several Spitfires damaged (including two that collided during the rush to take off) and two shot down: one pilot, Sergeant Charles Graysmark of 601 Squadron, was killed and another, Sergeant C. Bush of 603 Squadron, wounded. In turn, two Cant-1007s were claimed destroyed; a Ju 88 and an MC 202 probably destroyed; and a Ju 88 and three Bf 109s damaged, one of the latter by RAF ground defences at Ta'Qali. In fact, two Re 2001s of 2° Gruppo are reported to have crash-landed in Sicily as a result of battle damage; one pilot, Sergente Mario Marchio, subsequently dying of his injuries.[168] Although all the Italian bombers were attacked – 603 Squadron's Pilot Officer Eric Dicks-Sherwood was credited with the destruction of one while the Flight Lieutenant Lester Sanders and Flying Officer Richard Mitchell of the same unit jointly claimed another – just one S.84 was lost. Four crewmen abandoned their stricken aircraft before it crashed into a garden at Tal-Pitkal, near Dingli. The balers-out were spotted by Australian Sergeant John 'Slim' Yarra whose log book records: 'Did some dummy attacks on some dagoes coming down in 'chutes. Frightened them.'[169]

According to 185 Squadron's 'Gen and Doings':

Sgt Yarra . . . had quite an enjoyable time playing with some Dagoes who were coming down in parachutes after some destructive person had severely tampered with their Cant 1007 [sic]. The Italians took a rather poor view of Sgt Yarra's efforts to amuse them. These efforts took the form of placing the parachute canopy in the slipstream of a Spitfire. The canopy promptly collapses and the type has to fall a few hundred feet until the chute opens again. Consequently 4 very sick Dagoes landed in the water off the island.[170]

It would seem that Sergeant Yarra left the scene before the Italians descended. Flight Lieutenant Denis Barnham of 601 Squadron apparently arrived soon after, having returned from chasing one of the S.84s out to sea:

As I was recrossing the coast at St Paul's Bay, my mouth went dry: three dots were rushing head-on towards me. Three dots; 109s? three dots with white smudges above them! Parachutes! I turned quickly to avoid those three white parachutes – three Italians, swinging to and fro and drifting southwards with the earth far below us. Circling round and round them was rather fun, for the three Ice-cream Men, one slightly higher than the other two, appeared to go up and down like figures on a merry-go-round. As I watched them I became aware that they were staring back at me in terror: probably thought I was playing with them, that any second I would come in to attack them with blazing machine-guns or fly over the top of them to collapse their 'chutes as the Germans do to us – I gave them a wave. Immediate response – they all waved back, sinking towards the ground, yet jerking up and down as they waved. It was a glorious display of Italian friendliness! The lower we got the more and more swiftly the ground came up to meet us. I edged away, so that they could concentrate on their landings, for they were very nearly down on the cliff tops near Dingli. A gust of wind blew them over the edge and they fell another three hundred feet into the sea. I was powerless to help them, but, to make sure they were safe, I dropped down from the sky and my view, as I raced along the wave crests, was limited to the blue-green water sliding under my wings and the tall cliff rushing past. There they were: three white silk stains drifting in the swirling water; a lot of splashing too. I pulled up in a steep climbing turn over the cliff brink and back across a deserted landscape to dive again for another run past. A quick glimpse revealed the three of them trying to climb on a ledge. On

the third run I saw them all standing safe and sound.
They were waving happily.[171]

As Barnham's account clearly illustrates, one of the four
Italians must have landed some time before his three
companions. The War Diary of 1st Battalion The Durham
Light Infantry includes a strangely misleading entry that
obviously refers to this event, but is dated 5 May (when no
Italian bombers were actually lost over Malta): 'One Italian
bomber crashed in 'C' Coy Area, two burnt bodies were
found in the wreckage and one body was thrown clear and
found a few yards away. Three Italians were rescued from the
sea by launch off 'D' Coy Area (JEBEL CHANTAR).'[172]

The body 'thrown clear' was that of Aviere Scelto
Francesco Carabellese, as confirmed by a brief note included
with a file on Italian Prisoner's of War in Malta: 'The above
[personal details of Francesco Carabellese] are particulars of
the body of an Italian airman which fell near searchlight
station 335 220 on 12/5/42 and they were handed in
through CIB by the Durham Light Infantry.'[173] The map
reference (335 220) corresponds to an area known as Il-
Qaws, and is several hundred metres from where the S.84
came down, as opposed to the 'few yards' stated in the DLI
War Diary. How Carabellese died has not been ascertained.

From the entry in the same War Diary, it appears that two
of the crew remained inside the aircraft – but what of the
other three, last seen by Barnham below the cliffs near
Dingli? An entry in the War Diary of Malta Tanks RTR
records: 'Attempted rescue of parachutists off Dingli but
could not get to them.'[174] Presumably, some kind of vigil
would have been kept on three enemy airman, yet when a
rescue launch arrived on site that evening, only the body of
Sergente Eugenio Rivolta could be found. A few days later,
Barnham learned the fate of the hapless Italians: 'Some
persons unknown arrived on the cliff top before the rescue
party – or did the rescue men themselves commit the crime?
I do not know – but all that was found of the Italians was
crushed bodies, pulp and blood – someone had deliberately
rolled rocks over the cliff top.'[175]

85.   Map 3
AIRCRAFT: Supermarine Spitfire
PILOT: Sergeant Colin Finlay
UNIT: 185 Squadron
PLACE: In sea, off Wied iz-Zurrieq
DATE/TIME: 14 May 1942/0950 hours

Between 0900 and 1015 on 14 May, three Ju 88s escorted by
Bf 109s crossed the coast and proceeded to bomb Luqa and
Ta'Qali. Twenty-eight Spitfires were scrambled to intercept
the raid, seven of the pilots being credited with three Bf
109s and two Ju 88s destroyed, one Bf 109 probably
destroyed and two damaged. Some of these claims may relate
to a Ju 88 and two Bf 109s that crash-landed in Sicily on this
date, and one of three Ju 88s of KGr 806 that failed to
return from their mission over Malta.

In turn, one Spitfire was damaged when it belly-landed
after running short of fuel. Another was shot down an
estimated 400 yards off Wied iz-Zurrieq, the body of the
185 Squadron pilot, Sergeant Colin Finlay, being recovered
by personnel of 3rd Battalion The King's Own Malta
Regiment. Sergeant Finlay (who was killed just before
becoming tour expired) almost certainly fell to one of the
pilots of JG 53, at least three of whom submitted claims for
a fighter destroyed (including two misidentified as P-40s).[176]

86.   Map 3
AIRCRAFT: Supermarine Spitfire
PILOT: Sergeant John Boyd
UNIT: 185 Squadron
PLACE: Near west end of east–west Luqa runway
DATE/TIME: 14 May 1942/1305 hours

87.   Map 3
AIRCRAFT: Junkers Ju 88 (140166/M7+CH? or 140181/M7+FH?)
CREW: Feldwebel Günter Schwerdt (Pilot?), Gefreiter Rudolf Hertzler (Observer?),
             Feldwebel Paul Stahl (Wireless Operator?), Unteroffizier Johannes Meinel (Air
             Gunner?) (or) Hauptmann Emil Braun (Pilot?), Obergefreiter Karl-Heinz Stadtmann
             (Observer?), Unteroffizier Otto Richter (Wireless Operator?), Obergefreiter Rolf
             Hüppop (Air Gunner?)
UNIT: Kampfgruppe 806

PLACE: Ta'San Gakbu (Ta'Qali)
DATE/TIME: 14 May 1942/1235–1400

After the action in which Sergeant Colin Finlay was shot down (see previous entry), there was a respite of more than two hours before the next alert at 1235, when three Ju 88s approached, escorted by German and Italian fighters. Clearly, the Luftwaffe was taking minimal risks following its heavy losses of the 10th.

Seventeen Spitfires and four Hurricanes were scrambled. Four fighters of 185 Squadron engaged the Italians, Sergeant David Ferraby claiming one MC 202 probably destroyed. In turn, the unit lost another veteran who was due to be released from flying duties prior to his imminent return to the United Kingdom when Australian Sergeant 'Tony' Boyd was shot down by an unidentified fighter and crashed on the perimeter of Luqa aerodrome. Flight Lieutenant Denis Barnham, who was at readiness with other pilots of 601 Squadron, witnessed the event:

> A Spitfire came circling down in a medium turn just beyond the far side of the drome, as graceful as a bird, brown and then duck egg blue on its belly as it banked near us and away again. It was getting low now, very low. Surely that pilot is keeping it in that diving turn too late. I leapt to the top of a tall rock as the machine, beginning to flatten out, disappeared from sight at the far end of the aerodrome. A pause, then a gigantic bubble of flame shot up to 100 feet, seared right across the aerodrome and left no trace of smoke – a roar and then silence.[177]

The signal to scramble came moments later and Barnham soon found himself involved in the fight:

> On the northern horizon the blue sea meets the sky in a belt of white haze – suddenly, against the white – three tiny dots. Why only three? Must keep turning – where are those 109s? Approaching dots under my right wing – dots reappearing – certainly only three bombers – Ju 88s? Keep turning – bombers behind tail – turning – bombers on other side now – nearer – level out – check sun position,

finger up, shadow slightly left – keep over to the right – must stay invisible – this attack must be perfect. Blurrs round the bombers – 109s in close escort! Bombers under wing. Tighten circle a bit – must stay invisible. Bombers reappearing – hell of a strong escort – thirty, no forty 109s flying in twos and fours. Bombers behind tail – must go in quickly – enemy force reappearing – ideal position – this is it.

'In we go now, Exiles, each man cover the man in front. Destroy the bombers first. Straight in and straight out'.

With the 88s parading past in vic formation I'm diving fast on the tail of the nearest, black against the blue sea, black against the white houses of Valetta – 109s alive to our attack? No – still flying steadily. Harbour barrage – shells burst red and black, friendly shells, fired by our own side. Bomber growing larger, backwards towards me – gun sight spot on his port wing – 200 yards – on his port engine – fire now: quick white flashes along the wing, one, two, three, four on the engine – a great burst of black smoke gushing back. Swerving right and tilting – enemy fighters? No. Over my left shoulder the sky is filled with shellbursts; Spitfires behind other bombers; 109s breaking up too late from their tidy formation. Nearest Spit sliding up behind my burning bomber – strikes all down the bomber's fuselage, strikes along near wing, starboard engine splits into flame, bomber dropping below, tumbling downwards, pyre of blackness.[178]

The other attacking Spitfire was probably that flown by New Zealander Pilot Officer Mervin Ingram of 601 Squadron, who recorded:

Red and Blue sections intercepted 3 Ju 88s and 12 .109 escort at 16,000 feet over Grand Harbour. I attacked Ju 88 already damaged by F/Lt Barnham and fired 160 rounds into it. Strikes along starboard side and a/c crashed on Island. This a/c shared with F/Lt Barnham. All three bombers destroyed. *1 Ju 88 confirmed destroyed*.[179]

Flying Officer Richard Mitchell of 603 Squadron was also involved in this action, all three pilots being credited with shooting down the same bomber. Flight Sergeant John Hurst of 603 Squadron, together with AA gunners, was also credited with one Ju 88 destroyed. It would appear that Barnham, Ingram, Mitchell, Hurst and ground fire all contributed to the destruction of either Ju 88 M7+CH, piloted by Feldwebel Günter Schwerdt, or M7+FH, flown by Hauptmann Emil Braun. A Bf 109 'damaged' was also credited to Flight Lieutenant Lester Sanders of 603 Squadron. Barnham recalled a conversation with his fellow pilots shortly afterwards:

> 'That 88 you shot down on Takali the other day', a 'B' Flight pilot tells me. 'Bloody good show! We watched it all then went over to have a look. The German pilot was draped over the top of the wreckage – all burning –as the flames consumed him, so the muscles contracted in his right arm bringing it up in a Heil Hitler salute. Interesting to watch.'
>
> 'Yes', says another pilot with a bitter laugh, 'four more unhappy families in Germany – let 'em all sizzle. Have any luck today?'[180]

Hector Borg-Carbott, an official photographer who was also at the scene, remembered that the pilot was still alive but trapped in the burning wreck. According to him, a RAF officer prevented anyone from attempting a rescue and eventually used his revolver to shoot the unfortunate German.[181]

A pair of machine-guns were retrieved from the wreckage and added to the trophies in the Officers' Mess bar of 601 Squadron, until being taken by Barnham when he returned to England the following month. They were later stolen while being exhibited at a post-war display.

88.	Map 4
AIRCRAFT:	Junkers Ju 88 (140156?/M7+BL?)
CREW:	Unteroffizier Johannes (or Hans) Prokesch (Pilot), Obergefreiter Herbert Burger (Observer), Obergefreiter Hermann Köster (Wireless Operator), Obergefreiter Ferdinand Lechner (Air Gunner)
UNIT:	Kampfgruppe 806
PLACE:	Ta'Karach ridge, limits of Gudja and Ghaxaq
DATE/TIME:	14 May 1942/1811 hours

At 1713 hours on 14 May, the air raid sirens signalled yet another attack. Once again, three Ju 88s, accompanied by

Bf 109s and MC 202s, crossed the coast, this time bombing Gudja and Safi. Six Hurricanes and twenty-two Spitfires were scrambled, one of the latter being shot down into the sea taking Flight Sergeant Harold Fox to his death. The 249 Squadron pilot was later credited with a Bf 109 destroyed. There were several other claims by the RAF and AA, and at least one Ju 88 was brought down after being attacked by Flight Lieutenant Barnham on his third scramble of the day:

> I had to lead my boys straight across in front of thirty or forty 109s in close escort on the bombers. With the Vic of three 88s, tipped up big and black in front of my windscreen, I prayed hard for I expected we would have casualties. As I settled on to the tail of the nearest bomber I was aware of a 109 creeping into position behind me – I fired a steady three second burst, hitting the bomber all the time, watching cannon shells and bullets ripping into his black wing, a cascade of violent white sparks just inboard of his port engine – then, breaking violently left, flashed past the attacking 109 astonishingly close: saw its bright red propeller spinner, oval shaped like an elongated egg with a rippling highlight, rotating in strangely slow motion. The German pilot jerked his head up to look at me – then open sky and sudden panic as other 109s fastened on my tail. Did an aileron turn downwards, pulling fiercely up again. Saw the bomber dropping from the dog-fight above: its port wing, where my cannon shells had torn into it, had snapped off and was fluttering high above, while the rest of the machine, quite flat with flame gushing from its broken wing stump, was gyrating round and round, a great Catherine wheel. 109s on me again – we all had a hell of a fight to get home.[182]

At Kalafrana, RAF Armourer Phil Chandler watched as the bombers dived overhead

> amid pretty hot AA fire. One of them received a direct hit. Smoke poured forth immediately and he did a sharp turn, crossing the path of one of his comrades. This turn was perhaps too much for the stricken machine, for both

engines fell out. Then the whole box of tricks fell to pieces. The whole mainplane came off and spun lazily down, leaving a spiral of blue smoke, amid a shower of smaller fragments which continued to flutter down for some minutes afterwards. One got away by parachute.[183]

Later, a bitterly disappointed Barnham learned that the aircraft had been credited to AA gunners, 'despite the rear gunner, who baled out by parachute, confirming that I, the Spitfire leader shot him down'.[184]

The sole survivor was actually the observer, Obergefreiter Herbert Burger, who only just managed to escape after the aircraft went into a spin. Those killed were Unteroffizier Prokesch, and Obergefreiters Hermann Köster and Ferdinand Lechner. RAF Intelligence was able to compile a detailed report that revealed the considerable experience of at least two of the crew of Ju 88 M7+BL:

The observer, Burger, after completing his training was sent to the Russian front where his Unit was mainly engaged in attacks on shipping, though occasionally, as Prokesch's papers show, it carried out dive-bombing attacks in support of infantry. Burger's opinion of Russian men and material was low. He said he was sent to Sicily in December, 1941 . . .

Prokesch's papers show that he carried out 68 flights in the Mediterranean including 54 bombing attacks on military targets in Malta, 5 protective convoy patrols, 3 dive-bombing attacks on English convoys and 2 reccos. Burger had, he said, completed 80 operational flights in the Luftwaffe averaging almost one a day from Sicily and complained about the strain on his nerves particularly during the months of December, January and February. The attacks during March and April were not so wearing as by this time Malta's defences had weakened but he still reckoned Malta the toughest of all bombing propositions and was looking forward to his retirement from operational flying, which was possible, he thought, after about 100 operational flights.[185]

89.	Map 3
AIRCRAFT:	Messerschmitt Bf 109 (7295/Yellow 12?)
PILOT:	Leutnant Herbert Soukup
UNIT:	6/Jagdgeschwader 53
PLACE:	South of Marsa Creek
DATE/TIME:	15 May 1942/1536-1644 hours

Soon after 1530 on 15 May, a heavily escorted Junkers Ju 88 appeared over Malta. Six Spitfires were scrambled in response; two MC 202s and a Bf 109 were claimed destroyed, another Messerschmitt probably destroyed and one more damaged. One Bf 109 F-4 was certainly shot down by Squadron Leader Lord David Douglas-Hamilton of 603 Squadron who recorded:

> We were 'stooging' around at 25,000 feet for a considerable time; it was very cold and I even got frost-bite in a finger. We were bounced once by a pair of 109s but avoided them successfully. Eventually we were told to go down. Suddenly I saw a 109 sweeping down on my No 2. I warned him to break away, and turned towards the 109. It still came on, by this time at me, and we were approaching each other head-on at great speed. I resolved not to give way before he did, and he evidently made the same resolution. We were going straight at each other, and as soon as I got my sights on him I opened fire, and kept firing. He opened fire a second afterwards.
>
> It all happened in a flash, but when he seemed about fifty yards away I gave a violent 'yank' on the stick and broke away to the right. As I did so, his port wing broke off in the middle, and he shot past under me. I turned and looked back; his aeroplane did about five flick rolls to the left and broke up. Then a parachute opened.[186]

The Bf 109 smashed into the ground just inland from Marsa Creek. Leutnant Herbert Soukup of 6/JG 53, escaped with one arm broken by a 20mm cannon shell and drifted towards Zejtun, where his parachute canopy caught on the roof of a house, leaving the 21-year-old Sudetan German dangling just out of reach of angry locals. Eventually, he was rescued by the army and taken to Mtarfa hospital where he was allocated a bed alongside Flight Lieutenant Hugh 'Tim' Johnston of 126 Squadron who had been wounded following an encounter with a Bf 109 on 6 May. According to Johnston:

> [Soukup] knew very little English, but I learnt some of his history. He had previously been a Stuka pilot, but managed to get transferred on to fighters, and had made more than a hundred flights over Malta; he claimed five victories, one Blenheim, one Hurricane and three Spits. This was his first theatre of operations, although he'd been in the Luftwaffe more than two years. He seemed to have been assimilated by the Germans and, although he wasn't a party member, or noticeably a Hitler enthusiast, he identified himself with the *Herrenvolk*. His reasons for doing so were unconvincing and I thought he protested too much; it was probably self-interest. He said supposing we weren't English, but our country had been conquered by the English, wouldn't we fight for England? We said ask the Irish, but he didn't see the point.
>
> Douglas-Hamilton, who had shot him down, visited him in hospital and I couldn't help overhearing their conversation; when asked why 109 pilots shot up dinghies and parachutes he denied that they ever did so and described it as *Schweinerei*. A case had just occurred in which one of our pilots had been picked up in his dinghy, either dead or at the point of death, with a cannon-shell through his neck; he was told of this but refused to believe it. The cases of 1940 were then quoted, but he still said obstinately: '*Das glaub' ich nicht*' ['I don't believe it']. Nor would he admit that our rescue-launch had ever been attacked. I couldn't make up my mind whether he believed what he said or not.[187]

90.	Map 3
AIRCRAFT:	Supermarine Spitfire
PILOT:	Pilot Officer Peter Nash
UNIT:	249 Squadron
PLACE:	Bieb ir-Ruwa, limits of Rabat
DATE/TIME:	17 May 1942/1154-1234 hours

There was much activity off Malta's coast in the early hours of 17 May when searchlights illuminated what was thought to be four 'E' Boats (probably Italian Motor Torpedo Boats attempting to reconnoitre the Island preparatory to the proposed Axis invasion). These were engaged by coastal batteries, which reported hitting at least one vessel. At dawn, four Hurricanes of 229 Squadron were dispatched to strafe a stationary boat several miles offshore. It was eventually sunk following after further attacks by Messerschmitt Bf 109s.

During the night, there was a raid by eight aircraft, believed to be BR 20Ms, some of which dropped bombs on Malta and Gozo. Three were claimed destroyed by a Beaufighter of 89 Squadron. In fact, none were lost, but a Ju 88 of 2/KG 54 reportedly shot down south of Malta may have been misidentified by the crew of the night fighter.[188]

At about 0700, a reconnaissance Ju 88 was intercepted by two Spitfires of 249 Squadron and shot down by Flying Officer George 'Buck' Buchanan. An hour later, Flight Sergeant Thurne 'Tommy' Parks of 126 Squadron destroyed an air-sea rescue Dornier Do 24 flyingboat. Messerschmitt Bf 109s and Macchi C.202s were active over and around Malta at regular intervals during the rest of the morning. At 1154, another ASR Do 24 escorted by fighters was reported off the coast. Six Spitfires of 603 Squadron and two of 249 were scrambled; Flight Sergeant John Hurst and Pilot Officer Leslie Barlow of the former unit both attacked the Do 24 which was consequently written-off. Flight Sergeant Laurie Verroll of 249 Squadron was credited with a Bf 109 destroyed and one damaged, Pilot Officer Peter Nash of the same unit with another destroyed,[189] and Pilot Officer Neville King of 603 Squadron with one damaged. 5/JG 53 lost at least two aircraft on this date; Leutnant Wolfgang Hermann was killed while another pilot baled out off Cape Scaramia. One or both may have been victims of this engagement. Two claims for Spitfires destroyed were submitted by Unteroffizier Erich Paczia and Leutnant Hans Marklstetter of 6/JG 53;[190] the RAF suffering one loss when Pilot Officer Nash was shot down and killed north-west of Rabat.

91.   Map 4
AIRCRAFT: Reggiane Re 2001
CREW: Tenente Remo Cazzolli
UNIT: 152ª Squadriglia, 2º Gruppo Autonomo Caccia Terrestre
PLACE: North side of Fort San Leonardo, limits of Zabbar and Marsaskala
DATE/TIME: 18 May 1942/0545–0646 hours

At dawn on 18 May, approximately twenty fighters headed for Malta in support of a maritime/land reconnaissance of the Island.[191] The raid included eight Reggiane Re 2001s led by Tenente Remo Cazzolli of 152ª Squadriglia.

> That morning – so nice and bright – a big dog-fight began over the Island between the Re 2001s and Spitfires. There were many Spitfires and few Re 2001s, so when I ordered my pilots to break formation and engage, I found myself surrounded by Spitfires!
>
> As I opened fire, I saw before me in planform, like a cross, a Spitfire. I took aim and fired, seeing a long, black trail – possibly a sign that I had hit him.
>
> Minutes passed slowly like the years of youth; suddenly there was a terrible noise like thunder and my engine stopped; it was the fire of 20mm cannon, which overwhelmed my senses. An instant of infinite fear followed the realisation – my Re 2001 was shot down!
>
> I realised at once the situation, and my face was covered with blood (I still bear the sign of those injuries to this day); by instinct I sought to open the cockpit canopy, but it was stuck, a shell having struck behind the seat armour and crushed the canopy forward against the windscreen.
>
> I thought it was the end. I was in an aircraft with no power, a radiator shot away, a shattered aileron fluttering, with the earth of Malta coming up inexorably to meet me! I tried to recover control. I do not know what condition the tail of the aircraft was in, but that aircraft seemed to have a life of its own; it would not kill me!
>
> I saw a rock flush in the sea, there was an indescribable crash, and I passed out.[192]

Four Spitfires of 249 Squadron had been scrambled to intercept the raid, three pilots each claiming an Re 2001 destroyed. Sergeant Brennan recalled:

About 10 miles east of Zonkor [Zonqor] Point I spotted four aircraft silhouetted against the sea. They were three miles east of us, and about 2000 feet below. Having reported them to Ronnie [Flying Officer Ronald West], I headed straight for them. We circled above them. I think they must have mistaken us for 109s, and imagined we were those which had been south of the island come to join up with them. They were flying in two pairs, and were obviously Italians. I put them down as Macchis.

I told Ronnie to take the pair on the left, and, followed by my number two, Sergeant Pilot Johnny Gilbert, an Englishman whose home was in the Argentine, I dived on the right-hand pair. I gave one a short burst from dead astern. I saw some of my shells hit his port wing. He pulled away sharply, cutting right across Johnny's nose. I saw Johnny give him a squirt, and he went away pouring glycol. Meanwhile I had pulled on to the second one. He promptly went into a vertical dive. I followed him, caught him as he was pulling out of his dive at 2000 feet and, getting dead behind him, gave him a long burst. He hung there for a second, rolled on to his back, and hit the sea. As he crashed I saw another aircraft spin into the sea half a mile away. As I thought it might be one of our boys, I called up the others, and Ronnie told me he had just shot down one of the Eyetyes. As the other two Spits also answered my call, I knew the second aircraft to crash must also have been Italian. I told the section to return to base immediately.[193]

As far as can be ascertained, Tenente Cazzolli's Re 2001 was the only aircraft to have been shot down, and this crash-landed alongside Fort San Leonardo. Although the Reggiane survived the impact more or less intact, the pilot was badly injured and needed to be hospitalised for many weeks.

During interrogation, Cazzolli maintained that he was attacked from behind by Spitfires while flying at 6,000 feet. His aircraft was hit, and the engine began to pour black smoke. Cazzolli decided to seek cover in Malta's smoke screen, but had been unable to pull out of his dive in time. Interrogation also revealed details of the prisoner's varied, though somewhat dubious, background:

PILOT'S CAREER

9.   This pilot, a 28 year old Tenente Pilota, holder of 3 silver medals for military valour, already had his civil A Certificate in 1934.

10.   In 1935, after 34 hours' solo flying at Mondovi on Breda 15s and CR 20s he obtained his B Certificate; and in August of that year as Aviere Primo he went to Abyssinia with a CR 20 unit, returning to Italy in October to be demobilised.

11.   At the end of 1936 he rejoined the IAF and did his Primo Peridio at Foligno, and in March 1937 went to Spain as Sotto Tenente with the 7th Bandera of the Tercio (Spanish Foreign Legion), flying a CR 42.

12.   He was shot down in the battle of Guardalajara and taken P/W, but escaped from a prison camp at Barcelona and reached Italy. He returned to Spain and remained there until the end of the Civil War, being demobilised in May 1938, with a silver medal "Al Valore Militare" to his credit.

13.   After spending some months as a Civil Engineer in Libya, he was again called up in the autumn of 1938 and posted to the 2nd Stormo at Marmarica, then equipped with Breda 65s. The unit stayed at Tobruk until October 1938, when it moved to Castel Benito.

14.   P/W was then given leave to go to Turin to take an Engineer's Degree, and he rejoined the IAF early in 1939 but was posted to Gorizia, where he trained on CR 42s, G 50s and Macchi 200s.

15.   In April 1939 he joined the 152nd Squadriglia, then belonging to the 6th Stormo and equipped with G 50s, and went to Libya, where he was engaged in escorting German Stukas. He was awarded the EK II for 50 escorts.

16.   In May 1940 the unit moved to Tripoli and acted as Caccia sull' Alarme until September 1941. The unit then moved to Rome, where they spent two months at the

Gruppo Complementare, after which four months were
spent converting to Re 2001s at Ravenna.
17.   On May 17th 1942, P/W left for Catania on his
first and last operation in a Re 2001.[194]

As might be imagined, being captured for the second time
did not deter so colourful a character as Cazzolli. Later in the
summer he was moved from Malta to a PoW camp in
Scotland, from where he and two others managed to escape
in September, all three remaining on the run until the futility
of their attempt compelled the men to give themselves up.
Cazzolli, whose medical condition had deteriorated, was
then transferred to London. When his health failed to
improve, he was repatriated and returned to Italy on 24 April
1943.[195]

92.	Map 4
AIRCRAFT:	Reggiane Re 2001
PILOT:	Capitano Annibale Sterzi
UNIT:	358ª Squadriglia, 2º Gruppo Autonomo Caccia Terrestre
PLACE:	Ta'Garda, limits of Ghaxaq.
DATE/TIME:	26 May 1942/1519–1559 hours

There were ten alerts on Tuesday 26 May, but with the
exception of a bombing raid in the early hours, the enemy
concentrated on carrying out fighter patrols until evening,
when a number of fighter-bombers attacked the Luqa area.
At 1519 about eighteen Italian (and, possibly, German)
fighters crossed the coast at 27,000 feet. Eight Spitfires of 603
Squadron and four of 185 were scrambled at 1500 and 1515
respectively, followed at 1540 by four aircraft of 249
Squadron. Heavy anti-aircraft gunners fired pointer rounds
for the RAF; one Re 2001 being claimed damaged by Flight
Lieutenant Lester Sanders, and two destroyed by Pilot Officer
Leslie Barlow and Flying Officer Richard Mitchell, all of 603
Squadron.
    One Reggiane was definitely shot down, with the loss of
Capitane Annibale Sterzi, commander of 358ª Squadriglia.
The aircraft crashed at Ta'Garda, south of Ghaxaq, the force
of the impact leaving a crater that can be seen to this day.

93.	Map 3
AIRCRAFT:	Vickers Wellington
CREW:	Sergeant Raymond Hills (Pilot), Sergeant Eric (or Erix) Martin (Second Pilot), Sergeant (or Flight Sergeant) George Davis (Air Observer), Sergeant Andrew McColl (Wireless Operator/Air Gunner), Sergeant Elwyn Roberts (Wireless Operator/Air Gunner), Sergeant (or Flight Sergeant) Kenneth Ross (Air Gunner?)
UNIT:	104 Squadron
PLACE:	Il-Hotob, limits of Qormi/Birkirkara
DATE/TIME:	29 May 1942/2310 hours

Six Wellingtons were dispatched to bomb Catania aerodrome during the night of 29/30 May 1942. Five reached the target, and dropped a total of 17,630 lbs of high explosive, fragmentation and incendiary bombs. The sixth aircraft was forced to return early and crashed at Il-Hotob, between Attard and Qormi.

The War Diary of 11th Battalion The Lancashire Fusiliers said the 104 Squadron aircraft was 'returning from operations, during which it was badly damaged by AA . . . Three of crew thought to have been dead when plane crashed.'[196]

The pilot, Sergeant Raymond Hills, and second pilot, Sergeant Eric (or Erix) Martin, were rescued by personnel of the Royal Malta Artillery. Sergeants (or Flight Sergeants) George Davis and Kenneth Ross, and Sergeants Andrew McColl and Elwyn Roberts all died, one being killed when the aircraft fuel tanks exploded. Sergeant Martin succumbed to his injuries eight days later. The crew of another Wellington escaped injury when their aircraft crashed at Luqa.

94.	Map 4
AIRCRAFT:	Supermarine Spitfire (BR285)
PILOT:	Pilot Officer John Halford
UNIT:	185 Squadron
PLACE:	In sea, off Marsaxlokk
DATE/TIME:	2 June 1942/0910–0945 hours

Twenty Spitfires from 185, 249 and 601 Squadrons were scrambled for a raid between 0915 and 1040 on 2 June, when a large number of fighters escorted three Italian bombers across the coast. Claims were submitted by both sides. At least one aircraft was actually shot down; Pilot Officer J. Halford of 185 Squadron ditched his Spitfire VC in shallow water in the north of Marsaxlokk Bay where he was picked up by Seaplane Tender 338.

Re 2001 pilots, Maresciallo Luigi Jellici and Sergente Giovanni Dringoli of 2° Gruppo Autonomo CT, and Capitano Carlo Miani of 360ª Squadriglia, flying a MC 202, each apparently claimed a Spitfire destroyed during this engagement.[197]

95.	Map 3
AIRCRAFT:	FIAT BR 20M (MM24133?)
CREW:	(Believed to have been) Sottotenente Aldo Ruggieri (Pilot), Sergente Olinto Lentini (Second Pilot), Giovanni Ruggero (Wireless Operator), Aviere Scelto Bruno Gandolfi (First Engineer), Alberto Constantini (Air Gunner)
UNIT:	277ª Squadriglia, 116° Gruppo Autonomo Bombardamento Terrestre
PLACE:	Just north of Zebbug Cemetery
DATE/TIME:	17 June 1942/0150 hours

Shortly after 0130 on 17 June, there was a nuisance raid by a single Italian bomber. A Beaufighter was unable to intercept the intruder, which was eventually shot down by heavy AA, though not before it had released its bombs over Mellieha. Zebbug resident John Galea recalled:

> The BR 20 came down just off the cemetery with a big roar. It was carrying incendiaries and had not yet released them, hence it burned for a long time, illuminating the cemetery chapel . . .
>
> All five [of the crew] perished. Bits and pieces were scattered around and patches of blood remained on the nearby building for some time.
>
> I still have a few pieces of metal from the airframe in my possession.[198]

96.	Map 3
AIRCRAFT:	Fairey Albacore
CREW:	Sub Lieutenant P.A. Jordan (Pilot), Sub Lieutenant R.S. Todd (Observer)
UNIT:	(Probably) 828 Squadron
PLACE:	Tal Bakkari (between Bubaqra and Hal Far)
DATE/TIME:	19 June 1942/1045 hours

On 19 June, a Fleet Air Arm Albacore crashed soon after taking off for a test flight from Hal Far. Privates Sutton and

Downs, and Lance Corporals Williams and Winsor of 2nd
Battalion The Devonshire Regiment hurried to the scene
and extricated the wounded pilot, Sub Lieutenant P. Jordan,
and the body of the observer, Sub Lieutenant R. Todd.
Personnel of B and C Companies also helped to extinguish
several small fires in the surrounding area, caused when a
torpedo carried by the aircraft exploded.

97.	Map 5
AIRCRAFT:	Junkers Ju 87
CREW:	Sottotenente Fulvio Papalia (Pilot), Primo Aviere (or Aviere Scelto) Pietro Natale Gianini
UNIT:	239ª Squadriglia, 102º Gruppo, 5º Stormo Tuffatori
PLACE:	Near Qasam San Gorg, limits of Kercem and Victoria (Gozo)
DATE/TIME:	24/25 June 1942/2339–0014 hours

Bombs were dropped off the coast by two Ju 87s of 239ª
Squadriglia between the hours of 2339 and 0014 on the
night of 24/25 June. Flying Officer Robert 'Moose'
Fumerton and his observer, thought to have been Pilot
Officer Leslie (Pat) Bing, who were airborne in an
89 Squadron detachment Beaufighter, were credited with the
destruction of one Ju 87B-2. (The same machine may also
have been claimed by HAA gunners.) This crashed near
Kercem, in Gozo, probably in the area of Qasam San Gorg.
The body of Primo Aviere (or Aviere Scelto) Pietro Natale
Gianini was found close to the wreckage. The pilot,
Sottotenente Fulvio Papalia, was taken prisoner by the police
and later taken into custody by military authorities. During
interrogation, Papalia maintained that after flying south past
Malta, a radiator defect caused his aircraft to catch fire,
whereupon he had turned towards Gozo and ordered Gianini
to bale out before abandoning the aircraft himself. It had, he
said, been his first night flight. Papalia clearly made an
impression on his interrogator, who recorded:

P/Ws Roman blood together with his Southern upbringing
have produced a very decent, intelligent and security
minded man. He refused to answer any question, even when
disguised in a harmless conversation, that might have the
slightest bearing on military matters. His morale is very high

and his faith in Italy and "the cause" exemplary. This interrogation has, consequently been a failure, but as it is obvious that the P/W is a man of knowledge and experience, I venture to recommend that he be sent to ME by quickest route and placed in the hands of the "K" people there.[199]

98.	**Map 2**
AIRCRAFT:	Macchi C.202
PILOT:	Sergente Maggiore Alberto Porcarelli
UNIT:	151ª Squadriglia, 20º Gruppo, 51º Stormo Caccia Terrestre
PLACE:	800 metres north-east of Ghajn-Snuber Tower, limits of Mellieha
DATE/TIME:	2 July 1942/1944-2017 hours

There were at least five raids during daylight hours on 2 July. At 1921, five Bf 109s approached the Island, three of the fighters crossing the coast, apparently on reconnaissance. Twenty-five minutes later, Luqa and Hal Far were bombed by two aircraft identified as Cant-Z.1007s, escorted by up to fifteen fighters.

At 1900, 185 Squadron had scrambled four aircraft, followed twenty-five minutes later by seven of 249 Squadron, five pilots claiming a total of two MC 202s destroyed and three Bf 109s damaged. In turn, Flight Sergeant De Nancrede of 249 Squadron was shot up, crash-landing his damaged fighter at Ta'Qali. Another three or four Spitfires of 249 Squadron ordered up at 1855 as air cover for a minesweeper landed without incident, as did four more 185 Squadron aircraft scrambled at 1955.

Two Macchis of 151ª Squadriglia were actually destroyed, both by 185 Squadron: Flight Sergeant Haydn (Vic) Haggas accounted for Tenente Ennio Cherici, who baled out of his aircraft and was taken prisoner, and Flying Officer John Stoop shooting down Sergente Maggiore Alberto Porcarelli, who was killed when his fighter crashed in a field near Qasam Barrani, west of Mellieha.[200]

99.	**Map 2**
AIRCRAFT:	Junkers Ju 88 (1570/M7+GK? or 1348/3Z+BM?)
CREW:	Leutnant Oskar Kasimir (Pilot?), Unteroffizier Johann Haugenthal (Observer?), Unteroffizier Rüdiger Telle (Wireless Operator?), Feldwebel Walter Behnisch (Air Gunner?) (or) Unteroffizier Luitpold Martin (Pilot?),

Gefreiter Ludwig Ebner (Observer?), Unteroffizier Willi Böhmer (Wireless
Operator?), Obergefreiter Anton Fischer (Air Gunner?)

UNIT: Kampfgruppe 806 (or) 4/Kampfgeschwader 77
PLACE: Qawra
DATE/TIME: 4 July 1942/0015–0024 hours

An entry in the War Diary of 2nd Battalion The King's Own
Malta Regiment for 2218 hours, 16 July 1942, reads: 'Ju 88
crashes at KAURA TOWER. Four crew were killed. RAF
and C Coy provide guard.'[201]

Other available records fail to corroborate this account.
Indeed, no details at all can be found of a Ju 88 having been
lost over Malta on this occasion. The entry seems to refer to
an incident that actually occurred in the early hours of 4 July,
when at least two Beaufighters of 89 Squadron were
scrambled to intercept a raid comprising fourteen aircraft, ten
of which crossed the coast. Flight Lieutenant Henry Edwards
and his observer, believed to have been Sergeant J.G. Trebell,
attacked two Ju 88s, one of which apparently dived into the
sea while attempting to outmanoeuvre the night fighter. The
other was brought down in conjunction with AA and
crashed in flames near the Knights' watch tower at Qawra.
The two aircraft were almost certainly M7+GK, piloted by
Leutnant Oskar Kasimir of KGr 806, and 3Z+BM, flown by
Unteroffizier Luitpold Martin of 4/KG 77.[202]

100.   Map 4
AIRCRAFT: Savoia Marchetti S.84 Bis (MM24008?)
CREW: (Probably) Sergente Maggiore Romolo Cristiani (Pilot), (and) Sergente
               Maggiore Manca Gesuino (Second Pilot), Aviere Scelto Arduino Pelleschi
               (Wireless Operator), Primo Aviere Giovanni Genovese (Mechanic), Primo
               Aviere Gino Pascalizzi (Armourer), Aviere Scelto Giovanni Lunati
               (Photographer)
UNIT: 14ª Squadriglia, 4º Gruppo Autonomo Bombardamento Terrestre
PLACE: Ta'Garda, limits of Ghaxaq
DATE/TIME: 4 July 1942/0807–0908 hours

Luqa aerodrome appeared to be the target for the first
daylight raid of 4 July, although the nearby villages of Luqa
and Zurrieq also suffered. At least one civilian was killed, and
two injured.

Ten Spitfires of 249 Squadron were scrambled to meet the enemy, which consisted of three Savoia Marchetti S.84 Bis bombers heavily escorted by fighters. All three Savoias, misidentified by the RAF as Cant-Z.1007s, were claimed destroyed, as recounted by Squadron Leader Laddie Lucas:

We were close to 27,000 feet, flying north, with the sun behind us, and nicely placed at about five o'clock from Grand Harbour, when Woody's [Group Captain A.B. Woodhall] sonorous bass voice gave the news we wanted.

'Tiger leader, eighty plus approaching St Paul's Bay now, angels seventeen to twenty thousand. You should see them very soon at twelve o'clock six or seven thousand feet below you. Come in now and come in fast. There are some little jobs (enemy fighters) in your vicinity, but below you; so watch your tails'.

I was glad I had had time to add another 2000 or 3000 feet to our altitude. With such numerical odds stacked against us, it generated confidence in the Squadron to know the enemy was below.

The two section leaders and I spotted our prey almost simultaneously, dead ahead and some 6000 or 7000 feet below. Down-sun the gaggle was silhouetted against the hazy blue of the Mediterranean. 'OK, Woody', I said, 'we see them. Thanks. Out'.

Three Italian Cant Z 1007 bombers, with a strong escort of Me 109s, flying beautifully in their usual wide-open formation of fours abreast, were in a tight VIC, a hallmark of the Regia Aeronautica. Well astern of them was a token force of Macchi 202s and Reggiane 2001s also flying a tighter formation than their Luftwaffe counterparts. The raid looked to be heading for the airfield at Halfar, with a saver for Luqa.

To an old Island hand, the three Cants were an obvious decoy to tempt the defending Spitfires into battle while the superior forces of the Axis turned their guns on them. 249 weren't to be fooled with that kind of ruse. Surprise, born of height, sun and position, and a super-fast closing speed was the only plausible antidote for such a trap. With our extra height and the sun now blazing behind us, we clearly hadn't been spotted.

My instructions to the Squadron, with Raoul Daddo–
Langlois, leading Blue section to my left and Jack Rae and
his No 2, making Yellow section to my right, were
necessarily concise. With such an experienced lot, they
could have followed the tactics blindfold.

'OK, fellers', I said, 'turning hard to port and going
down now. My Red section will take the bomber to the
port of the VIC. Raoul, you and Blue section take the
starboard bomber. And Jack, you and your number two,
cover Red and Blue sections as we go in. If you're not
engaged, and have the chance, take a good poke at the
leading big job. After the attack, all Tiger aircraft are to
break downwards fast and go straight down to the deck.
There are far too many 109s about to stay and mix it.

'OK, Raoul?'

'Roger'.

'And Jack, OK?'

'Roger'.

'Right, fellers, going in now. Let's get in close to the
bombers'.

The plan worked. With all the advantage of being
unseen, and with height, sun and speed compounding the
opportunity, we cut straight through the opposing fighters
and closed quickly with three bombers, seconds before the
escort spotted us. It was a diamond-sharp bounce, a
chance in a thousand.

My emotions, as we tore through a covey of
unsuspecting 'dirty black crosses', and on to the three
bombers, are vivid still. I had no feeling of apprehension
or fear – only a buoyed-up excitement and determination
to close right in with the port bomber and take a shot
which might never recur. Every atom of concentration I
possessed was riveted on the port Cant as Red section
swung naturally in behind me and we turned a beam
attack into a nicely curved quarter attack.

It was all over in seconds as these interceptions always
were. But it had produced, for me, exactly the sense of
exhilaration which I had become accustomed to on the
rugby field . . .

A quick look in the rear mirror confirmed that only
Red 2, 3 and 4, each immaculately positioned, were

behind. Then, disregarding the Italian rear gunners' rather desultory fire, I pressed the attack on the port Cant until, at what seemed like point-blank range, I let the shells from the four cannons in my Spitfire VC rip into the port side of the aircraft's fuselage and engine. The bomber seemed almost to be disintegrating as I flew through a mass of debris severed from airframe and port motor.

As I broke away fast downwards, telling the rest of my section to follow, I could see the 109 escort spreadeagling all over the sky as the leaders suddenly became alive to the enormity of the affront to which 249 and Woodhall had subjected them. A *Schwarm* of four Messerschmitts gave a face-saving chase after my section, but they were too late. As our speed built up in the dive for the deck, and we turned now and then towards them, they never had a hope of getting inside us with a worthwhile deflection shot.

Meanwhile, an upward glance or two told me that the three Cants, in various stages of disrepair, were falling out of the sky. The port aircraft, which I had attacked, was ablaze and smoking, shortly to plunge into the sea 5 miles or so from Delimara Point. I was glad to see two parachutes open from it.

The starboard aircraft, which Daddo-Langlois and his aggressive Canadian No 2, Bob Middlemiss, had sent smoking earthwards, looked as if it must crash within gunshot of Halfar.

Finally, the leading bomber, which had been Jack Rae's responsibility with his No 2, was streaming black smoke as it went into a terminal dive southwards before hitting the sea a few miles from Kalafrana. More parachutes were floating down from it. Jack's attack on it, precisely timed to synchronize with those of Red and Blue sections on the two flanking bombers, was a professionally executed assault.[203]

It would seem that one damaged S.84 did, in fact, manage to return to Sicily, while two bombers were actually brought down. One crashed offshore, possibly the 15ª Squadriglia machine piloted by Tenente Raffaele Notari;[204] the other fell

at Ta'Garda, between Ghaxaq and Birzebbuga. This is
thought to have been MM24008, flown by Sergente
Maggiore Romolo Cristiani of 14ª Squadriglia. The only
survivor from this machine was the W/T operator, Aviere
Scelto Arduino Pelleschi, on his first operation over Malta.
Pelleschi was severely wounded when his aircraft was hit by
AA shortly after releasing its bombs and prior to being
attacked by 249 Squadron. He baled out and landed in the
sea from where he was rescued by the crew of HSL 128. The
24-year-old, whose injuries resulted in the loss of one hand,
was visited in hospital by several pilots involved in the
destruction of the S.84s. The event left a lasting impression
on Laddie Lucas, who assumed that Pelleschi had been
wounded by a cannon shell. Thereafter, the Squadron Leader
discouraged his pilots from visiting badly wounded prisoners
so that others might be spared a repetition of his own
traumatic experience.

101.	Map 2
AIRCRAFT:	Junkers Ju 88
CREW:	(Unidentified)
UNIT:	(Unidentified)
PLACE:	Approximately 150 metres south-west of Zammitello Palace, Mgarr
DATE/TIME:	6 July 1942/0336-0440 hours

There were two alerts during the night of 5/6 July, the
second commencing at 0336 and lasting just over an hour as
a dozen aircraft crossed the coast individually before dropping
bombs in various locations. A Beaufighter of 89 Squadron,
crewed by Pilot Officer Neville Reeves and Sergeant Arthur
'Mike' O'Leary, accounted for one Ju 88 that crashed in a
field close to Zammitello Palace, on the outskirts of Mgarr.
At least two bodies were found near the wreckage.[205]

102.	Map 3
AIRCRAFT:	Supermarine Spitfire (AB500 or BR165)
PILOT:	Flight Sergeant David Ferraby (or) Flight Sergeant Thurne Parks
UNIT:	185 (or) 249 Squadron
PLACE:	Ta'San Gwakkin, limits of Qormi
DATE/TIME:	7 July 1942/0730-0810 hours

103.	Map 3
AIRCRAFT:	Supermarine Spitfire (AB500 or BR165)
PILOT:	(As above)
UNIT:	(As above)
PLACE:	Near the Chapel of Our Lady of the Abandoned, Zebbug
DATE/TIME:	(As above)

Eleven Spitfires of 249 Squadron and six of 185 were scrambled at 0730 on 7 July as up to a dozen Ju 88s approached, escorted by a large number of Bf 109s and MC 202s. At Luqa a Beaufort was destroyed and two more damaged. One airman sustained slight injuries. In the air, four enemy fighters were claimed destroyed and two others plus a Ju 88 damaged. Actual Axis losses are not known, but the RAF lost three Spitfires, two of which were shot down by fighters. Flight Sergeant David 'Nick' Ferraby of 185 Squadron abandoned AB500 and parachuted to safety near Zebbug, while 249's Flight Sergeant Bob Middlemiss, in BR251, came down off the coast from where he was later rescued. Another 249 Squadron Spitfire was hit by anti-aircraft fire, Flight Sergeant Thurne 'Tommy' Parks baling out of BR165 and landing in the same town as Ferraby. All three pilots were injured.

Ferraby later described his own involvement in this action:

First two Spits to take off left a dust cloud right down the take off track . . . I took off by myself as close to the dust cloud as I could . . . My Number Two failed to take off due to dust. I hoped I would be able to join up with some other Spits, but as was often the case, I didn't see a plane in the sky and climbed to 10,000 feet by myself. I can't have kept a good enough look-out, because there was a loud bang and flames belted into the right side of cockpit. Hood was open (we mostly flew with them open for better visibility), I pulled harness release handle and shot half out cockpit. I have very long legs and my knees jammed on rim of windscreen. Still got the scars. So I had to pull myself back in and straighten my legs. Parachute had caught on head pad, which stuck out a few inches behind one's head. Plane was going down at about 45°

with engine still on. Forgot to shut throttle and there was no control from stick. Anyway, I got out in the end and pulled rip cord. I much enjoyed floating down and saw a Spit circling me. Turned out it was [Flight Sergeant William] Dodd, Canadian and a good pal. Just missed a 10 foot wall in a village. 'Chute went over the wall and I landed in a lane. I suppose all the women who gathered round didn't know if I was English or Jerry, but they kept touching my bleeding knees for some reason. Burns were just down my right leg from knee down. I'd been flying in shorts and gym shoes.[206]

Records show that one of the Spitfires came down near Zebbug and the other near Qormi, but according to Ferraby:

As far as I can tell, my Spitfire, after I'd baled out, showed a plume of smoke for a while and flew itself, gradually losing height, till it more or less landed in the sea somewhere: I should think on the south-east side of the island.[207]

An altogether different opinion is held by Zebbug resident, John Galea:

I am positive that both David Ferraby and his Spitfire fell in the same area, David against a wall in a narrow street . . . and his plane in a field not far from his fall . . . a woman who was a girl then . . . told me that she remembers seeing the plane going round in circles at speed until it crashed in a low-lying field beside a chapel . . . I saw David sitting in a RAF jeep with those who came to pick him up just off the church.[208]

In September 1998, wreckage found in a field directly below the Chapel of Our Lady of the Abandoned, on the outskirts of Zebbug, provided indisputable evidence that an aircraft had indeed crashed where John Galea said. Was it Ferraby's or Parks'? Or have events been confused with those of 6 May 1942, when Flight Lieutenant Hugh Johnston of 126 Squadron baled out of Spitfire VC BR116 which also come down in the area?

104. Map 3
AIRCRAFT: Cant-Z.1007 Bis
CREW: Tenente Francesco Antonelli (Pilot), Sottotenente (or Tenente) Giovanni
Casadio (Probably Second Pilot), Primo Aviere Gaetano Pisarra,
(Probably) Aviere Scelto Giuseppe Buratti, (Probably) Sergente Calogero
Dragotta
UNIT: 60ª Squadriglia, 33º Gruppo, 9º Stormo Bombardamento
PLACE: Ta'Brija Street, Siggiewi, and limits of Ta'l-Ghasfur
DATE/TIME: 7 July 1942/1716–1741 hours

The third and last daylight raid of 7 July was a short but
violent affair that began at 1716 with the approach of five
high level Cant-Z.1007s and the usual fighter escort. These
crossed the coast at Marfa and proceeded to the south-east
of Malta before bombing. Two civilians and a soldier were
wounded by AA splinters; Lance Bombardier Francis Vella
of 3rd Light Anti-Aircraft Regiment Royal Malta
Artillery, died of his injuries soon after. Of at least fifteen
Spitfires airborne during the attack, two 185 Squadron
machines were lost together with Flight Sergeants Haydn
Haggas and Peter Terry, one of whom probably fell to
Reggiane pilot Maresciallo Olindo Simionato of 150ª
Squadriglia.[209] Flight Sergeant Jack Yarra of 185 Squadron
escaped injury when his aircraft was damaged in combat,
though not before he had claimed two Re 2001s destroyed.
Pilot Officer W.L. Miller of 126 Squadron and Flight
Sergeant J.E. MacNamara of 185 were credited with
damaging one and two Cants respectively, and heavy AA
with one Cant destroyed. In fact, one MC 202 of 353ª
Squadriglia was shot down (probably by Yarra) and its pilot,
Tenente Fabrizio Cherubini, killed, while a Cant-Z.1007
Bis piloted by Tenente Francesco Antonelli was hit by AA
and blew up over Siggiewi; some of the wreckage landed
on a house in the town and injured a civilian, and other
parts fell nearby at Ta'l-Ghasfur. Four of the five-man crew
were seen to leave the aircraft, but their parachutes
apparently either failed to deploy or were rendered useless
by AA fire. There were no survivors from the 60ª
Squadriglia machine.

105.   Map 5
AIRCRAFT: Supermarine Spitfire (BR108)
PILOT: Flight Lieutenant Lester Sanders
UNIT: 603 Squadron
PLACE: In sea, Marsalforn Bay, Gozo
DATE/TIME: 8 July 1942/0732–0800 hours

Malta's first raid on 8 July began shortly after 0730 and involved seven Ju 88s and a number of fighters. Bombs were dropped at Siggiewi and on and near Luqa aerodrome where a Beaufighter was slightly damaged. Eight Spitfires of 603 Squadron and several of 126 were already airborne and were joined at 0740 by eight more Spitfires of 249 Squadron. Nine pilots claimed three Bf 109s destroyed, one probable and several fighters and bombers damaged. Luftwaffe records indicate that all its aircraft returned to base. However, the RAF reported the loss of two Spitfires.

After being scrambled at 0630, Flight Lieutenant Lester Sanders led 603 Squadron's B Flight to intercept the raid. When it arrived an hour later, Pilot Officer Edward Glazebrook attacked two Ju 88s before his guns jammed. Another bomber was claimed damaged by Pilot Officer Dudley Newman. Flight Sergeant James Ballantyne and Flying Officer Richard Mitchell were also each credited with a Bf 109 damaged while Flight Lieutenant Sanders and, apparently, Pilot Officer Neville King attacked a Messerschmitt, which was seen to emit black smoke. The pair then turned their attention to some Ju 88s which were returning to Sicily. Sanders attacked one, whereupon the armoured windscreen of his aircraft was hit by retaliatory fire. The Spitfires disengaged. By this time they were perilously low and, in turning, the wing of King's aircraft dipped into the sea causing the fighter to spin out of control and disappear with the pilot into the Mediterranean.

Sanders was now set upon by a pair of Bf 109s that proceeded to chase him at low level around Gozo. Finally, with the engine hit in the glycol coolant system and in imminent danger of seizing due to overheating, Sanders was forced to ditch in Gozo's Marsalforn Bay. Overhead, the victors circled the scene as Sanders struggled to escape his rapidly sinking Spitfire.[210] The Germans made no attempt to intervene, allowing a small boat to put out to rescue the pilot, whose only injury was a bruised eye caused when he hit his face on the gunsight during the crash.

Spitfire VC BR108 remained submerged in only 10 metres of water until the summer of 1973 when the engine, cockpit section and port wing were recovered, parts of which are now displayed in Malta's National War Museum.

106.	Map 3
AIRCRAFT:	Junkers Ju 88 (5513/3Z+ET?)
CREW:	Unteroffizier Herbert Schlitt (Pilot?), Unteroffizier Josef Forster (Observer?), Gefreiter (or Obergefreiter) Andreas Pollack (Wireless Operator?), Unteroffizier Franz Schmiedl (Air Gunner?)
UNIT:	9/Kampfgeschwader 77
PLACE:	Callus Street, Mosta
DATE/TIME:	9 July 1942/0852–0923 hours

Shortly before 0900 on 9 July, six Ju 88s, escorted by an estimated twenty fighters, raided Ta'Qali where an airman was wounded and a bus destroyed. Up to twenty-four Spitfires were airborne, two pilots each claiming a Ju 88 damaged. Another bomber was hit by AA, one of the crew baling out only to have his parachute catch on the tail of the doomed aircraft which crashed in flames in Callus Street, Mosta, demolishing several houses. There were no survivors from Unteroffizier Herbert Schlitt's 9/KG 77 Ju 88.

107.	Map 3
AIRCRAFT:	Junkers Ju 88 (6579/3Z+FS?)
CREW:	Feldwebel Karl Bonk (Pilot?), Unteroffizier Johann Gerstel (Observer?), Unteroffizier Gerhard Priewisch (Wireless Operator?), Unteroffizier Josef Pohl (Air Gunner?)
UNIT:	8/Kampfgeschwader 77
PLACE:	Near the junction of Salvu Sacco and Nerik Xerri Streets, Kirkop
DATE/TIME:	20 July 1942/2346 hours

There were two raids during the night of 20/21 July, the second between 2252 and 0025 when at least eight aircraft crossed the coast. These proceeded individually towards their targets, bombing Zejtun, Luqa, Safi and Hal Far. The crew of a Beaufighter, airborne from the previous raid, reported seeing one aircraft flying 1,000 feet above and in the opposite direction to themselves, but were unable to intercept. However, three Ju 88s were claimed by AA gunners, as related by Lance Bombardier Stan Fraser:

Last night we witnessed a fine example of the co-operation which has developed between the forces on this island.

The moon is nearing the half now and so the enemy's night activity is increasing. At about 1030 pm – I was writing by the light of a candle at the time – the siren sounded, heralding the approach of the enemy raiders and after a short interval I heard the drone of their engines overhead.

Upon going out into the moonlight I could see the target, already illuminated at the apex of a concentration of searchlight beams. The moon was almost full and, with the searchlights, caused a beautiful pool of light to be reflected in the waters of the bay below. I ran for my camera, and placed it in a good position to take a time exposure by the aid of this light and also by the lights of the guns which intermittently flashed, as the enemy planes were greeted by the gunners. Within a minute of the plane being caught in the beams, it crashed near the centre of the island and burst into flame. I took a photo just as it crashed.[211]

The 8/KG 77 machine demolished a building on the western edge of Kirkop and all four crewmen were killed (their remains being 'buried at sea' at Wied iz-Zurrieq).[212]

No sooner had this plane crashed than another was caught in the beams as it crossed the coast near the OP. I thought I could see a trace of smoke trail as it passed overhead, maybe it was the exhaust fumes, but as the AA shells burst around him he took strong avoiding action, let his bombs drop – they glistened in the beams as they fell – and then he dived straight down one beam and on into the sea, where he burst into flame on the water. Two victims within about ten minutes!

Still another came in by the same way as the others and, as before, was caught and held in the beams, but not before several flares had been dropped over the bay, followed by several bombs one of which, unfortunately, wiped out a Bofors gun detachment on the edge of the water.[213]

Lance Sergeant Fidele Zarb MM and Gunners Saviour Sillato, Francis Baldacchino, Albert Zammit, Joseph Ellul and Francis Agius of 3rd Light Anti-Aircraft Regiment Royal Malta Artillery were all killed when their gun post (XLS 31) received a direct hit, while Gunner Gauci, duty telephonist at B Troop headquarters, was seriously wounded. (Corporal William Hearl of 2nd Battalion The Devonshire Regiment, was also killed while visiting a Beach Patrol in the area.)

Their deaths were avenged, however, when this third plane was brought down into the sea just off Delimara Point, causing another large spread of flame over the water.

AA were responsible for definitely two of these victims, if not the third, which may have been lamed by a night fighter out at sea. However, the fact remains that it was a very creditable feat and a spectacle worth remembering.[214]

Two of the Ju 88s destroyed were credited to HAA and the third jointly to HAA and LAA. XHB 8, a gun position of 4th HAA Regiment located at Il-Mara (Benghisa), claimed two of the bombers. Searchlights were also instrumental in the night's work, the operators being highly praised in a letter to Brigadier C.J. Woolley from Major General C.T. Beckett MC, Commander Royal Artillery:

Will you please convey my congratulations to the 4th SL Regiment, RA and RMA for the excellent work they did on the night 20–21 July. They were not only very quick in initial pick-up, but once picked up, the drill for holding the targets which took great evasive action was excellent. As you know, three aircraft were destroyed that night, I am sure that not one of these would have been destroyed had it not been for Searchlight work. It was a great show of team work and drill co-operation. I am very pleased.[215]

108.	Map 3
AIRCRAFT:	Junkers Ju 88 (140247/M7+KH?)
CREW:	Leutnant Sepp Hörmann (Pilot), Obergefreiter Josef Popp (Observer),
	Leutnant Heinz Heuser (Wireless Operator), Unteroffizier Wolfram Quass (Air
	Gunner)
UNIT:	Kampfgruppe 806
PLACE:	Mnajdra/Hagar Qim (south coast)
DATE/TIME:	24 July 1942/1039–1115 hours

Twenty-four Spitfires, drawn equally from 1435 Flight, 126 and 185 Squadrons, were scrambled between 1015 and 1040 on Friday, 24 July, to intercept five Ju 88s escorted by approximately twenty fighters. Two Spitfires of 603 Squadron were also ordered up as minesweeper protection. Three bombers and a Bf 109 were claimed destroyed by the RAF, and a number of machines probably destroyed or damaged. Among those involved in the action was Pilot Officer Roderick Smith, a Canadian in 126 Squadron, who claimed his first enemy aircraft shot down:

> We were vectored onto five Ju 88s coming south at 18,000 feet. We met them at their height virtually over the centre of the island. Their fighter escort was lagging badly behind them. They were several hundred yards to our left. I was on the front left corner of our formation of eight, and therefore nearest to them. I began my 180 degree turn to port, to get in behind them, slightly ahead of the rest of our pilots. I came in behind and made a port quarter attack on the one on the extreme left of their formation, which was the nearest one of course.
>
> My Spitfire was a tropical VB, each of its two cannons having 60 round drums . . . Its four Brownings had been ripped out immediately on arrival in Malta, being almost ridiculous because they were .303 and not .50 (less than one quarter the weight of the latter) and couldn't penetrate the armour which was installed in all military aircraft in 1940. Ripping them out eliminated 200lb of weight, but the considerable installation drag of their many little bumps and holes remained.
>
> I chose the port engine of the 88 to start with (a bigger target from behind than a 109 in fact) and fired a six

second burst, from 250 yards closing to 150, emptying both drums. The port engine immediately streamed black and white smoke and caught fire, and I shifted my aim to the wing root and then the fuselage, both of which became enveloped in flames. (Glycol gave off white smoke, fuel black; the white didn't last long as there were only a few gallons of glycol for each engine.) The whiteness of fuel-fed flames surprised me, as I had thought they would be orange. Many pieces came off the aircraft. When I finished firing I broke violently down into a diving aileron turn to the left, and kept in it until my ailerons hardened up, my speed being well over 400 mph by then. When I came out of the dive I was all alone and saw the 88 coming down streaming fire and smoke in a great downward arc to the south. I then noticed a parachute high up over the centre of the island, and I could see the figure of a man in it. I hadn't noticed anyone bale out but some of the pieces coming off the aircraft were quite large, and it was hard to distinguish between them and a man while concentrating on firing. I was back on the ground in a mere two or three minutes, my entire sortie being logged as 20 minutes.[216]

Rod Smith's older brother, Jerrold, also a Pilot Officer in 126 Squadron, noted in his diary:

Got off late on a scramble. Joined the others just as they attacked the Bombers. Started to aim at Port JU 88, when Rod opened fire, it went down in flames. Moved over to next one and opened fire, putting port engine aflame. Was hit in glycol and force landed on Luqa (third time this month). A Sergeant saw my JU 88 go into the sea.[217]

Rod's own account continues:

126 Squadron's dispersal was along the west-south-west quadrant of Luqa. We could see almost the whole of Malta from there. The arc of black smoke the 88 had trailed behind it remained in the air for quite a long time. The wreckage burned for a very long time, giving off a pillar of black smoke all the while. The ground crew brought me a burnt piece of aluminium sheeting they said had

fluttered down to the aerodrome from the 88. The
parachute seemed to take ages to come down, and it
drifted slowly to the north. As it got close to the ground it
disappeared behind a low ridge to the north-west.[218]

The parachutist was twenty-year-old Leutnant Heinz
Heuser, who merited a special mention in the RAF
interrogation report.

The crew contained 2 Lieutenants one a pilot, the other
Heuser the W/T Operator. This unusual feature results
from the fact that until recently (probably 29/6/42)
Heuser was ground staff officer (W/T). From June to
December 1941, he was on the Russian Front and in
November 1941 had his last leave at home in Germany. In
the beginning of 1941 he was sent to Pantellaria where he
worked for 2 months on the W/T Staff. He first started
operational flying from Sicily from where he had made 11
flights over Malta, some by day and some by night.

According to the same document:

The P/W's Junker was at 15,000 feet in formation when it
was attacked from the port side and below by a Spitfire
with the result that an engine was hit, the machine caught
fire and only the P/W . . . was able to bale out.[219]

The similarities between this account and those of the two
brothers indicate that Rod Smith was responsible for
destroying Heuser's aircraft. However, other Spitfires of 185
Squadron were also involved in attacking the formation,
Sergeants Claude Weaver and A. Drew sharing one Ju 88
destroyed, and Sergeant Leonard Reid being credited with
one destroyed, the latter recording:

Intercepted four Ju 88s together with large fighter escort.
Dived straight down on one at a 45 degree angle, opening
up with cannon at 500 yards closing in to 100 yards,
giving one long burst. Hit top of cockpit and starboard
engine which immediately gave off black smoke and [it]
went into a spin. One Ju 88 destroyed.[220]

It will be noted that when Rod Smith commenced his attack there were five Ju 88s, but by the time 185 Squadron became involved, there were just four. Certainly, one Ju 88 was brought down on land, between the ancient ruins of Mnajdra and Hagar Qim and yet the RAF interrogation report states that Heuser's aircraft crashed in the sea. This, and Jerry Smith's account, would suggest that at least two bombers were destroyed. If this were so, which of these came down on land? Rod Smith believes that the Ju 88 he attacked, 'crashed about midway and a bit south of a line between Luqa and Rabat . . . about a mile south-west of Siggiewi and therefore about three miles south-west of Luqa'.[221] The area of Mnajdra/Hagar Qim is on the south coast, one and three quarter miles south of Siggiewi, three and a half miles south-west of Luqa village, and considerably less from Luqa aerodrome.

In an obvious reference to Heuser's Ju 88 the Malta police reported: 'Enemy bomber crashed in flames in fields in the limits of Qrendi. One crew member landed, slightly injured, taken away by Military ambulance; two others found dead in the aircraft.'[222]

Howard Bell thought there were no survivors from the aircraft brought down close to his gun position (XHB 10) although, as his testimony shows, it must have been difficult to assess just how many died in the crash: 'We picked up remnants of bodies in sandbags, the crash and explosion was so bad . . . no one could have survived.'[223]

In 1990, Rod Smith was amazed to receive a telephone call from Heuser, who had sought to contact the pilot responsible for shooting him down forty-eight years previously: 'Heinz's first words to me were, "You saved my life!" I'm sure he was right, but I didn't tell him that was not my intention. I'm very glad it happened though. I was always glad to see enemy aircrew bale out; I was always keen to destroy enemy aircraft but not their crews.'[224]

A list of German aircrew buried in Malta and later exhumed for reinterment in Sicily includes a Leutnant Hermann Zepp, who died on 25 July 1942. This is obviously Heuser's pilot, whose body was either identified from the remains recovered at Mnajdra, or else found some distance from the crash site (thereby supporting the police view that only two of the crew were found dead in the wreckage). No further information is available with regard to a second Ju 88 brought down on this date.

109.	Map 5
AIRCRAFT:	Macchi C.202 (MM7842)
PILOT:	Sergente Maggiore Faliero Gelli
UNIT:	378ª Squadriglia, 155° Gruppo, 51° Stormo Caccia Terrestre
PLACE:	Between Dabrani and Ta'Kuljat, limits of Zebbug (Gozo)
DATE/TIME:	27 July 1942/0915 hours

There were ten air-raid warnings on Monday 27 July. The third sounded at 0912 as nine Ju 88s were escorted to their targets by German and Italian fighters. Eight Spitfires of 126 Squadron were still airborne from the previous alert. These were soon joined by eight more of 185 Squadron and at least five from 249. Two 603 Squadron aircraft were also scrambled to provide cover for a Catalina flyingboat.

Both 126 and 249 Squadrons sighted the Ju 88s, but were unable to reach them in time to prevent Ta'Qali from being bombed, as a result of which the aerodrome was rendered temporarily unserviceable. Afterwards, 126 Squadron was able to catch up with the bombers, claiming one probably destroyed and two damaged.

185 Squadron headed north from Kalafrana, but also failed to intercept the Ju 88s. The Spitfires then turned back, claiming a Bf 109 destroyed south of Gozo. Meanwhile, 249 Squadron had flown south-west of the Island where they met the enemy fighter escort turning north-west. Two MC 202s and three Bf 109s were claimed shot down, and a Bf 109 damaged.

At least two Macchis were actually destroyed, as described by Canadian Sergeant George 'Screwball' Beurling of 249 Squadron, a remarkable fighter pilot who was to claim twenty-six and a third aircraft destroyed during four months of operations:

I spotted four Macchis running in line astern and took Number Four. They saw me coming and pulled into a climbing turn to the right. As they did I came up on my man's starboard quarter and let him have a burst. it was a straight deflection shot which went into his engine and radiator. He flicked into a spin, but managed to pull out and crash-landed on Gozo . . .

A second or so later I got Number Three exactly the same way. The poor devil simply blew to pieces in the air.[225]

Sergente Faliero Gelli of 378ª Squadriglia crash-landed in a field below Ta'Kuljat, in Gozo, where the injured pilot was captured. Beurling's second victim was Capitano Furio Doglio Niclot, commander of 151ª Squadriglia, who was killed.

The rudder of Gelli's machine was soon dismantled and the 'Cat and Mice' emblem of 51° Stormo CT cut from the fuselage. Later, Beurling posed with the trophies in what is probably his best-known photograph.

110.	Map 4
AIRCRAFT:	Junkers Ju 88 (14075/3Z+HP?)
CREW:	Unteroffizier Albert Führer (Pilot), Gefreiter Peter Bolten (Observer), Unteroffizier Karl Max Bauer (Wireless Operator), Unteroffizier Gustav Frick (Gunner)
UNIT:	II/Kampfgeschwader 77
PLACE:	Wolseley Camp (near Il-Biez), limits of Marsaxlokk
DATE/TIME:	28 July 1942/1745 hours

At least three Ju 88s and about a dozen fighters crossed the coast between 1741 and 1747 hours on 28 July. Spitfires of 126, 185 and 1435 Squadrons intercepted, shooting down all the bombers and also claiming a Bf 109 destroyed. It would appear that two, possibly three, of the Junkers crashed into the sea while another came down on land.[226] According to the RAF Daily Intelligence Summary, Squadron Leader Anthony Lovell of 1435 Squadron, Pilot Officer John Mejor of the same unit, and Wing Commander George Stainforth of 89 Squadron flying, on this occasion, with 1435, all shared in the destruction of a Ju 88 along with 126 Squadron's Pilot Officer Rod Smith. Another bomber was shared between Pilot Officers J. (Paul) Baril and James Guthrie of 185 Squadron, and Sergeants A. Tiddy and Nigel Park of 126, and a third between Pilot Officers Bill Thompson, Jerrold Smith and F.D. Thomas, Flight Sergeant Gordon Farquharson and Flying Officer Ripley Jones, all of 126 Squadron.[227]

Rod Smith recalled:

This 88 was my second enemy aircraft destroyed. In the late afternoon the squadron, while being vectored north-east at 18,000 feet, intercepted three escorted Ju 88s heading west over Kalafrana Bay at the same height. We turned left into them and this time I was on the side farthest away and therefore last into them. One of the 109 escort came right down among us blazing away but we ignored him. As was common, most of our pilots attacked the nearest 88. The one on the left side of their formation, and a couple of them attacked the one in the centre. Both of them caught fire and started down in seconds. I flew across and opened fire at the port engine of the one on the far side, which no one else had attacked.

I was flying a Mark VC, all of which originally arrived in Malta with four cannon but had had two ripped out on arrival because a single Merlin couldn't possibly throw four cannons around with any panache. Each cannon was belt-fed with 120 rounds, good for 12 seconds of fire. The port engine of my 88 caught fire immediately, and I carried my aim into the port wing root and then the fuselage, and then the starboard engine, all of which also caught fire. The aircraft headed downwards but I kept firing for the full 12 seconds. Finally the engines came out, the wings fell off, and all the burning pieces fell like a shower of golden rain . . .

I think that firing all my ammunition in one 12 second burst was an emotional reaction from being fired upon so often before, with rarely a chance to fire myself. (The 109 F, which was the one the Huns used at that time, went much faster and went higher and got up there faster than we could.) A 12 second burst was unnecessary and very dangerous because every second spent looking through a gunsight when there were enemy fighters around was a second you were not watching your tail. I resolved never to fire longer than necessary in the future and I kept that resolution.

I was amazed to find later that three of the crew got out. They must have been quick off the mark, perhaps put on their toes by the other two 88s going down seconds before. I hadn't noticed them among the big pieces that were coming off all the time . . .'[228]

The combat report of Pilot Officer Guthrie shows that he also attacked the same aircraft:

I was flying Green two in a section of three. We climbed to 22,000 feet South of Zonker [Zonqor], and sighted three Ju 88s coming in at about 18,000 feet. All Green section dived towards these aircraft over Hal Far, but by the time we got near them, two had already been shot down. I delivered a short *head-on* attack on the remaining Ju 88 closing to 50 yards, and then pulled left on a climbing turn. When I completed the turn, the Ju 88 was going down in pieces. The Ju 88 was already damaged when I attacked it.[229]

Rod's brother in 126 Squadron, Pilot Officer Jerry Smith reported:

Turned port into bombers. Fired from 200 yards closing at port 88 a two or three second burst and aircraft immediately burst into flames around port engine and front of fuselage. It turned to port and down.
I turned into the middle Ju 88 and fired a short burst and saw a trail of white smoke but cannot remember from which engine it came.
Observed the starboard 88 going down almost vertically in flames. Also saw four Spits chasing an 88 at deck level 5 miles SE of Kalafrana, which trailed white smoke, turned to port and crashed into the sea.[230]

The four Spitfires chasing the Ju 88 were almost certainly from 1435 Squadron. In his combat report, Wing Commander Stainforth claimed that Squadron Leader Lovell 'dived on a Ju 88 *which was then untouched* flying East, followed by the rest of the section . . .' Two crew members were seen to bale out before Stainforth commenced the first of two attacks, following which the aircraft, 'went into a spiral dive in flames . . .'[231]
Was this bomber one of the first two targeted by 126 Squadron which, perhaps, had dived in an attempt to escape,

before being set upon by 1435 Squadron? If, by this time, the damaged glycol tank was empty and any flames had been extinguished in the dive, there may not have been any smoke or other obvious sign that the aircraft had already been attacked. Another explanation, of course, is that this was a separate Ju 88.

Rod Smith remembered that, 'three or four minutes after 126's three 88s had gone down, when I was approaching Luqa to land, I heard Tony [Lovell] and other 1435 pilots on the R/T calling to each other in some kind of drawn-out affray . . .'[232]

Of further significance is the combat report of Jerry Smith, who also recorded in his diary that the three Ju 88s intercepted by 126 Squadron, 'were in flames within fifteen seconds and a fourth 88 was shot down'.[233]

On the basis of available information it does seem that on this occasion the RAF DIS is mistaken in its claims assessment. It appears that Sergeants Tiddy and Park, Pilot Officers Thompson, Jerry Smith and Thomas, Flight Sergeant Farquharson and Flying Officer Jones all participated in the destruction of the first or second Ju 88; Pilot Officers Rod Smith, Guthrie and, probably, Baril attacked the third, while Squadron Leader Lovell, Pilot Officer Mejor and Wing Commander Stainforth shared in the shooting down of what seems to have been another machine altogether.

At Kalafrana, Leading Aircraftman Phil Chandler recorded in his diary that he observed the third bomber coming down, 'on, fire, right above. One of the crew baled out, but his parachute only half opened and he would be lucky to get away with his life. The machine hit some buildings on the other side of the bay and became a huge mass of flames . . . one of two more parachutists hit the sea not far out.'[234]

This was without doubt the Ju 88 singled out by Pilot Officer Rod Smith. When the aircraft began to break up after his attack, he watched as pieces fell 'into Kalafrana Bay, I would say midway between . . . Kalafrana and Birzebbuga, but a quarter to half a mile from the shore.'[235]

After scattering a trail of debris as it crossed Marsaxlokk Bay in a north-easterly direction, the remains of the II/KG 77 machine crashed at Wolseley Camp, one mile north of

Delimara in the south-east of the Island. The W/T operator, Unteroffizier Karl Max Bauer and gunner, Unteroffizier Gustav Frick, both baled out into the sea from where they were picked up by Seaplane Tender 338 from Kalafrana. The pilot, Unteroffizier Albert Führer and observer, Gefreiter Peter Bolton, were killed. One was found near Fort Tas-Silg after his parachute failed to deploy. The body was kept overnight at an army post but quickly began to decompose in the scorching weather, much to the disgust of the post's occupants and the next morning was buried at sea off Il-Qali.

111.	Map 2
AIRCRAFT:	Supermarine Spitfire (BR362)
PILOT:	Pilot Officer James Guthrie
UNIT:	185 Squadron
PLACE:	Limits of Zebbieh
DATE/TIME:	2 August 1942/1414–1445 hours

There was a half-hour alert at 1412 on 2 August when a number of fighters and up to four high-level bombers were reported to be approaching Malta. However, 15 miles from Gozo the bombers turned north, leaving only the fighters to continue. Twenty-five Spitfires intercepted the raid and a number of dog-fights took place over Gozo and Comino with claims by both sides. 185 Squadron lost two Spitfires, one possibly falling to Oberleutnant Gerhard Michalski of 4/JG 53, and the other to Leutnant Karl Eberle of 2/JG 77.[236] Sergeant Matthew McLeod, a New Zealander, was reported missing in Spitfire VC BR321 while Pilot Officer James Guthrie was killed in BR362, which crashed in a field midway between Zebbieh and Dwejra Lines.

112.	Map 4
AIRCRAFT:	Supermarine Spitfire (EN973)
PILOT:	Pilot Officer George Beurling
UNIT:	249 Squadron
PLACE:	Ta'Salib, limits of Gudja
DATE/TIME:	8 August 1942/1050 hours

Seven Spitfires of 249 Squadron were scrambled soon after 0930 on 8 August. Two were obliged to return early, leaving

Blue Section with three aircraft. Shortly afterwards, Blue Section, consisting of Pilot Officer Frank Jones, Sergeant Ernie Budd and newly promoted Pilot Officer George Beurling, sighted six Bf 109s overhead and turned towards them, whereupon two others swept in to attack the Spitfires from behind. Eight more Messerschmitts then joined the fight. The Spitfires spiralled down to 10,000 feet, turning into the enemy fighters, the action continuing to 500 feet during which Blue Two (Sergeant Budd) claimed to have damaged a Bf 109, before being shot up and wounded in the shoulder. He broke in front of Pilot Officer Jones, closely followed by his assailant, who was fired at by the section leader before he was, in turn, attacked. At about the same time, Blue Three (Pilot Officer Beurling) also hit a Bf 109; the latter pair of Messerschmitts were observed to dive towards the sea, streaming glycol. Beurling described what happened next:

I hadn't any more than begun to dive when I got mine – a couple of bullets right in the engine. The throttle wouldn't grab hold and after a minute or so the engine decided it would like to call it a day and seize up. There was I, spang in the middle of a skyful of Jerries, and my motive power gone lame!

A couple of Huns were perched above me, slightly off to one side, but didn't see me, thank God, or I'd have been cold turkey for them. I didn't dare call Jonesey on the R/T and tell him my plight, or he'd have quit the dogfight of which he was the centre of attraction and come hurrying over to help me – bringing all his friends with him, no doubt. Over to the north I could see Georgia split-assing all over heaven, entertaining four or five Jerries. No use calling him, either. So I decided to quietly get the hell out of there – if I could.

The old Merlin wouldn't give me any more than 160 miles an hour and was heating up fast. The Spit was sinking slowly. It began to look like a baling job. Thank God, the Huns didn't seem to have registered my departure! By the time I reached the Maltese coast I was down to 2,000 feet and doubting strongly my ability to get home. I prepared to bale. That's what orders tell you to do, if in trouble below 3,000 feet and not over an aerodrome. Then I made the discovery that my parachute straps were pretty loose and said to myself: "If you ever try jumping into that rig, you're going to rupture yourself when the umbrella opens my friend!" Before that I'd undone my Sutton harness, to free myself from the cockpit, and by the time I'd snapped it on again, so as not to fall forward in a crash landing, I'd lost another big piece of height and was skipping cross-country about 200 feet above the ground. By this time the engine was finished and the prop dead. Right ahead I could see a nice ploughed field, about an acre in size, surrounded by low stone walls. If I could sneak into that I'd be okay.

I skithered along, cutting the glide fine, but not too fine. It's damned easy to flick these Spits and spin in when you try keeping that nose high. As I came close in over the near wall I put the left wing down on the ground. The wing absorbed the wallop and stopped me cold, which was okay by me. The far wall was too near for comfort. I climbed out, unhurt except for a superficial cut in one arm, and looked the ship over. She had taken little damage, apart from those bullets in the engine.[237]

Nevertheless, Beurling's Spitfire VB EN973 was a complete write-off. One other Spitfire was shot down, the pilot, Sergeant Clarence Kelly of 1435 Squadron (scrambled at 1020), being reported missing. Sergeant Budd, in spite of his injury, managed to land safely. The Luftwaffe claimed one Spitfire shot down by Oberfeldwebel Herbert Rollwage of 5/JG 53, while Oberleutnant Siegfried Freytag and Feldwebel Otto Pohl, both of I/JG 77, were apparently each credited with a Curtiss P-40![238]

Luftwaffe losses fail to substantiate the two Bf 109s claimed destroyed by Beurling and Jones.

113.	Map 3
AIRCRAFT:	Vickers Wellington (DV542)
CREW:	Pilot Officer Douglas Shepherd (Pilot?), Sergeant John Maslin (Second Pilot?), Sergeant Harry Fox (Wireless Operator/Air Gunner), Sergeant Keith Thompson (Wireless Operator/Air Gunner), Sergeant Jacob Langley (Air Gunner)

UNIT: (Probably) 221 Squadron
PLACE: Tal-Ibrag, between Zebbug and Luqa
DATE/TIME: 13 August 1942/0500 hours

'Pedestal' was the codename for the most famous of the
Malta convoys and resulted in the delivery of around 32,000
tons of supplies, as well as thirty-seven Spitfires flown off
HMS *Furious*. Of the fourteen merchant vessels involved,
only the *Rochester Castle*, *Melbourne Star*, *Port Chalmers*,
Brisbane Star and *Ohio* reached Malta. The *Deucalion*, *Empire
Hope*, *Clan Ferguson*, *Waimarama*, *Almeria Lykes*, *Wairangi*,
Glenorchy, *Santa Elisa* and *Dorset* were lost, together with the
carrier HMS *Eagle*, the cruisers *Cairo* and *Manchester*, and the
destroyer *Foresight*. As many as 387 seamen are believed to
have died, as well as 28 Fleet Air Arm personnel and 25 men
of The Maritime Regiment Royal Artillery. The Royal Air
Force also suffered casualties, and heavy losses were sustained
by the Luftwaffe and the Regia Aeronautica, both of which
had been greatly reinforced for operations against
'Pedestal'.[239]

During the period 11–15 August, as 'Pedestal' steamed
eastward through the Mediterranean, ten or so Malta-based
aircraft were shot down, otherwise written-off, or damaged
while landing. The losses include a Wellington bomber
which was involved in two sorties against Còmiso aerodrome
during the night of 12/13 August. During the second
operation, it was probably damaged by flak, and on returning
to Luqa crashed on the dining hall of an airfield defence post
(LQ14) where it was burnt out. The rear-gunner, Sergeant
Harry Fox, was killed, while the remainder of the crew
sustained various injuries.

114.   Map 3
AIRCRAFT: Supermarine Spitfire (EP207)
PILOT: Flight Sergeant George Hogarth
UNIT: 249 Squadron
PLACE: 800 metres north of XHB 10 HAA gun position, limits of Qrendi
DATE/TIME: 14 August 1942/Approximately 1845 hours

At 1823 hours on 14 August, the air-raid sirens announced
the approach of at least a dozen enemy fighters. The RAF

was already providing air cover for the battered oil tanker *Ohio*, still struggling to reach Malta with her escort. Now, twelve Spitfires of 249 Squadron were also scrambled, the pilots reporting six Bf 109s, which they were unable to intercept, several thousand feet above Ta'Qali. About 15 minutes later, the Spitfires engaged three Bf 109s which were sighted at 22,000 feet, orbiting between Luqa and Hal Far. In the ensuing action, one Spitfire was shot down and claimed by Oberleutnant Gerhard Michalski of II/JG 53;[240] Canadian Flight Sergeant George Hogarth managing to bale out into the sea three miles east of Zonqor, where he was rescued by HSL 128. His Spitfire VB crashed on the south coast, 800 metres north of gun position XHB 10, and just south of the present-day Ta'San Niklaw reservoir, west of Qrendi. (Flight Sergeant Hogarth would be killed after being wounded and crash-landing his battle-damaged fighter in the same area less than two months later.)

115.	Map 4
AIRCRAFT:	Bristol Beaufort (DW805)
CREW:	Pilot Officer Ernest Moody (Pilot), Sergeant Griffith (Navigator?), Sergeant O. Pritchard (Wireless Operator/Air Gunner?), Sergeant S. Gill (Air Gunner?)
UNIT:	Overseas Aircraft Delivery Unit
PLACE:	In sea, 1,300 metres north of Ghar id-Duhhan, limits of Marsaskala
DATE/TIME:	21 August 1942/Approximately 0930 hours

Shortly after taking off to deliver a Beaufort to the Middle East on the morning of Friday 21 August, Pilot Officer Ernest Moody was obliged to return to Malta when the aircraft developed engine trouble. Unable to maintain height after the port engine failed, he successfully ditched the machine 1 kilometre off the north-east coast, the crew immediately taking to their dinghy. They were rescued by HSL 128 shortly afterwards.

In 1977, information provided by a local resident enabled a visiting seaman to locate the Beaufort with echo-sounding equipment. Members of the Island's RAF Sub Aqua Club, accompanied by representatives of the National War Museum, soon confirmed the aircraft type, but it would take many more dives and be another fifteen years before the identification of Beaufort Mk I DW805 was established

following the recovery of a shoebrush stamped with Ernest
Moody's pre-war airman's number. The retired Squadron
Leader was traced to his home in Cornwall, and, in October
1993, invited to RAF St Mawgan to be presented with the
shoebrush and other personal items he had last seen more
than fifty-one years before!

A foolhardy attempt to move DW805 to another location
in order to turn it into a tourist attraction further damaged
the already fragile wreck. It has since been broken up by
rough seas.

116.	Map 5
AIRCRAFT:	Junkers Ju 88
CREW:	Feldwebel Ernst Klaus (Pilot), Unteroffizier Franz Rohringer (Observer), Unteroffizier Kurt Klawitter (Wireless Operator), Unteroffizier Franz Diedl (or Riedl) (Air Gunner)
UNIT:	8/Kampfgeschwader 77
PLACE:	Ta'Tingi, limits of Xewkija, Gozo
DATE/TIME:	27 August 1942/0003–0104 hours

At eight minutes past midnight on 27 August, about a dozen
Ju 88s approached Malta and bombed Luqa, Safi, Hal Far,
Kirkop, Paola and Gharghur. One of the Junkers was
intercepted by a patrolling 89 Squadron Beaufighter crewed
by Squadron Leader Paul Evans and his observer, believed to
have been Flight Sergeant J.K. Houston. The pilot reported:

> I was scrambled at 2340 hours and climbed to Angels 15.
> Went over to FASHION[241] and received numerous vectors,
> eventually resulting in a contact. I closed in and identified
> as a Ju 88. I gave a short burst of cannon and machine gun
> at 150 yards and his starboard engine caught fire. He
> started to dive – I followed and saw only exhaust flames
> from port engine. I gave another short burst but missed,
> owing to violent evasive action. I closed in for a third time
> to 50 yards and gave a long burst. There were strikes all
> over and the port motor streamed glycol. About 1 minute
> later I saw an aircraft crash on Gozo.[242]

The 8/KG 77 machine came down at Ta'Tingi, just south of
Xewkija. The pilot, Feldwebel Ernst Klaus and radio operator,

Unteroffizier Kurt Klawitter were taken prisoner. The observer, Unteroffizier Franz Rohringer and gunner, Unteroffizier Franz Diedl (or Riedl) both perished in the crash.

117.	Map 4
AIRCRAFT:	Bristol Beaufighter (V8268)
CREW:	Flight Lieutenant John Waddingham (Pilot), Pilot Officer Alfred Cumbers (Observer)
UNIT:	89 Squadron
PLACE:	200 metres north-east of XHE 33 HAA gun position, limits of Naxxar
DATE/TIME:	26 September 1942/2005–2036 hours

There was one night alert on 26 September when, between 2005 and 2036 hours, two enemy bombers approached the Island and one dropped its bombs into the sea just north of Madliena. Two Beaufighters of 89 Squadron were airborne, one of which was obliged to return early. George Nottage, then a Flight Lieutenant in 89 Squadron, recalled:

Flight Lieutenant John Waddingham . . . had been my Flight Commander in 141 Squadron, where he was awarded the DFC. The manner of his death was a tragedy. He was scrambled at night and once he was clear of the Island, the AA was put to 'Guns Free', i.e. they could fire at any aircraft. 'Waddie' had an engine failure . . . but he was at height and was a highly competent pilot, so there was no problem. The AA was put to 'Guns Tight' i.e. fire only at aircraft identified as enemy. This was a well-established procedure and the message reached every gun site on the Island except, incredibly, a site on the approach to Luqa! As 'Waddie' came in at a few hundred feet with wheels and flaps down, this site opened up at him. They did not hit him but he decided it was safer to try and go round again, so he raised the wheels and flaps and opened up the good engine. There was insufficient height however, and he had to crash-land, which he did quite successfully, although the aircraft caught fire.

The Beaufighter crashed in a field south-east of Gharghur, not far from gun position XHE 33 of 10th HAA Regiment. Nottage continues:

The next day, I saw his navigator, Alf Cumbers, in hospital
and he described how he tried to get out but his top hatch
was jammed. As the flames came back he drew his pistol
to shoot himself as he had no intention of burning to
death. Then two soldiers came along, and seeing him in
the light of the flames, they started to kick the side of the
fuselage. By astonishing good fortune, they picked the
only spot that was free of 'clobber' and they were able to
reach in and help Alf out, quite badly burned though he
recovered okay.

Pilot Officer Cumbers undoubtedly owed his life to
Lieutenant C.J. Arnold RA and his men who carried out the
rescue in spite of the signal lights and ammunition exploding
around them. 'As he lay on the grass, Waddie, who had got
out through his top hatch with only minor burns, came
along and asked how Alf was, and seemed to be in good
spirits. That night, however, he died of shock.'[243]

Flying Officer Rod Smith had recently been admitted
with sinus trouble to Number 45 General Hospital at
St Patrick's.

I was with a dozen or so other officers in a . . . ward on
the upper floor which faced north or north-west and gave
an uninterrupted view of the bay.

The night of September 26/27 was beautiful and clear,
with a full moon or close to it. Although the moon was
behind us, it lit up everything to the north of us, and the
reflected light lit up the ward surprisingly well. Sometime
before midnight, when we were lying in our beds but still
awake, we heard an aircraft approaching from the north at
a very low altitude. Its engine sound was unfamiliar and it
seemed to be flying quite slowly.

A few of us rose and went to the windows. We saw a
Beaufighter which, though headed right in our direction,
was obviously going to pass about 50 feet over the
hospital. It was flying on one engine only . . . I had heard
that a Beaufighter had marginal performance on one
engine and I also knew there was a rocky ridge close
behind the hospital which rose quite far above its roof. I
realised the aircraft was doomed.

In a very few seconds a brilliant flash lit up the whole area and in another second or two the engine sound stopped abruptly . . .

In a surprisingly short time the pilot and the AI operator were brought into the ward on wheeled stretchers and placed on beds at the far end of the ward. Doctors and nurses came in with them and stayed a long time. They were badly burned. Their faces were a brownish grey and had loose skin on them. For some reason the lights in the ward were not turned on nor were the curtains drawn. Several semi-circular metal frames were placed over each bed however, inside of which small inwardly reflecting lights were attached and over which ran curtains that could be raised and lowered in sections as desired.

The rest of us kept silent and listened, sensing unusual concern. The pilot talked a lot about what had happened. The AI operator spoke very little and I felt he would die. I eventually went to sleep and when I woke up I found I was wrong. The pilot died before dawn and the AI operator survived. I never got to speak to him because he was much subdued and I left a day or two later.[244]

118.	Map 4
AIRCRAFT:	Supermarine Spitfire (BR368?)
PILOT:	Sergeant T.R.D. Kebble (or Kebbell)
UNIT:	1435 Squadron
PLACE:	In sea, St Julian's/Balluta Bay
DATE/TIME:	12 October 1942/0940–1030 hours

On 10 October 1942, the Luftwaffe and the Regia Aeronautica launched the first in a series of attacks in a final concerted effort to crush Malta. The October Blitz began in earnest the next morning. It continued until the 17th, and was one of the most eventful periods during nearly two and a half years of Axis operations against the Island.

At 0907 on 12 October, the air raid warning sounded for the twelfth time in twenty-four hours as an estimated eighteen bombers crossed the coast in two waves, each accompanied by Bf 109 and MC 202 fighters. The main targets were Ta'Qali and Luqa and a number of aircraft were damaged at the latter airfield.

Between 0840 and 0950, some forty Spitfires were scrambled from 229, 249, 126, 1435 and 185 Squadrons. Claims include three Ju 88s, two Bf 109s and a Macchi destroyed, though only RAF losses can be verified: Sergeant John Vinall of 185 Squadron was shot down and killed, while Sergeant T. Kebble (or Kebbell) of 1435 Squadron baled out and landed in Valletta. Both were almost certainly victims of II/JG 53. Another Spitfire was badly damaged.

Flying Officer Rod Smith, who was off duty at the time, was watching the battle from his mess at 184 Main Street, in St Julian's:

> We had access to the roof of the third floor. On the north-west corner of this roof there was . . . a small stone flat-roofed square structure . . . its roof afforded a view of the whole bay.
>
> On this day some action was taking place high up and a little to the south-west. Rip Jones [Flying Officer Ripley Jones] and I climbed onto this small structure to get a better look. We saw a parachute high up to the south-east, and we became aware of the roar of an aircraft in a very fast dive. It was not whining . . . so its constant speed unit was obviously still controlling the propeller revolutions within the limits, but the roar was increasing so relentlessly it indicated distress.[245] We suddenly spotted a diving Spitfire seven or eight thousand feet up to the south-east, streaming flame and smoke . . . it kept a perfectly straight course and an unchanging attitude, but . . . its dive was about thirty degrees off the vertical and it appeared to be coming absolutely straight at us.
>
> For a second or two I considered rushing down below but I realised I wouldn't get far enough to make any difference. Rip and I just stood staring upwards, mesmerized by the sight of the oncoming aircraft and its ever-increasing roar. After a few more seconds we noticed that we could see slightly more of its underside than its top. It began to look as if it were going to pass over us, and it did, roaring incredibly by then. It hit almost dead in the centre of the bay with an enormous splash. It left a yellowy-green patch on the surface which lasted a surprisingly long time. I turned to Rip and said, "You'll

never see another sight like that as long as you live!", or something like that. This so amused him he kept repeating it to others the rest of the day.

I remember our being told that the pilot had baled out and that the parachute we had seen was his.[246]

119.	Map 4
AIRCRAFT:	Macchi C.202
PILOT:	Sottotenente (or Maresciallo) Maurizio Iannucci
UNIT:	352ª Squadriglia, 20º Gruppo, 51º Stormo Caccia Terrestre
PLACE:	In sea, off Tignè
DATE/TIME:	13 October 1942/1310–1344 hours

During the height of the October Blitz, at 1300 hours on the 13th, the sirens signalled the start of yet another raid as some fifty aircraft, including at least six Ju 88s, approached Malta. Twenty-four Spitfires were airborne, drawn equally from 185, 229 and 126 Squadrons. 185 Squadron first sighted the enemy 25 miles north of Zonqor, and climbed to engage the top cover at 26,000 feet. 229 Squadron was next to attack as the bombers and fighter escort headed north-west some 20,000 feet above south-west Malta. After completing their bombing run, the Ju 88s were engaged by two aircraft of 185 Squadron south of Kalafrana at 12,000 feet. 126 Squadron also reported attacking the departing bombers and their escort eight miles north of Zonqor.

In 20 minutes or so of aerial combat, one Spitfire was shot down and the pilot, Sergeant Alex MacLeod of 185 Squadron, killed. Three Spitfires were also damaged. At the same time, Sottotenente (or Maresciallo) Maurizio Iannucci of 352ª Squadriglia was killed in an attack by Flying Officer Rod Smith, who recalled:

Prosser Hanks [Wing Commander, Luqa] was leading 126 Squadron and we got into position a couple of thousand feet above the 88s over Luqa heading the opposite way. Prosser tried to half-roll down to come in behind them but he wasn't high enough above them for that. He came down though them and wound up under them, too low to shoot. His aircraft was badly riddled by return fire.

I was sure we weren't high enough above the 88s to half-roll down to them without coming out below them, so I did a half-spiral down to the left and though I found myself level with them I was behind them, now heading north–west as they were, but considerably out of range. I was faced with the prospect of trying to overhaul them from a position directly underneath their escort, not a safe tactic. I suddenly saw a Macchi 202 not far below me to my right, heading east for some reason, and I decided to attack it.

I made a half spiral down to the right and attacked it from the starboard quarter, firing a three second burst with slight deflection from about 250 yards. Strikes appeared on his engine, and it began to stream smoke. I fired another three second burst and got more strikes on it. It went into a very tight and almost vertical spiral dive towards the mouth of Sliema Bay. As it neared the water I could tell that one or more of its guns were firing because, before it made its own great splash, a pattern of little splashes had appeared on the surface which exactly matched its tight spiralling. It was the fifth enemy aircraft I destroyed, and I realised, with some satisfaction I must admit, that I had become an 'ace'.[247]

The police reported that an 'Me [sic] crashed in flames into the sea opposite Ghar-id-Dud, Sliema seafront'. According to Rod Smith, it fell between Dragut Point and Fort St Elmo.[248]

120.	Map 4
AIRCRAFT:	Supermarine Spitfire
PILOT:	Pilot Officer James Stevenson
UNIT:	126 Squadron
PLACE:	Near Gharghur Cemetery
DATE/TIME:	18 October 1942/1543-1654 hours

On 18 October, the Luftwaffe suddenly changed tactics as daylight bomber sorties were replaced by fighter sweeps and fighter-bomber attacks: more than seventy-five raiders were plotted high above Malta at 1547 on this date. Gharghur was bombed 13 minutes later followed, at 1640, by Luqa where

a Wellington was slightly damaged. During the course of the
raid, thirty-six Spitfires were airborne with 1435, 126, 185
and 249 Squadrons each providing eight aircraft and 229
scrambling four. One Bf 109 was claimed damaged by
Sergeant J.S. Hamilton of 1435 Squadron. However, 126
Squadron lost Pilot Officer James Stevenson when his
Spitfire dived into a field south-west of Gharghur, close to
HAA gun position XHE 27. Whether the crash resulted
from battle damage or some other cause has not been
ascertained.

121.	Map 2
AIRCRAFT:	Messerschmitt Bf 109 (10524/Black 12?)
PILOT:	Unteroffizier Heribert Wagner
UNIT:	5/JG 53
PLACE:	Zebbieh
DATE/TIME:	23 October 1942/Approximately 0700 hours

122.	Map 3
AIRCRAFT:	Supermarine Spitfire (EP685)
PILOT:	Flying Officer Alec Lindsay
UNIT:	185 Squadron
PLACE:	Ta'Netta ta'Falzon, limits of Dingli
DATE/TIME:	23 October 1942/0640–0738 hours

About thirty-five fighters and fighter-bombers approached
Malta between 0637 and 0736 on 23 October. A number of
aircraft aborted their mission while still 20 miles north of
their objective, but others carried out at least two swift
raids, dropping bombs in the areas of Saint Paul's Bay,
Mosta and Mtarfa. 185 and 1435 Squadrons each scrambled
eight Spitfires, and 249 four more. Some Bf 109s that
dived on Dingli from the west were intercepted by a
section of 185 Squadron. Sergeant Raymond Saunders
(who would be killed the following day) was credited
with one destroyed, and Flight Lieutenant Kenneth
Charney with one damaged. Anti-aircraft gunners also
claimed two Bf 109s destroyed, one of which slammed into
a field at Zebbieh and exploded, the flaming wreckage
hurtling down a narrow lane and partly demolishing a farm
building before coming to rest a few metres further on. The

body of Unteroffizier Heribert Wagner of 5/JG 53 was
found nearby. In turn, 185 Squadron lost Flying Officer
Alec Lindsay when he was shot down on the outskirts of
Dingli.[249]

123.	Map 3
AIRCRAFT:	Supermarine Spitfire (EP138)
PILOT:	Pilot Officer Russell Wright
UNIT:	1435 Squadron
PLACE:	Near Tal-Hlas Chapel, limits of Zebbug
DATE/TIME:	1 November 1942/1210–1225 hours

At 1205 hours on 1 November, four Spitfires of 1435
Squadron were scrambled in anticipation of a raid that failed
to materialise. A short while later, one of the aircraft crashed
and Pilot Officer Russell Wright, a Rhodesian, was killed.
The event was witnessed by recently promoted Flight
Lieutenant Rod Smith:

> I was on readiness when poor Wright was killed. I have
> no personal recollection of him whatever, although he
> must have been in the mess at Saint Julian's Bay because he
> was in 1435 Squadron . . . I remember hearing his name
> at the time though and have never forgotten it, I think
> because I felt so sorry for his bad luck.
>   126 Squadron's dispersal was at the west end of the east-
> west runway at Luqa, and 1435's was at the other end of
> it. Once in a while the two squadrons would be scrambled
> at the same time, and the aircraft of each would have to
> pass those of the other while taking off in opposite
> directions in clouds of dust . . .
>   [Wright] had just got airborne, heading west, and was
> barely past the west end of the east-west runway when his
> engine gave a cough and quit cold. He was in a hopeless
> position because there was a rocky steep-sided terraced
> ravine off the west end of the runway, and the plots in it
> were tiny and surrounded by low stone fences. He had no
> choice but to glide straight ahead into the ravine. he went
> out of sight from where I was standing. There was a
> sickening crunch and a column of thick black smoke
> appeared above the edge of the ravine . . .[250]

Presumably the incident caused a degree of apprehension among Malta's fighter pilots as it warranted a special mention in the RAF Daily Intelligence Summary three days later:

> The crash . . . was due to engine failure, 20 minutes after take-off. The failure was immediately investigated and found to be due to a number of valve spring failures in both cylinder blocks. The consistent nature of the failures suggests that the springs were from a batch of faulty material.
>
> Both cylinder blocks were received in the Island with seven others as serviceable spares. The remaining seven blocks have been located and will not fly until they have been tested and suspect springs changed. This case may be regarded as a very isolated instance of unwarranted technical failure and should not be held as a reflection on the general reliability of the Merlin engine.[251]

124.	**Map 3**
AIRCRAFT:	**Vickers Wellington (Z8590)**
CREW:	**Sergeant (or Flight Sergeant) Lincoln Craig (Pilot), Flying Officer Samuel Morrison (Second Pilot), Sergeant (or Flight Sergeant) Herbert Earney (Observer), Sergeant (or Flight Sergeant) Alastair Paterson (W/T Operator), Sergeant Oliver Holmes (Air Gunner), Sergeant Keith Donald**
UNIT:	**104 Squadron**
PLACE:	**Gebel Cantar, limits of Siggiewi**
DATE/TIME:	**7 November 1942/Approximately 2040 hours**

By November 1942, Malta was firmly on the offensive. On the 7th, RAF day and night fighters were active over and around the Island, and 69 Squadron was also busy conducting photographic reconnaissances and shipping searches. That night, between 2002 and 2040, six Wellingtons of 104 Squadron left to bomb Decimomannu and Elmas aerodromes in Sardinia. Wellington II 'D', the last off, ran into difficulties almost as soon as it cleared the runway. Charlie Savage of the King's Own Royal Regiment was in A Company stores at Gebel Cantar. He recalled: 'We heard a RAF Wellington outside circling to gain height. Unfortunately, its undercarriage was still down, so we were told, and touched a wall and [the aircraft] crashed nearby, all crew killed, the bodies being brought into the dining room and screened off.'[252]

Later, an RAF bomb disposal team arrived to blow up the Wellington's six DA bombs, the blast scattering debris and causing some damage to army billets in the area.

125.	Map 4
AIRCRAFT:	Handley Page Halifax (DT542)
CREW AND PASSENGERS:	Major The Lord Allen Apsley DSO, MC, TD, MP (1st Royal Gloucestershire Hussars, RAC), Leading Aircraftman Cyril Browne (138 Squadron), Leading Aircraftman Richard Clegg (138 Squadron), Pilot (or Flying) Officer Krzysztof Dubromirski (or Dubromisski) (138 Squadron), Flight Lieutenant Peter Earle (138 Squadron), Corporal Douglas Hounslow (138 Squadron), Flying Officer Zbigniew Idzikowski (138 Squadron), Aircraftman 1 Stanley Kelly (138 Squadron), Sergeant (or Flight Sergeant) Alfred Kleniewski (138 Squadron), Major Arthur Millar (or Curtis-Miller) (Indian Army), Flying Officer Stanislaw Pankiewicz (138 Squadron), Sergeant Dennis Spibey (138 Squadron), Flight Lieutenant Leonard Vaughan DSO, DFC (40 Squadron), Sergeant Alexander Watt (138 Squadron), Squadron Leader Jefferson Wedgwood DFC (92 Squadron), Sergeant Roman Wysock (or Wysocki) (138 Squadron), Flight Sergeant Oskar Zielinski (138 Squadron)
UNIT:	138 Squadron
PLACE:	Between Il-Bajjada and Ta'San Girgor, limits of Zejtun
DATE/TIME:	18 December 1942/0405 hours

The night of 17/18 December 1942 saw the year's last heavy raid by the Luftwaffe when, between 2307 and 0015 hours, an estimated forty Ju 88s bombed Luqa, Qrendi, Siggiewi, Gudja and Safi. Earlier, thirteen Wellingtons of 40 and 104 Squadrons had taken off to bomb targets at Tunis and La Goulette, all aircraft returning to base in time to be caught on the ground.[253] Nine Wellingtons were destroyed and a Baltimore and four Spitfires damaged. It was reported that six civilians were killed and four servicemen and a civilian injured. One Ju 88 was claimed destroyed at 2344 by Flying Officer James (Nigel) Young and Pilot Officer A.L. Webber in their 89 Squadron Beaufighter.[254]

A few hours later, in the early hours of the 18th, 'a four engined bomber flew low over Zejtun with engines failing and crashed east of Zejtun'.[255] The aircraft, a Halifax of 138 Squadron carrying passengers en-route from the Middle East to the UK, came down between Il-Bajjada and Ta'San Girgor. Seventeen Air Force and Army personnel were killed.

The cause of the crash is open to conjecture, however, the Halifax would have made a low-level approach, at night, shortly after Malta's first major raid for weeks. The Island's defenders would certainly have been wary of any aircraft, and at least one account claims that the Halifax was mistakenly shot down by AA.[256] If so, no mention of this could be found in official records, some of which omit altogether any reference to the incident, while the Operations Record Book of 40 Squadron merely states that the aircraft 'crashed on landing after being recalled'.[257]

AXIS UNITS OPERATING OVER MALTA

REGIA AERONAUTICA

At the outbreak of hostilities between Italy and Great Britain, responsibility for neutralising Malta fell to 2ᵃ Squadra Aerea (superseded in December 1940 by Comando Aeronautica Sicilia). The Squadra Aerea (Air Fleet) was essentially a command structure responsible for a particular geographic area. The Squadra could vary in size considerably, both in area and establishment. It comprised two or more Divisioni Aerea (Air Divisions) which, in turn, comprised at least two Brigati Aerea (Air Brigades). Within the Brigata Aerea were a number of Stormi (Wings) each normally comprising two Gruppi (Squadrons), and usually equipped throughout with one specific aircraft type. The Gruppo was the basic operating unit, and comprised two Squadriglie (flights comprising nine aircraft) in the case of multi-engined aircraft, and three Squadriglie for single-engined types. Units of the Regia Aeronautica were designated by the formation number and the role, e.g. 195ᵃ Squadriglia, 90° Gruppo, 30° Stormo Bombardamento Terrestre (land-based bomber Group). The following Italian unit types are mentioned in this book:

Aerosiluranti (AS or Sil)	Torpedo bomber
Autonomo (Aut)	Autonomous. (Classification for an independent unit)
Bombardamento Terrestre (BT)	Bomber, land-based
Bombardamento a Tuffo (BaT)	Dive bomber
Caccia Terrestre (CT)	Fighter, land-based

LUFTWAFFE

In January 1941, the Luftwaffe's X Fliegerkorps commenced operations against Malta. A Fliegerkorps (Flying Corps) could operate either within or independently of a Luftflotte

(Air Fleet), which had a role broadly similar to that of the Italian Squadra Aerea. Both the Fliegerkorps and the Luftflotte varied considerably in strength and comprised all types of flying units. The Geschwader (Group) was the largest German formation with a nominal fixed strength. Normally confined to one role, a Geschwader typically comprised three Gruppen (Wings) plus a Stab (Staff Flight) with four machines. A Gruppe usually consisted of a Stab with three aircraft and three Staffeln (Squadrons), each comprising nine machines. Luftwaffe units were commonly designated by an abbreviation of the unit type, prefixed by the Gruppe (in Roman numerals), the Staffel (in Arabic numerals), or with Stab; eg, III/ZG 26, ie, third Gruppe of the 26th Zerstörergeschwader (heavy bomber Group). The following German unit types are mentioned in this book:

Jagdgeschwader (JG)	Fighter Group
Kampfgeschwader (KG)	Bomber Group
Kampfgruppe (KGr)	Bomber Wing
Küstenfliegergruppe (KüFlGr)	Coastal Reconnaissance Wing
Lehrgeschwader (LG)	Instructional/Operational Development Group
Nachtjagdgeschwader (NJG)	Night Fighter Group
Schlachtgeschwader (SchG)	Fighter-Bomber Group
Seenotdienststaffel (Seenotst)	Air-Sea Rescue Squadron
Stukageschwader (StG)	Dive-Bomber Group
Zerstörergeschwader (ZG)	Heavy Fighter Group

COMPARATIVE RANKS

The following is a guide to comparative ranks of the Royal Air Force, the Regia Aeronautica and the Luftwaffe. The Luftwaffe also used three Officer Candidate grades: Fahnenjunker, which was prefixed to the ordinary NCO rank, eg Fahnenjunker Unteroffizier; Fähnrich and Oberfähnrich.

RAF	Regia Aeronautica	Luftwaffe
—	—	Reichsmarschall
Marshal of the RAF	Maresciallo dell'Aria	Generalfeldmarschall
Air Chief Marshal	Generale di Armata Aerea	Generaloberst
Air Marshal	Generale di Squadra Aerea	General der Flieger
Air Vice-Marshal	Generale di Divisione Aerea	Generalleutnant
Air Commodore	Generale di Brigata Aerea	Generalmajor
Group Captain	Colonnello	Oberst
Wing Commander	Tenente Colonnello	Oberstleutnant
Squadron Leader	Maggiore	Major
Flight Lieutenant	Capitano	Hauptmann
Flying Officer	Tenente	Oberleutnant
Pilot Officer	Sottotenente	Leutnant
—	Aiutante di Battaglia	—
Warrant Officer	Maresciallo (1°, 2°, 3° Classe)	Stabsfeldwebel
Flight Sergeant	Sergente Maggiore	Oberfeldwebel
Sergeant	Sergente	Feldwebel
—	—	Unterfeldwebel
Corporal	Aviere Scelto	Unteroffizier
—	—	Hauptgefreiter
Leading Aircraftman	Primo Aviere	Obergefreiter
Aircraftman 1	Aviere	Gefreiter
Aircraftman 2	—	Flieger

MUSEUMS AND COLLECTIONS

Established by a group of local enthusiasts on 29 July 1974, the National War Museum Association (NWMA) is a voluntary organisation dedicated to maintaining a record of Malta's role as a fortress, with particular emphasis on the Second World War, through the collation of archive material and the collection and preservation of related artefacts. On 30 May 1975, the Association opened a War Relics Exhibition at Lower Fort Saint Elmo, in Valletta. The success and rapid expansion of the collection led to the inauguration of the National War Museum on 5 November 1979.

At Fort Saint Elmo, the wartime role of the Armed Forces, Police and other formations as well as the fortitude of the Islanders, is depicted in a series of photographic panels. Medals, uniforms and equipment donated by the public are displayed, along with numerous other items acquired by the Association. Principal exhibits include the George Cross, awarded to Malta on 15 April 1942; the restored fuselage of Gladiator N5520 (soon to be fitted with recently acquired wings); a restored Motoscafo Turismo Modificato (MTM) such as that used in the abortive Italian attack of 26 July 1941; a Willys Jeep used during their visits to Malta by General Dwight D. Eisenhower in the run-up to Operation 'Husky' and, later, by President Franklin D. Roosevelt, and the Merlin engine and part of the cockpit of Spitfire VC BR108, ditched by Flight Lieutenant Lester Sanders of 603 Squadron during a dogfight with Messerschmitt Bf 109s on 8 July 1942 (see pages 184–5).

At one end of the museum there is an impressive display of aviation artefacts. Many are wartime souvenirs which have been presented to the museum. Other items have been found in and around the Maltese Islands. While retaining an interest in excavating potential land sites, the NWMA tends to concentrate of the recovery of offshore aircraft wrecks, some of which were found by scuba divers and, more recently, by the Italian Navy using the latest search techniques. The remains of others have been recovered, albeit unintentionally, by dredgers and fishing vessels. In 1975 a Pegasus 9 aero engine was found off Marsa by the Port Dredger *Anadrian*. The following year parts of a Spitfire of 1435 Squadron were recovered from the bay below the cliffs at Dwejra, in Gozo, where it was deposited after crash-landing nearby on 27 March 1943. On 11 September 1976, the wreckage of a Messerschmitt Bf 109 F snagged in the nets of the trawler *Hannibal*, by which time the Director of Agriculture and Fisheries had issued a departmental order to all government trawlers to retain for the museum any non-hazardous wreckage recovered during trawling operations. Before the year was over, scuba divers also raised a Wright 14-cylinder engine from a 69 Squadron Maryland shot down by Bf 109s on 15 February 1942 (see pages 111–12). In 1977, divers recovered various items from Beaufort DW805 which ditched on 21 August 1942 (see pages 201–2). Early in 1978, parts of a Junkers Ju 88 were trawled from off Salina and on 29 January 1981, the *Nalout* caught in her nets the wreckage of an unidentified British machine, believed to be a bomber. The propeller and an MG 17 machine gun were retrieved by divers from a Ju 87 Stuka off Zonqor during the summer of 1982. Subsequently, a second gun and the Junkers Jumo 211 engine were also recovered. The remains of what was probably another Ju 88 were brought to the surface by the trawler F1138 on 16 October 1983 (and then disposed of at a local rubbish dump!). In May 1990, two Hispano cannon were removed from the wreckage of a Spitfire off Dragunara Point. Additional items were salvaged from Beaufort DW805 in October 1992 and in April of the following year the mainspar was retrieved from the Spitfire off Dragunara. Another Junkers Jumo 211 engine was recovered from the sea off Ahrax Point on 12 September 1993 (see pages 147–8), followed, in October, by a DB601 engine from Bahar ic-Caghaq.

Artefacts not put on display are usually placed in storage, exchanged for sought-after items or retained for use in aircraft rebuild projects. The first such venture was the restoration of Spitfire Mk IX EN199, the remains of which were recovered from the Pembroke area in the mid-1970s. It was completed in time for the 50th anniversary of the Victory in Europe (VE) celebrations and is now on loan to the Malta Aviation Museum Foundation. The MAMF was formed on 1 November 1994, by a number of individuals and organisations whose ultimate aim is the establishment of an aviation museum. This will be situated at the former RAF Station at Ta'Qali, and involves the relocation of two hangars from Hal Far and Kalafrana. Presently, the Foundation is also engaged in rebuilding Hurricane Mk II Z3055 which crashed off the south coast on 4 July 1941, with the loss of its pilot, Sergeant Thomas Hackston (see pages 89–90).

Many of Malta's growing number of military and aviation enthusiasts belong to organisations such as the Malta Historic Aircraft Preservation and Restoration Group, and the Arms, Armour and Militaria Society, and these regularly hold exhibitions, both independently and in collaboration with each other, providing the public with an opportunity to view some of the unique artefacts held in private collections.

NOTES

1. Philip Vella, *Malta: Blitzed But Not Beaten*, pp. 2–4.
2. Christopher Shores, Brian Cull, Nicola Malizia, *Malta: The Hurricane Years 1940–41*, p. 2.
3. Christopher Shores, Brian Cull, Nicola Malizia, *Malta: The Hurricane Years 1940–41*, p. 2.
4. Philip Vella, *Malta: Blitzed But Not Beaten*, pp. 17–18 and 216–20.
5. Ian Cameron, *Red Duster, White Ensign, The Story of the Malta Convoys*, p. 38.
6. HMSO, *The Air Battle of Malta*, pp. 23–4.
7. Christopher Shores, Brian Cull, Nicola Malizia, *Malta: The Hurricane Years 1940–41*, p. 225.
8. Christopher Shores, Brian Cull, Nicola Malizia, *Malta: The Hurricane Years 1940–41*, pp. 304–5.
9. Letter to the author from P.B. 'Laddie' Lucas, dated 15 September 1995.
10. Philip Vella, *Malta: Blitzed But Not Beaten*, p. 98 and Christopher Shores, Brian Cull, Nicola Malizia, *Malta: The Hurricane Years 1940–41*, pp. 130–1.
11. Philip Vella, *Malta: Blitzed But Not Beaten*, p. 100.
12. Wing Commander Tim Johnston DFC, *Tattered Battlements – A Fighter Pilot's Diary*, pp. 78–9.
13. *After The Battle* Number 10, edited by Winston Ramsey, p. 15.
14. Diaries of Stan Fraser.
15. Cajus Bekker, *The Luftwaffe War Diaries*, p. 239.
16. *The Air Battle of Malta*, p. 67. Although he is not named in the Ministry of Information publication, the identity of Flying Officer Mitchell has since been established.
17. Denis Barnham, *One Man's Window, An illustrated account of ten weeks of war Malta, April 13th to June 21st 1942*, p. 155.
18. Introduction by Laddie Lucas in Lord James Douglas-Hamilton, *The Air Battle for Malta – The Diaries of a Fighter Pilot*, pp. 17–18.
19. Laddie Lucas, *Five Up – A Chronicle of Five Lives*, pp. 59–60.
20. Letter to the author from Leo Nomis.
21. Based on figures in *Malta: The Hurricane Years 1940–41*, pp. 362–3, and *Malta: the Spitfire Year 1942*, pp. 645–6, both by Christopher Shores, Brian Cull and Nicola Malizia, Axis losses during the battle amount to at least 320 German aircraft in 1941–42, and 105 Italian machines between 11 June 1940 and 31 December 1941, alone. (According to Richard Mifsud, *Flames over Malta*, p. 77, the Luftwaffe and the Regia Aeronautica admitted to losing 357 and 210 machines respectively up to November 1942.) During the siege, some 300 British fighters were lost in the air, mostly as a result of enemy action. Many others force/crash-landed or were destroyed on the ground. Numerous bombers and reconnaissance aircraft were also written-off. According to *After The Battle*, number 10, p. 19, edited by Winston Ramsey, RAF

losses amounted to 547 in the air and 160 on the ground, in addition to 504 damaged in the air and 231 damaged on the ground.

22. The number and timings of air-raid warnings for Malta's first year under attack are taken from Army and Police records. On 22 June 1941, the RAF in Malta began to record events in a Daily Intelligence Summary. This includes details of air-raid alarms and provides the basis for subsequent entries.

23. Christopher Shores, Brian Cull, Nicola Malizia, *Malta: The Hurricane Years 1940–41*, pp. 31–2.

24. Sottotenente Luigi Illica Magnani, Sergente Dante Becherucci, Primo Aviere Silla Bussaglia, Primo Aviere Antioco Giovanni Chessa and Sergente Maggiore Pietro Gori, believed to have been in the same crew, were all reported missing on this date. The mortally wounded crewman from one of the damaged bombers is believed to have been Primo Aviere Dino Calzolari of 194ª Squadriglia.

25. Christopher Shores, Brian Cull, Nicola Malizia, *Malta: The Hurricane Years 1940–41*, p. 37.

26. War Diary of 1st Battalion The Dorsetshire Regiment, Public Record Office (PRO), Kew, ref: WO 169/910.

27. The story behind 'Faith', 'Hope' and 'Charity' is covered in detail in *Malta: The Hurricane Years 1940–41*, by Christopher Shores, Brian Cull and Nicola Malizia.

28. Christopher Shores, Brian Cull, Nicola Malizia, *Malta: The Hurricane Years 1940–41*, p. 41.

29. 'Jock' Barber interviewed by Brian Cull in 1976.

30. War Diaries held at the PRO place the crash site of Gladiator N5519 as follows: 1st Battalion The King's Own Malta Regiment (1 KOMR), WO 169/905: 'just off beach near Fort Leonardo'; 2nd Battalion The Devonshire Regiment, WO 169/909: 'just off beach near Fort Leonardo', amended to, 'just off beach near Fort Ta-Silch'; 2nd Battalion The Queen's Own Royal West Kent Regiment, WO 169/912: 'on the coast'. The War Diary of 3 KOMR, WO 169/907, records that the pilot baled out, 'landing in the sea off Il-Hofra il-Kebira'. The Operations Record Book of RAF Kalafrana, AIR 28/409, states that the, 'Gladiator burst into the sea'. However, the Malta Police, whose records are among the most reliable, reported: 'Air-Craft fell at Zabbar – Parachutist seen gliding towards Kalafrana – Parachutist observed coming down into the sea in the vicinity of Tas-Silg Fort': Report Regarding Air Raids, via Robert Farrugia.

31. 'Jock' Barber interviewed by Brian Cull in 1976. Sergeant Robertson's first recorded flight after his accident was in Hurricane P3731 on 12 August.

32. *Malta: enemy prisoners of war interrogation reports* (June 1940–May 1941), PRO, ref: AIR 40/1862.

33. Christopher Shores, Brian Cull, Nicola Malizia, *Malta; The Hurricane Years 1940–41*, p. 71.

34. Combat report of Sergeant Fred Robertson, via the NWMA.

35. *Malta: enemy prisoners of war interrogation reports* (June 1940–May 1941), PRO, ref: AIR 40/1862.

36. Christopher Shores, *Aces High*, Volume 2, p. 115.

37. War Diary of 2nd Battalion The Devonshire Regiment, PRO, WO 169/909.

38. Letter to the author from Jim Pickering.

39. Letter to the author from John Galea, dated 22 May 1995.

40. Combat report of Sergeant Fred Robertson, via the NWMA.

41. PRO, ref: WO 169/3284.

42. Donald Caldwell, *The JG 26 War Diary, Volume One, 1939–1942*, pp. 103–4.

43. Extracts from the diary and log book of James MacLachlan, via Roland Symons.

44. 'Malta was his Battleground' (extracts from the diary of an unnamed pilot, since identified as C.D. Whittingham), *The Royal Air Force Quarterly*, Volume XIII, Number 3, June 1942, p. 162.

45. Donald Caldwell, *The JG 26 War Diary, Volume One, 1939–1942*, pp. 105–6.

46. Diary of James MacLachlan, via Roland Symons. The entry is incorrectly dated 3 March 1941.

47. Christopher Shores, Brian Cull, Nicola Malizia, *Malta: The Hurricane Years 1940–41*, pp. 164–5.

48. Donald Caldwell, *The JG 26 War Diary, Volume One, 1939–1942*, p. 106.

49. Luftwaffe loss register, listed as 'Luftwaffe Losses' at the Imperial War Museum (IWM), ref: GER/MISC/MCR 18.

50. Combat report of Sergeant Fred Robertson, via the NWMA. Robertson's log book (via Robert Farrugia) records that he, 'Climbed to 10,000 feet over the Island and baled out. Machine crashed about ½ mile South of Rabat'.

51. Donald Caldwell, *The JG 26 War Diary, Volume One, 1939–1942*, pp. 108–9.

52. Luftwaffe Losses, IWM, ref: GER/MISC/MCR 18.

53. Donald Caldwell, *The JG 26 War Diary, Volume One, 1939–1942*, p. 110.

54. PRO, ref: WO 169/3284.

55. According to *Malta: The Hurricane Years 1940–41*, by Christopher Shores, Brian Cull and Nicola Malizia, Pilot Officer Claude Hamilton of 261 Squadron, 'attacked and claimed shot down' the Ju 87 piloted by Leutnant Werner Zühlke, the aircraft crashing, 'just behind the hangars at Takali'. Both crewmen were killed. Official records confirm that while one enemy aircraft was definitely destroyed, this fell at Il-Maghtab; the General Staff Malta Command War Diary (PRO, ref: WO 169/3259) recording: '1 Ju 87 was shot down on land, 4130, by ground defences, (strong claim by 2 R Ir F to have shot this machine down with SA fire). 1 Ju 87 probably shot down by fighters.'

56. PRO, ref: AIR 40/1862.

57. Interrogation conducted on 6 May 1941, PRO, ref: AIR 40/1862. The report includes a reference to the prisoners' unit, which is recorded as, '5th Staffel, 2nd Gruppe of unknown KG'. Luftwaffe Losses, IWM, ref: GER/MISC/MCR 18, identifies it as 9(K)/LG 1.

58. Christopher Shores, Brian Cull, Nicola Malizia, *Malta: The Hurricane Years 1940–41*, p. 194.

59. Christopher Shores, Brian Cull, Nicola Malizia, *Malta: The Hurricane Years 1940–41*, pp. 205–6, and *Malta: The Spitfire Year 1942*, p. 13.

60. PRO, ref: AIR 27/1142.

61. Donald Caldwell, *The JG 26 War Diary, Volume One, 1939–1942*, p. 112.

62. Christopher Shores, Brian Cull, Nicola Malizia, *Malta: The Hurricane Years 1940–41*, p. 195.

63. PRO, ref: WO 169/3284.

64. PRO, ref: WO 169/3277.

65. PRO, ref: WO 169/3282.

66. PRO, ref: WO 169/3278.

67. PRO, ref: WO 169/3283.

68. Malta Police Reports compiled by Philip Vella and listed as 'Aircraft Losses, Malta, 1940/41', via the NWMA.

69. Christopher Shores, Brian Cull, Nicola Malizia, *Malta: The Hurricane Years 1940–41*, pp. 260–1, describes how the unfamiliar Cant-Z.1007 Bis may have been misidentified due to the angle of approach of attacking fighter pilots.

70. Diary of Second Lieutenant J.Q. Hughes RA, IWM, ref: 81/24/1. The entry is incorrectly dated 28 July 1941.

71. Royal Air Force Daily Intelligence Summary, PRO, ref: AIR 22/391.

72. PRO, ref: AIR 27/1142.

73. Two Ju 87s seem to have been lost on this date together with Sottotenente Bragadin and Sergente Maggiore (or Maresciallo) Gatti, and Sergente (or Sergente Maggiore) Armando Tosi and Aviere Scelto Amleto Bruttini; the former crew being listed as killed and the latter as missing.

74. PRO, ref: AIR 50/49.

75. PRO, ref: AIR 50/49.

76. PRO, ref: AIR 22/391.

77. Quote from the diary of Second Lieutenant J.Q. Hughes RA, IWM, ref: 81/24/1.

78. Philip Vella, *Malta: Blitzed But Not Beaten*, p. 50.

79. Donald Stones, *Operation "Bograt" – From France to Burma*, p. 61.

80. Malta: German prisoners of war interrogation reports (December 1941–October 1942), PRO, ref: AIR 40/1863. A report dated 12 February 1942 states that Leutnant Brauns, 'recently recovered consciousness'.

81. PRO, ref: AIR 22/391.

82. Although a night fighter, this Ju 88 is reported by RAF Intelligence to have been carrying eight 50 kilogramme bombs, a not uncommon practice. PRO, ref: AIR 40/1863.

83. Diaries of Stan Fraser.

84. Luftwaffe Losses, IWM, ref: GER/MISC/MCR 18, lists the aircraft as a Ju 88 C4.

85. Log book of Sergeant Garth Horricks.

86. PRO, ref: AIR 50/49.

87. PRO, ref: AIR 50/49.

88. Letter to the author from John Galea, dated 22 May 1995.

89. Diaries of BSM F.G.R. Packington, IWM, ref: 86/69/1.

90. Christopher Shores, Brian Cull, Nicola Malizia, *Malta: The Spitfire Year 1942*, p. 38.

91. Letter to the author from Charlie Savage, dated 11 August 1997.

92. Malta: German prisoners of war interrogation reports (December 1941–October 1942), PRO, ref: AIR 40/1863.

93. PRO, ref: WO 169/7382.

94. Letter to the author from Charlie Savage, dated 11 August 1997.

95. Luftwaffe Losses, IWM, ref: GER/MISC/MCR 18, identifies the pilot of Ju 88 0149/R4+MM as Leutnant Felix-Dieter Schleif.

96. Combat report of Flight Lieutenant Nigel Kemp, PRO, ref: AIR 50/92.

97. One of the Ju 88s may have been a I/KG 54 machine reported to have been lost on this date.

98. PRO, ref: AIR 27/1498.

99. Jochen Prien, *'Pik-As', Geschichte des Jagdgeschwaders 53, Teil 1*, pp. 452–3.

100. Letters to the author from Peter Thompson, dated 5 July and 23 July 1995.

101. Diaries of Stan Fraser.

102. Jochen Prien, *'Pik-As', Geschichte des Jagdgeschwaders 53, Teil 3*, p. 1669.

103. Diaries of Oliver Ormrod, via Captain J.M. Ormrod.

104. Quote from the diaries of Stan Fraser. Official records state that one Ju 88 was destroyed and another damaged by HAA. A third, credited to LAA, was reported to have crashed in the sea south of Dingli at about 1000 hours. RAF fighters also claimed two Bf 109s destroyed. At least one Ju 88 was actually brought down.

105. Diaries of Phil Chandler.

106. The cutting, from *The Times of Malta*, 23 February 1942, carried the headline, 'AIR BATTLES OVER MALTA', and consisted of a Situation Report issued by the Information Office the day before. The actions of Sergeants Sutherland and Eastman are recounted thus:

'ME' FALLS TO GUNS OF SERGEANT PILOT

The 'ME 109' was shot down by a Sergeant Pilot [Sutherland]. He flew so close to press home his attack that he had to break off to avoid a collision. Black smoke was then pouring from the Messerschmitt's engine. Another pilot saw the starboard wing fall off, the fighter then spinning into the ground. The Sergeant Pilot then attacked a 'JU 88', damaging it and silencing the rear-gunner.

Another Sergeant Pilot [Eastman] attacked in turn two 'JU 88s' and two 'ME 109s'. His tracer bullets ripped the fuselage of one bomber, the underneath side of the other and hit the rear gunner of the second. Bursts of tracer also hit both the fighters.

107. 185 Squadron diary, PRO, ref: AIR 27/1142.

108. By the time they reached Sicily, the Bf 109s were dangerously low on fuel. At least three force/crash-landed on return including the Kapitän of 8 Staffel, Oberleutnant Hans-Joachim Heinecke, and Oberfeldwebel Hipper, who was killed: Jochen Prien, 'Pik-As', Geschichte des Jagdgeschwaders 53, Teil 1, pp. 472, 475 and 523.

109. The War Diary of 2nd Battalion The Devonshire Regiment, PRO, ref: WO 169/7426, records that this Bf 109 crashed on F Range; that of 2nd Battalion The Royal Irish Fusiliers, PRO, ref: WO 169/7430, gives the location as E Range; and that of 11th Battalion The Lancashire Fusiliers, PRO, ref: WO 169/7432, as near C Range stop butts. According to the diaries of Mrs A.B. Marjoribanks-Egerton, IWM, ref: 85/47/1, the Messerschmitt came down on C Range. It seems likely that the crash site is under the reverse osmosis plant now at this location.

110. Malta: German prisoners of war interrogation reports (December 1941–October 1942), PRO, ref: AIR 40/1863.

111. Unteroffizier Engelmann is named in Malta: German prisoners of war interrogation reports (December 1941–October 1942), PRO, ref: AIR 40/1863. Luftwaffe Losses, IWM, ref: GER/MISC/MCR 18, lists Unteroffizier Friedrich Engelbert as the observer of Ju 88 1392/7T+JK.

112. Letter to the author from Tony Busuttil, dated 30 June 1995.

113. Letter to the author from Phil Wigley, dated 12 July 1996.

114. The War Diary of Headquarters Royal Artillery Malta, PRO, ref: WO 169/7382, credits HAA with the destruction of one Ju 88, while the War Diary of 225th Light Anti-Aircraft Battery, Royal Artillery, PRO, ref: WO 169/7419, claims that the Ju 88 brought down at Hal Far was destroyed by LAA.

115. Jochen Prien, Chronik des JG-53 Pik-As, Band 1, p. 482, and 'Pik-As', Geschichte des Jagdgeschwaders 53, Teil 3, p. 1669. Recent findings indicate that Hauptmann Krahl's 24th victory was a Spitfire destroyed at 1710 hours on 10 March 1942.

116. Jochen Prien, 'Pik-As', Geschichte des Jagdgeschwaders 53, Teil 1, p. 488.

117. Laddie Lucas, Malta – The Thorn in Rommel's Side, Six Months that Turned the War, pp. 62–3.

118. Jochen Prien, 'Pik-As', Geschichte des Jagdgeschwaders 53, Teil 3, p. 1669.

119. Diaries of Stan Fraser.

120. Letter to the author from George Lord, dated 30 June 1995.

121. Letter to the author from Howard Bell, dated 9 July 1995.

122. Letter to the author from George Lord, dated 1 August 1995.

123. Letter to Gavin Cooper (nephew of Douglas Leggo) from Hermann Neuhoff, dated 10 February 1999.

124. 185 Squadron diary, PRO, ref; AIR 27/1142.

125. Luftwaffe Losses, IWM , ref: GER/MISC/MCR 18, identifies this pilot as Unteroffizier Franz Pilz. The RAF AI1(k) Report, Number 61A/1942, PRO, ref: AIR 40/2410, names him as Hans Pelz. The letters 'JP' on a flying helmet said to have belonged to a German fighter pilot shot down over Malta might provide another clue. No

such pilot with these initials has been identified, unless Hans is a corruption of Hannes, i.e. Johannes.

126. Eyewitness account via Robert Farrugia.

127. In the Operations Record Books of RAF Station Ta Kali, PRO, ref: AIR 28/807, and 126 Squadron, PRO, ref: AIR 27/926, Pilot Officer Nash, Flight Sergeant Fletcher and Flying Officer Buchanan are each credited with destroying a Ju 87. The ORB of 249 Squadron, PRO, ref: AIR 27/1498, confirms the victories of Nash and Buchanan, while the RAF Daily Intelligence Summary, PRO, ref: AIR 22/392, confirms those of Nash and Fletcher, but lists Buchanan's as 'probably destroyed'. It also records that two Ju 87s fell to AA fire.

128. Pilot Officer Paul Brennan DFC, DFM, Pilot Officer Ray Hesselyn DFM and Bar, Henry Bateson, Spitfires Over Malta, p. 35.

129. Malta: German prisoners of war interrogation reports (December 1941–October 1942), PRO, ref: AIR 40/1863. Luftwaffe Losses, IWM, ref: GER/MISC/MCR 18, also includes the loss on this date of a second Ju 87 of III/StG 3 together with Unteroffizier Helmut Süchlich.

130. 185 Squadron diary, PRO, ref; AIR 27/1142.

131. Hal Far is at an altitude of 200 feet.

132. Letters to the author from Phil Wigley, dated 8–18 June 1995.

133. Jochen Prien, Chronik des JG-53 Pik-As, Band 1, p. 500.

134. Diary of Second Lieutenant J.Q. Hughes RA, IWM, ref; 81/24/1. 'Schirop' and 'Munsharr' are corruptions of the Maltese Xrobb (il-Ghaghin) and Munxar.

135. Phil Wigley always maintained that Hauptmann Krahl's Bf 109 was shot down as described in this letter to the author, dated 8 June 1995. However, a somewhat different version of events is provided by Pilot Officer Oliver Ormrod, whose diary records that, 'two Me 109s came towards Hal Far from Safi on a ground strafing attack. One was hit by machine gun fire as he came over the ridge beyond the Albacore dispersals, where we now keep Hurricanes. He hit the ground and blew up with a vivid flash and a puff of black smoke . . . This is the second time I've seen a low flying Messerschmitt shot down on coming over that ridge'. (The first occasion was on 7 February 1942, when Oberfeldwebel Otto Göthe was killed: see pages 108–10)

136. Diary of Ian McKay.

137. AI1(k) Report, Number 84C/1942, PRO, ref: AIR 40/2410.

138. PRO, ref: AIR 27/1419.

139. Jochen Prien, 'Pik-As', Geschichte des Jagdgeschwaders 53, Teil 3, p. 1670.

140. Letter to the author from Phil Wigley, dated 8 June 1995.

141. Diary of Pilot Officer Peter Nash, via Brian Cull.

142. Jochen Prien, 'Pik-As', Geschichte des Jagdgeschwaders 53, Teil 3, p. 1670.

143. Diary of Denis Barnham, via Oliver Barnham.

144. Jochen Prien, 'Pik-As', Geschichte des Jagdgeschwaders 53, Teil 3, p. 1670.

145. Diary of Denis Barnham, via Oliver Barnham. A similar account in Barnham's book, One Man's Window, An illustrated account of ten weeks of war Malta, April 13th, to June 21st, 1942, pp. 96–7, attributes the shooting down of what is clearly Flight Sergeant Brooks' Hurricane to AA fire.

146. Jochen Prien, *'Pik-As', Geschichte des Jagdgeschwaders 53, Teil 3*, p. 1670.

147. Diary of Denis Barnham, via Oliver Barnham.

148. Luftwaffe Losses, IWM, ref: GER/MISC/MCR 18, identifies the observer of Ju 88 5717/L1+GM as Sonderführer Doktor Eduard Perertil.

149. Diary of Miss G.M. Bates, IWM, ref: 90/30/1.

150. Malta: German prisoners of war interrogation reports (December 1941–October 1942), PRO, ref: AIR 40/1863.

151. Diary of 603 Squadron by Squadron Leader Lord David Douglas-Hamilton and Flight Lieutenant William Douglas, among the papers of Wing Commander J.L. Jack held at the IWM.

152. Jochen Prien, *'Pik-As', Geschichte des Jagdgeschwaders 53, Teil 3*, p 1670.

153. Pilot Officer Paul Brennan DFC, DFM, Pilot Officer Ray Hesselyn DFM and Bar, Henry Bateson, *Spitfires Over Malta*, pp. 61–2.

154. Denis Barnham, *One Man's Window, An illustrated account of ten weeks of war Malta, April 13th, to June 21st, 1942*, pp. 110–12.

155. Laddie Lucas, *Malta – The Thorn in Rommel's Side, Six Months that Turned the War*, pp. 106–7.

156. The only claims for Ju 88s destroyed on 8 May 1942 were for the 0835–1011 raid. The only recorded loss appears to have been Ju 88 5709/M7+KL of KGr 806 (Unteroffizier Gerhard Andrae killed, and Leutnant Heinz Möller, Unteroffizier Hermann Bräuer and Obergefreiter Erich Kaluza missing): Luftwaffe Losses, IWM, ref: GER/MISC/MCR 18.

157. *Malta: German prisoners of war interrogation reports (December 1941–October 1942)*, PRO, ref: AIR 40/1863.

158. Christopher Shores, Brian Cull, Nicola Malizia, *Malta: The Spitfire Year 1942*, p. 247. Another possibility is that the two missing Spitfires were shot down by Leutnant Dietrich Kasten of 8/JG 53 and Oberleutnant Franz Götz of 9/JG 53, who are each credited with a P-40 destroyed at 1015 and 1020 respectively: Jochen Prien, *'Pik-As', Geschichte des Jagdgeschwaders 53, Teil 3*, p. 1670.

159. War Diary of Headquarters Royal Artillery Malta, PRO, ref: WO 169/7382.

160. Jochen Prien, *'Pik-As', Geschichte des Jagdgeschwaders 53, Teil 3*, p. 1670, credited Hauptmann Belser with a Spitfire destroyed at 1816 on 9 May 1942.

161. HMS 'Welshman' – Report on a Combined Services Operation, attached to the War Diary of the General Staff, Malta Command, PRO, ref: WO 169/7381.

162. Diaries of Stan Fraser.

163. Pilot Officer Paul Brennan DFC, DFM, Pilot Officer Ray Hesselyn DFM and Bar, Henry Bateson, *Spitfires Over Malta*, pp. 69–70.

164. RAF Daily Intelligence Summary, PRO, ref: AIR 22/392. By 13 May 1942, the tally had risen to 23:20:24 (including eight destroyed by AA). Pilots' log books also indicate that some claims were later upgraded.

165. *The Times of Malta*, 11 May 1942.

166. Message attached to the War Diary of Headquarters Royal Artillery Malta, PRO, ref: WO 169/7382.

167. Aircraft Losses, Malta, 1942, via the NWMA, confirms that a, 'Ju87 crashed in flames at Senglea; pilot killed', apparently between 1810 and 1949, while AI1(k) Report Number 101D/1942, PRO, ref: AIR 40/2410, states that Unteroffiziers Rastinnes and Rauer were, 'shot down by AA fire' at 1700 (presumably GMT).

168. Christopher Shores, Brian Cull, Nicola Malizia, *Malta, The Spitfire Year 1942*, p. 264.

169. Log book entry via Chris Shores.

170. PRO, ref: AIR 27/1143. The entry is incorrectly dated 11 May 1942.

171. Denis Barnham, *One Man's Window, An illustrated account of ten weeks of war Malta, April 13th, to June 21st, 1942*, pp. 140–1.

172. PRO, ref: WO 169/7428.

173. PRO, ref: AIR 40/1868.

174. PRO, ref: WO 169/7395.

175. Denis Barnham, *One Man's Window, An illustrated account of ten weeks of war Malta, April 13th, to June 21st, 1942*, pp. 154–5.

176. Jochen Prien, *'Pik-As', Geschichte des Jagdgeschwaders 53*, Teil 3, p. 1670.

177. Diary of Denis Barnham, via Oliver Barnham.

178. Denis Barnham, *One Man's Window, An illustrated account of ten weeks of war Malta, April 13th, to June 21st, 1942*, pp. 146–7.

179. Entry in the log book of Mervin Ingram, via Chris Shores.

180. Denis Barnham, *One Man's Window, An illustrated account of ten weeks of war Malta, April 13th, to June 21st, 1942*, p. 154.

181. Some of the most enduring images of the Battle of Malta are photographs attributed to Hector Borg-Carbott of a crewman trapped in the burning wreckage of the Ju 88 at Ta'Qali on 14 May 1942. The story of the crewman being shot dead has not been substantiated, but former RAF Fitter, Bill Metcalf, recalled that it was an officer in the Army, not the RAF, who took charge at the crash site.

182. Denis Barnham, *One Man's Window, An illustrated account of ten weeks of war Malta, April 13th, to June 21st, 1942*, pp. 147–8.

183. Diaries of Phil Chandler.

184. Denis Barnham, *One Man's Window, An illustrated account of ten weeks of war Malta, April 13th, to June 21st, 1942*, p. 148.

185. Malta: German prisoners of war interrogation reports (December 1941–October 1942), PRO, ref: AIR 40/1863.

186. Squadron Leader Lord David Douglas-Hamilton, 'With a Fighter Squadron in Malta', *Blackwood's Magazine*, May 1944.

187. Wing Commander Tim Johnston DFC, *Tattered Battlements – A Fighter Pilot's Diary*, p. 136.

188. Christopher Shores, Brian Cull, Nicola Malizia, *Malta: The Spitfire Year 1942*, p. 273.

189. According to his log book, completed by an unknown hand after his death, Pilot Officer Nash was involved in two scrambles on 17 May, shooting down a Bf 109 on both occasions: PRO, ref: AIR 4/81.

190. Jochen Prien, *'Pik-As', Geschichte des Jagdgeschwaders 53*, Teil 3, p. 1670.

191. This was an attempt by the Italians to reconnoitre the coastal defences. At least one man was landed on the Island, and later captured. The

Italians also put ashore a spy, Carmelo Borg Pisani, a Maltese Fascist. He, too, was taken prisoner, and eventually executed. A full account of this episode can be read in Philip Vella's, *Malta: Blitzed But Not Beaten*, pp. 142–4.

192. Christopher Shores, Brian Cull, Nicola Malizia, *Malta: The Spitfire Year 1942*, pp. 683–4.

193. Pilot Officer Paul Brennan DFC, DFM, Pilot Officer Ray Hesselyn DFM and Bar, Henry Bateson, *Spitfires Over Malta*, pp. 83–4.

194. AIK Report Number 317/1942, PRO, ref: AIR 40/2411.

195. Christopher Shores, Brian Cull, Nicola Malizia, *Malta: The Spitfire Year 1942*, p. 684.

196. PRO, ref: WO 169/7432.

197. Christopher Shores, Brian Cull, Nicola Malizia, *Malta: The Spitfire Year 1942*, p. 300.

198. Letter to the author from John Galea, dated 22 May 1995.

199. Italian PoWs: Interrogation Reports 1940–42, PRO, ref: AIR 40/1868.

200. Information about Italian pilots from Christopher Shores, Brian Cull, Nicola Malizia, *Malta: The Spitfire Year 1942*, pp. 385 and 671.

201. PRO, ref: WO 169/7421.

202. Luftwaffe Losses, IWM, ref: GER/MISC/MCR 18.

203. Laddie Lucas, *Malta – The Thorn in Rommel's Side, Six Months that Turned the War*, pp. 161–4.

204. The S.84 piloted by Tenente Raffaele Notari is believed to have been crewed by Aviere Scelto Giorgio Bolgioni, Tenente Mario Daniele, Aviere Scelto Egidio Fioretti, Aviere Scelto Giovanni Maddaloni and Aviere Scelto Mario Pozzoli, all of whom were posted as missing.

205. At about 1900 hours on 6 July 1942, a Ju 88 of KGr 806, believed to have been 1595/M7+CL, ditched off Malta with the loss of Oberfeldwebel Peter Wilbertz. Gefreiter Heinz Stiller, Feldwebel Sebastian Krumbachner and Flieger Hans Albrecht were taken prisoner. Luftwaffe Losses, IWM, ref: GER/MISC/MCR 18, includes details of at least two more Ju 88s missing during operations over Malta on this date: 3636/3Z+JN of 5/KG 77 with Leutnant Reinhold Böger, Unteroffizier Heinz Brunner, Obergefreiter Reimund Geideble and Unteroffizier Josef Pfiefer, and 5729/3Z+FP of 6/KG 77 with Hauptmann Leo Behlau, Feldwebel Paul Pohlau, Feldwebel Karl Kraus and Unteroffizier Paul Jaffke. Another Ju 88, 1096 of 4/KG 77, apparently also ditched after fighter attack, but is listed as being 80 per cent damaged, indicating that it probably came down on the Sicilian coast. No details of the crew are given. A fifth machine, Ju 88 C-6 360191/R4+DK of I/NJG 2, was also reported missing together with its crew – Leutnant Georg Wiedow, Unteroffizier Karl Danzinger and Unteroffizier Alfred Felix – though neither the area nor mission is stated.

206. Letter to Brian Cull from Dave Ferraby, dated 4 July 1989.

207. Letter to the author from Dave Ferraby, dated 12 October 1995.

208. Letter to the author from John Galea, dated 28 November 1995.

209. Christopher Shores, Brian Cull, Nicola Malizia, *Malta: The Spitfire Year 1942*, p. 398.

210. Leutnant Heinz-Edgar Berres of I/JG 77 has since been credited with shooting down Flight Lieutenant Sanders, yet an account attributed to Unteroffizier Horst Schlick of the same unit suggests that he and Berres were actually responsible for shooting down two Spitfires of 249 Squadron later in the day, when Flying Officer John Smith and Sergeant John Gilbert were killed: Jochen Prien, *Geschichte des Jagdgeschwaders 77, Teil 3*, p. 1232.

211. Diaries of Stan Fraser.

212. As already disclosed, the remains of badly mutilated airmen were sometimes buried where they were found. The burial 'at sea' of enemy dead also seems to have been a not uncommon practice in Malta at this stage of the battle.

213. Diaries of Stan Fraser.

214. Diaries of Stan Fraser. The War Diary of 4th Heavy Anti-Aircraft Regiment, Royal Artillery, PRO, ref: WO 169/7410, records that three Ju 88s were brought down by HAA, and that the last to crash was, 'believed to have been badly dazzled by S/Ls, from his erratic behaviour'. According to Luftwaffe Losses, IWM, ref: GER/MISC/MCR 18, Feldwebel Otto Rutschmann, Oberfeldwebel Ernst Weiss, Stabsfeldwebel Georg Engle and Oberfeldwebel Ernst Ulmer of KüFlGr 606 were reported missing in Ju 88 140200/7T+GH on 20 July 1942, probably as a result of becoming disorientated. Ju 88 140065/3Z+CS of 8/KG 77 was also reported missing during an operation against Malta together with Leutnant Rolf Haekel, Gefreiter Georg Kiefer, Unteroffizier Hilmar Krazat and Unteroffizier Günter Brzeske.

215. War Diary of 4th Searchlight Regiment, Royal Artillery and Royal Malta Artillery, PRO, ref: WO 169/7406.

216. Letter to the author from Rod Smith, dated 2 August 1995.

217. Diary of Jerry Smith, via Chris Shores.

218. Letter to the author from Rod Smith, dated 2 August 1995.

219. Malta:German prisoners of war interrogation reports (December 1941–October 1942), PRO, ref. AIR 40/1863.

220. Christopher Shores, Brian Cull, Nicola Malizia, *Malta: The Spitfire Year 1942*, p. 428.

221. Letter to the author from Rod Smith, dated 2 August 1995.

222. Aircraft Losses, Malta, 1942, via the NWMA.

223. Letter to the author from Howard Bell, dated 9 July 1995.

224. Letter to the author from Rod Smith, dated 2 August 1995.

225. Flying Officer George F. Beurling DSO, DFC, DFM and Bar, and Leslie Roberts, *Malta Spitfire – The Story of a Fighter Pilot*, p. 81.

226. Luftwaffe Losses, IWM, ref: GER/MISC/MCR 18, includes details of three Ju 88s of II/KG 77 missing on this date during operations against Luqa. All were almost certainly brought down in the 1741–1747 hours raid.

227. PRO, ref: AIR 22/392.

228. Letter to the author from Rod Smith, dated 2 August 1995.

229. PRO, ref: AIR 22/392.

230. PRO, ref: AIR 22/392.

231. PRO, ref: AIR 22/392.

232. Letter to Chris Shores from Rod Smith, dated 11 April 1992.

233. Diary of Jerry Smith, via Chris Shores.

234. Diaries of Phil Chandler.

235. Letter to the author from Rod Smith, dated 2 August 1995.

236. Jochen Prien, 'Pik-As', Geschichte des Jagdgeschwaders 53, Teil 3, p. 1677, and Geschichte des Jagdgeschwaders 77, Teil 3, p. 1252.

237. Flying Officer George F. Beurling DSO, DFC, DFM and Bar, and Leslie Roberts, Malta Spitfire – The Story of a Fighter Pilot, pp. 86–8. In this account, Sergeant Budd has evidently been confused with Flight Lieutenant Eric Hetherington or Sergeant R. Lamont, and misidentified as Sergeant Vasseure 'Georgia' Wynn: Budd is stated to have, 'turned back with engine trouble', and Wynn is credited with damaging a Bf 109. However, the ORB of 249 Squadron does not include Sergeant Wynn among those involved in this action, but records that Flight Lieutenant Hetherington and Sergeant Lamont returned early. It also credits Budd with a Bf 109 'damaged': PRO, ref: AIR 27/1498.

238. Jochen Prien, 'Pik-As', Geschichte des Jagdgeschwaders 53, Teil 3, p. 1677, and Geschichte des Jagdgeschwaders 77, Teil 3, p. 1253. (Geschichte des Jagdgeschwaders 77, Teil 4, p. 2421, lists the victories of Oberleutnant Freytag and Feldwebel Pohl as Spitfires).

239. The epic of 'Il-Convoy ta'Santa Marija' has been fully documented in several publications: a selected bibliography is provided at the end of this book. Casualty figures are from Malta, Defiant & Triumphant, Rolls of Honour, 1940–1943, edited by Captain E.A.S. Bailey CBE DSC Royal Navy.

240. Jochen Prien, 'Pik-As', Geschichte des Jagdgeschwaders 53, Teil 3, p. 1677.

241. FASHION: air sector code name.

242. Combat report of Squadron Leader P.M.J. Evans, PRO, ref: AIR 22/392.

243. The History of No 89 Squadron RFC/RAF, (unpublished manuscript), pp. 68–9, produced by the 89 Squadron Reunion Club.

244. Letter to the author from Rod Smith, dated 2 August 1995.

245. In describing another crash he witnessed, Rod Smith explained:

> The constant speed unit of an aircraft which had been hit hard in its engine usually failed to keep control of the engine rpm. This was because the oil pressure which adjusted the angle of the propeller blades (or the electrical power which adjusted the angle in the case of German propellers and some American ones) failed. A single engined aircraft so stricken usually went into a dive, and the increasing air stream past the propeller blades began to make them rotate so fast that the tips of the blades went faster than sound. This produced a whining roar which got louder and more high pitched as the speed of the dive increased.

246. Letter to the author from Rod Smith, dated 2 August 1995.

247. Letter to the author from Rod Smith, dated 2 August 1995.
248. Aircraft Losses, Malta, 1942, via the NWMA. Rod Smith also explained that at the time:

> I was uncertain whether it was a Macchi or a 109, as they were quite hard to tell apart in the air and one was often claimed as the other. I had never been close to any Italian fighter before. I had noticed that this aircraft had a white band about two feet wide around its fuselage between its cockpit and its tail, which I knew was a key Italian marking . . .
>
> When I got back to our mess in St Julian's Bay, Wally McLeod [Flight Lieutenant Henry McLeod] and another 1435 Squadron pilot, both of whom happened to be walking by Sliema Bay when the Macchi went in, told me that they thought it was a 109 and explained that German aircraft in the Med also had the white band. I therefore changed my claim to a 109 the next day.

249. According to Christopher Shores, Brian Cull, Nicola Malizia, *Malta: The Spitfire Year 1942*, p. 633, Flying Officer Lindsay was shot down by Bofors fire.
250. Letter to the author from Rod Smith, dated 2 August 1995.
251. PRO, ref: AIR 22/392.
252. Letter to the author from Charlie Savage, dated 11 August 1997.
253. Six Wellingtons of 40 Squadron and seven of 104 Squadron were dispatched between 1720 and 2240 hours on 18 December. One aircraft of 40 Squadron developed generator trouble and so diverted to attack Comiso aerodrome. Another of 104 Squadron returned early. The remainder dropped nearly 18 tonnes of bombs on Tunis and La Goulette.
254. This was probably Ju 88 140389/3Z+NK of 2/KG 77, reported missing on a sortie to Malta on 18 December 1942, together with Oberfeldwebel Herbert Bunde, Gefreiter Karl Saft, Unteroffizier Albert Zimmermann and Unteroffizier Friedrich Stelting: Luftwaffe Losses, IWM, ref: GER/MISC/MCR 18.
255. War Diary of 1st Battalion The Dorsetshire Regiment, PRO, ref: WO 169/7427.
256. Christopher Shores and Clive Williams, *Aces High*, p. 623.
257. PRO, ref: AIR 27/412.

SELECT BIBLIOGRAPHY

Agius, John A. MBE and Galea, Frederick R., *Lest We Forget, Royal Air Force and Commonwealth Air Forces Servicemen Lost in the Defence of Malta*, Malta Aviation Museum Foundation, 1999.

Bailey, Captain E.A.S. CBE DSC Royal Navy (ed), *Malta, Defiant & Triumphant, Rolls of Honour, 1940–1943*, E.A.S. Bailey, 1992, and *Addenda & Amendments* (as at 31 December 1997).

Barnham, Denis, *One Man's Window, An illustrated account of ten weeks of war Malta, April 13th, to June 21st, 1942*, William Kimber, 1956.

Bekker, Cajus, *The Luftwaffe War Diaries*, Macdonald, 1968.

Beurling, Flying Officer George F. DSO, DFC, DFM and Bar, and Roberts, Leslie, *Malta Spitfire – The Story of a Fighter Pilot*, Hutchinson, 1943.

Bonner, Robert A., *The Ardwick Boys went to Malta. A British Territorial Battalion during the siege 1940–1943*, Fleur de Lys Publishing, 1992.

Borgiotti, Alberto and Gori, Cesare, *Gli Stuka Della Regia Aeronautica 1940–45*, Stem Mucchi Modena, 1976.

Brennan, Pilot Officer Paul DFC, DFM, Hesselyn, Pilot Officer Ray DFM and Bar, Bateson, Henry, *Spitfires Over Malta*, Jarrolds, 1943.

Caldwell, Donald, *The JG 26 War Diary, Volume One, 1939–1942*, Grub Street, 1996.

Cameron, Ian, *Red Duster, White Ensign, The Story of the Malta Convoys*, Frederick Muller, 1959.

Cull, Brian, *249 At War, The Authorised History of the RAF's Top-Scoring Fighter Squadron of WWII*, Grub Street, 1997.

Douglas-Hamilton, Squadron Leader Lord David, 'With a Fighter Squadron in Malta', *Blackwood's Magazine*, April and May 1944.

Douglas-Hamilton, Lord James, *The Air Battle for Malta – The Diaries of a Fighter Pilot*, Mainstream Publishing, 1981.

Gibbs, Wing Commander Patrick DSO, DFC and Bar, *Torpedo Leader*, Grub Street, 1992.

Hamlin, John F., *Military Aviation in Malta G.C., 1915–1993, A comprehensive history*, GMS Enterprises, 1994.

HMSO, *The Air Battle of Malta*, 1944.

Johnston, Wing Commander Tim DFC, *Tattered Battlements – A Fighter Pilot's Diary*, William Kimber, 1985.

Lucas, Laddie, *Five Up – A Chronicle of Five Lives*, Sidgwick and Jackson, 1978.
——, *Malta – The Thorn in Rommel's Side, Six Months that Turned the War*, Stanley Paul, 1992.

Mahlke, Helmut, *Stuka, Angriff: Sturzfleug, Verlag* E.S. Mittler & Sohn, 1993.

Malizia, Nicola, *Inferno su Malta*, Mursia, 1976.

McAuley, Lex, *Against All Odds, RAAF pilots in the Battle for Malta 1942*, Hutchinson Australia, 1989.

Mifsud, Richard, *Flames over Malta*, Richard Mifsud, 1989.

Neil, Wing Commander T.F. DFC★, AFC, AE, RAF Ret'd, *Onward to Malta, Memoirs of a Hurricane pilot in Malta – 1941*, Airlife, 1992.

Nolan, Brian, *Hero: The Falcon of Malta*, William Blackwood, 1982.

Poolman, Kenneth, *Faith, Hope and Charity, Three Planes against an Air Force*, William Kimber, 1954.

——, *Night Strike From Malta, 830 Squadron RN and Rommel's Convoys*, Janes Publishing Company, 1980.

Prien, Jochen, *Chronik des JG-53 Pik-As Band 1*, Flugzeug Publikations GmbH.

——, *'Pik-As', Geschichte des Jagdgeschwaders 53, Teile 2 und 3*, Struve-Druck, 1990 and 1991.

——, *Geschichte des Jagdgeschwaders 77, Teile 3 and 4*, Struve-Druck.

——, *Messerschmitt Bf 109 im Einsatz bei der II/Jagdgeschwader 3*, Struve-Druck, 1996.

Radtke, Siegfried, *Kampfgeschwader 54*, Schild Verlag, 1990.

Ramsey, Winston (ed), *After the Battle* (magazine), number 10, Battle of Britain Prints, 1975.

Rolls, Flight Lieutenant W.T. DFC, DFM, AE, *Spitfire Attack*, William Kimber, 1987.

Shankland, Peter and Hunter, Anthony, *Malta Convoy*, Collins, 1961.

Shores, Christopher, *Aces High, Volume 2*, Grub Street, 1999.

——, Cull, Brian, Malizia, Nicola *Malta: The Hurricane Years 1940–41*, Grub Street, 1987.

——, *Malta: The Spitfire Year 1942*, Grub Street, 1991.

Shores, Christopher and Williams, Clive, *Aces High*, Grub Street, 1994.

Smith, Peter C., *Pedestal, The Malta Convoy of August 1942*, William Kimber, 1987.

Spooner, Tony, DSO, DFC, *Warburton's War, The Life of Wing Commander Adrian Warburton, DSO*, DFC**, DFC (USA)*, William Kimber, 1987.

Stones, Donald, *Operation 'Bograt' – From France to Burma*, Spellmount, 1990.

Vella, Philip, *Malta: Blitzed But Not Beaten*, Progress Press, 1985.

INDEX